CW00971306

BRAND-NEW
FANTASY DISCOVERIES!

WHAT WOULD YOU DO? . . . If you had to flee an elevator 500 miles up, if pirates accused you of ESP powers, or the plastic trees began to crush your jungle shelter?

WOULD YOU KNOW? . . . What software would interface with pure evil, how there are monsters among us, why the U.S. would bodyguard Hitler? . . . and whose ashes to sow in your garden?

COULD YOU GUESS WHY? . . . Outer space might kill you inside, a robot might be sly, a starship might dream a nightmare? . . . and why Edgar Allan might not be Poe?

CAN YOU IMAGINE? . . . an insect as landlord on Earth, a dying woman in Panama *and* among the stars, a lost man who is everywhere?

Read These Winning stories
The Finest and Latest in SF Tales
by The Best of The New Breed!

L. RON HUBBARD

PRESENTS

WRITERS

OF THE

FUTURE

VOLUME III

L. RON HUBBARD

PRESENTS

WRITERS
OF THE
FUTURE

VOLUME III

14 Great New Tales from the
Writers of The Future
International Talent Search

Plus Essays on the Art and Craft of Writing by
L. RON HUBBARD
FREDERIK POHL
GREGORY BENFORD
JERRY POURNELLE

Edited by
ALGIS BUDRYS

NEW ERA Publications UK Ltd.

CONTENTS

FEATURES:

ACKNOWLEDGMENTS

The continuing growth of L. Ron Hubbard's Writers of The Future program is due to the dedicated participation of noted SF authors. They judge the winners of the writing competition and often give generously of their expertise and support in many other ways.

In the 1986 year, these individuals were:

Gregory Benford
Stephen Goldin
Larry Niven
Jerry Pournelle
Jack Williamson
Roger Zelazny

Algis Budrys
Anne McCaffrey
Frederik Pohl
Robert Silverberg
Gene Wolfe

It is through their contributions of time and attention that this volume has been made possible and the significance of the Writers of The Future program has been assured.

Frank Frazetta

L. Ron Hubbard called him the "King of Illustration" and indeed Frank Frazetta is one of our century's very few great masters. Credited with transforming and popularizing fantasy art illustration, he developed whole new trends in the genre, setting uniquely brilliant standards of quality. We are pleased and honored to have his latest work gracing the covers of *Writers of The Future Vol. III.* To symbolize the boundless scope of the Writers of The Future anthologies, Frazetta's cover art depicts the meeting of fantasy and science fiction in a magical universe.

A Growing Thing
by
Algis Budrys

About the Author

Algis Budrys is the editor of the Writers of The Future anthology series, and Coordinating Judge of the Writers of The Future contest. He also directs the invitational Writers of The Future workshops, where Writers of The Future winners and finalists polish their skills after having been judged.

Budrys, a speculative-fiction fan since childhood, wrote his first SF story at the age of nine, and then underwent the usual extended learning process for twelve years thereafter while attending various writing clubs and classes. He entered the ranks of SF pros with a dozen sales in 1952, and simultaneously began an editorial career which took him from Gnome Press and Galaxy Magazine on up through the ranks in and out of the SF world.

He has published eight SF novels and three short-story collections while also pursuing other careers. A collection of his SF book review columns, Benchmarks: Galaxy Bookshelf by Algis Budrys, won the Locus Award as the 1985 nonfiction book of the year on SF, and a successor volume is being readied. He is also at work on a new novel.

He has taught SF writing extensively, particularly at the Clarion SF Writing Workshop where he has been an instructor since 1977.

Of his participation in the Writers of The Future

program, he says, "I feel this is the most important thing could be doing with all the things I've learned in my life.'

This is the third annual volume in a series that has become the talk of the SF world. It's the immediately visible result of a talent-discovery program whose dimensions are unique in literature. L. Ron Hubbard's Writers of The Future Contest was designed by him to be meaningful to entrants, effective in bringing attention to large numbers of new authors and their talent, and providing outstanding, fresh, new stories to the reading public.

You'll find fourteen such stories here, and fourteen new authors to join those appearing in *L. Ron Hubbard's Writers of The Future* volumes. All were winners or finalists in the Contest, which is publicized to the entire English-speaking world and sees entries from residents of many nations. If our experience of past volumes is any guide, some of the stories here signal the start of meteoric careers, and all of them stem from talents to be reckoned with. We know there are more. The Contest will find them, and future volumes of this series will bring them to you.

(If you don't know already, the Contest is open to new and amateur writers, features quarterly judging, and confers outright grants of $1000, $750, $500, respectively, on the three prize-winners each quarter. An additional prize of $4000 is awarded annually, with the L. Ron Hubbard Gold Award trophy, to the author of the Writers of The Future Story of the Year. The judges are among the very best and most famous SF writers in the world. Complete rules appear in the back pages of this book, or can be obtained by sending a stamped, self-addressed envelope to Writers of The Future Contest, P.O. Box 110, Tonbridge, Kent TN9 2TY.)

By definition, the Contest was designed by an outstanding expert on breaking into popular writing. There are many difficulties that sometimes make achieving success a discouraging process. Every one of them is an obstacle that Hubbard had to deal with when he was first learning not only how to direct his own talent as a wordsmith but to bring it to the attention of editors and publishers. It's also a fact of life that beginning writers almost invariably lack practical support—money, sound advice, and meaningful encouragement from those who have preceded them along the road to achievement. These things have no effect on talent, but they have everything to do with its freedom to develop.

The stories in this book are drawn from the quarterly Contest winners and some of the top runners-up in the 1986 contest year. We confidently expect they'll meet with the same public enthusiasm and critical praise that were accorded to their predecessors. The judges' only criterion within the Contest rules is that the stories be good. We don't judge what kind of speculative fiction they happen to represent, what their writing style is, or even what their author's career motivations are. Why should we? Writing to professional standards is hard enough... and good writing often springs from impulses and approaches that the experts have dismissed. In the judging, which is done with the authors' names removed from the manuscripts, all we care about or can care about is whether a story is good to read.

Come to think of it, that's probably why the W.O.T.F. volumes are good to read... and why these books, unencumbered by dictates of fad, mode or theory, sell enormously. (SF authorities have recognized Writers of The Future as the best-selling SF anthology of all time. So we also want to thank you, for your support and for replenishing our faith in the public's taste for good SF of whatever length and approach.)

We find these writers, we encourage them with awards and publication, and, if they so desire, we then invite them to master-class workshops where major SF-writing figures share their expertise and experience with them. The object is to help these people sustain their careers after the first flush of success.

Why do we do this? In part because each of us has a certain personal knowledge of how hard it is to hoe one's way toward success as a writer, and then to keep it going. Almost all of us owe something to the tutelage of older writers who took us under their wings when we were first breaking in. That's an old tradition in the arts, and particularly in SF, whose "Good Old Days" weren't all that long ago. There were no academies, so there had to be masters and apprentices if our literature was going to live and evolve.

No one observed these phenomena more acutely than L. Ron Hubbard, who in the 1930s and '40s was one of the most prolific, enthusiastic and well-received authors of SF, and a major factor in the fondly remembered "Golden Age." What Hubbard saw, in SF and in other fields, was that few were as fortunate as he. He was a legend for the speed of his writing, for his ability to develop ideas into rousing stories, and for his maintenance of a career as a writer. The writers' magazines of the time frequently published how-to articles written by Hubbard in an attempt to teach his methods to others. At the time, that was the best he could do for them.

His design for the Writers of The Future program represents the last and biggest thing he did along that line. As a talent search, it is unique in that it provides meaningful recognition financially and in other significant ways, while costing nothing to enter and conferring its awards purely on merit. We don't even reserve any rights in the entered stories; when these anthologies are put together, we contact the authors and make them an entirely separate—and generous—offer for limited use of their stories. They are under no obligation to accept it (although it's *quite* generous.)

The contest is still evolving, in keeping with Hubbard's concept of how creativity works. It is developing additional means of offering no-strings assistance to would-be and beginning professionals. It's significant that so many established major talents have enthusiastically supported this effort, serving as judges, contributing their own words of expert advice, and acting as teachers and advisors in our growing program of workshops. If you're wondering, our judges receive token honoraria, and the very real satisfaction of seeing creative talent develop in aspiring writers who progress from unknown contest-entrants to full-fledged finalists and winners. L. Ron Hubbard's Writers of The Future has become clearly recognized as probably the major philanthropic vehicle within SF.

Great numbers of entries in to the contest from all over the world, additional volumes of these anthologies are being launched, and more and more writers we have published are now appearing as novelists, and as regulars on the tables of contests of major SF magazines. Each year, a W.O.T.F. story has been selected by a major anthologist as one of the best of the year, and the list of W.O.T.F. authors nominated for leading awards is a long and growing one. The most recent winner of the John W. Campbell, Jr., award for the Best New Writer of the year is Karen Joy Fowler, whose story, "Recalling Cinderella", appears in Vol. I.

We don't do that last part—those nominations originate with the readers of these volumes. That's who these volumes are for, after all, and we're glad you're pleased.

L. Ron Hubbard left this life in January, 1986, nearly 75. For several years before that he had devoted considerable attention to the writing of epic science fiction novels that now appear steadily on best-seller lists. With his passing, his publishers have taken over the administrative support of the Writers of The Future program, out of respect to his memory, out of deference to his creative direction, and as a gesture of good will to the SF-reading public. It's unusual to see a business enterprise volunteer for the expense and effort this will cost. But everyone who has felt the multi-faceted enthusiasm for the W.O.T.F. program wants it to flourish, and never mind the immediate economics. We'll all be better off in the long run, and, it's a lot of fun and satisfaction.

This is a good thing we all—you and we—are doing. It means there will be more, and better, SF in years to come. That will have desirable practical results. In the words of the late Frank Herbert, from his essay of advice in a previous *Writers of The Future,* "The more good writers there are, the more good readers there will be. We'll benefit—readers and writers alike!"

The writers and stories you'll find in this book are fully worthy of whatever good fortune now comes their way. Like their predecessors, they represent a broad spectrum of world-views and life experiences. Their ages vary—this year, remarkably. They include people who almost didn't enter, people who have had a great deal of formal instruction and others who've had almost none, some who've been years in working toward publication and others who began quite recently. There is no magic pattern. There is only talent, and the courage to lay it on the line. Because they are here, they are therefore extraordinary people.

But what really counts is whether they can make *you* glad you're here among us, ready to see what they've brought you. I don't think they will fail you in that respect, either.

Eric M. Heideman	First Place, First Quarter
L. E. Carroll	Second Place, First Quarter
R. V. Branham	Third Place, First Quarter
M. Shayne Bell	First Place, Second Quarter
Carolyn Ives Gilman	Second Place, Second Quarter
Lori Ann White	Third Place, Second Quarter
Martha Soukup	First Place, Third Quarter
Tawn Stokes	Second Place, Third Quarter
Jean Reitz	Third Place, Third Quarter
Dave Wolverton	First Place, Fourth Quarter
J. R. Dunn	Second Place, Fourth Quarter
Mary Catherine McDaniel	Third Place, Fourth Quarter
Christopher Ewart	Finalist, Fourth Quarter
Paula May	Finalist, Fourth Quarter

There were many excellent stories among the other finalists; we wish we had the pages in which to offer them publication. Perhaps some day we will. To them, to all the contest entrants and the judges, and to the indefatigable people at the companies which publish these volumes, as well as Writers of The Future Contest Administrative Consultant Fred Harris, and to L. Ron Hubbard's impetus and energy, we express our thanks.

Introducing L. Ron Hubbard On Art and Communication

L. Ron Hubbard (1911-1986) was born in the American West at a time when the Frontier ethic still placed a heavy responsibility on a man. The responsibility was to survive without being a burden on others; to be a positive force; to not merely survive, but to contribute. Nothing said you couldn't have fun in the process, and there is plenty of evidence that Hubbard loved taking the world apart to see how it ticked, and putting parts of it back together in ways that baffled some and often afforded him enormous merriment.

Even in his earliest teens, he displayed an omnivorous thirst for information, at first hand and from books. That's not rare in someone who'll be a writer, but his intensity was. Too, his personal circumstances were such that he could explore sea and land personally, while also coming into contact with some unusually effective teachers. He made observations and formed opinions that were not always usual, and developed a manner that dared you to dispute them. If you put up a good argument, so much the better; if you couldn't, so be it. Either way, both of you had had the opportunity to test some feature of the universe, that wonderful box full of marvelous toys and elegant instruments.

Something led him to share his discoveries, and his delights in them, and his occasional consternations at what he found there. He became an entertainer; specifically, a writer of popular "pulp" fiction. Soon enough, even more specifically, a writer of speculative fiction.

Science fiction and fantasy are where the ultimate speculations can go and turn into dramas. The supposed worlds they embody are based on our common understanding of reality, as they must be, but they can be taken apart and put into unique configurations that amaze, and yet work in human terms . . . work elegantly, sometimes, to the edification and the delight of the reader.

All his life as a writer, Hubbard devoted constant attention to to making his writing more effective; to reaching larger and larger audiences, and to making them want more of his work. He wanted to know why people read so avidly for "entertainment" and perhaps he wanted to know why he himself was so strongly drawn to provide it.

He concluded that underneath it all, the audience wants to learn something; that storytelling is not pure diversion. Teaching is essential to entertainment, and background gives meaning to action. Oh, you had better not preach, and you had better not stop the action for an expository paragraph or two cribbed from some encyclopedia. That would lose your audience. But your story had to be about something, or why should the reader care to enjoy it?

Many years after his rise to fame as a writer, Hubbard,

on looking back on how it all worked, dictated a few paragraphs on "Message." Here's some of what he had to say:

Successful works of art have a message.

It may be implicit or implied, emotional, conceptual or literal, inferred or stated. But a message nonetheless.

This applies to any form of art: paintings, sculpture, poetry, writing, music, architecture, photography, cine, any art form that depends on art, even advertising brochures and window displays.

Art is for the receiver.

If he understands it, he likes it. If it confuses him, he may ignore it or detest it.

It is not enough that the creator of the work understands it; those who receive it must.

Many elements and much expertise go into the creating of successful works of art. Dominant among them is message for this integrates the whole and brings comprehension and appreciation to those for whom it is intended . . . a message is fundamental to understanding.

This view is guaranteed to raise some hackles among established arbiters of these matters. It is, however, a view promulgated by one of the most successful communicators we have ever seen, by someone who was a widely popular writer and top producer while still in his twenties, and whose final work, the ten-volume Mission Earth *dekalogy, legitimately rides today's best-seller lists, attracting enthusiastic readers by the muliple tens of thousands.*

Hubbard knew how to reach them. And he knew how to teach it. Here is some more of his expertise. . . .

Art and Communication
by
L. Ron Hubbard

When a work of painting, music or other form attains two-way communication, it is truly art.

One occasionally hears an artist being criticized on the basis that his work is too "literal" or too "common." But one has rarely if ever heard any definition of "literal" or "common." And there are many artists simply hung up on this, protesting it. Also, some avant-garde schools go completely over the cliff in avoiding anything "literal" or "common"—and indeed go completely out of communication!

The return flow from the person viewing a work would be contribution. True art always elicits a contribution from those who view or hear or experience it. By contribution is meant "adding to it."

An illustration is "literal" in that it tells everything there is to know. Let us say the illustration is a picture of a tiger approaching a chained girl. It does not really matter how well the painting is executed, it remains an illustration and it IS literal. But now let us take a small portion out of the scene and enlarge it. Let us take, say, the head of the tiger with its baleful eye and snarl. Suddenly we no longer have an illustration. It is no longer "literal." And the reason lies in the fact that the viewer can fit this expression into his own concepts, ideas or experience: he can supply the why of the snarl, he can compare the head to someone he knows. In short he can CONTRIBUTE to the head.

The skill with which the head is executed determines the degree of response.

Because the viewer can contribute to the picture, it is art.

In music, the hearer can contribute his own emotion or motion. And even if the music is only a single drum, if it elicits a contribution of emotion or motion, it is truly art.

That work which delivers everything and gets little or nothing in return is not art. The "common" or overused melody, the expected shape or form gets little or no contribution from the hearer or viewer. That work which is too unclear or too poorly executed may get no contribution.

Incidental to this, one can ask if a photograph can ever be art, a controversy which has been raging for a century or more. One could say that it is only difficult to decide because one has to establish how much the photographer has contributed to the "reality" or "literalness" in front of his camera, how he has interpreted it, but really the point is whether or not that photograph elicits a contribution from its viewer. If it does, it is art.

Innovation plays a large role in all works which may

become art. But even this can be overdone. Originality can be overdone to the point where it is no longer within any possible understanding by those viewing or hearing it. One can be so original one goes entirely outside the most distant perimeter of agreement with his viewers or listeners. Sometimes this is done, one suspects, when one has not spent the labor necessary to execute the work. Various excuses are assigned such an action, the most faulty of which is "self-satisfaction" of the artist. While it is quite all right to commune with oneself, one cannot also then claim that it is art if it communicates with no one else and no other's communication is possible.

The third flow, of people talking to one another about a work can also be considered a communication and where it occurs is a valid contribution as it makes the work known.

Destructive attitudes about a work can be considered as a refusal to contribute. Works that are shocking or bizarre to a point of eliciting protest may bring to themselves notoriety thereby and may shake things up; but when the refusal to contribute is too widespread, such works tend to disqualify as art.

There is also the matter of divided opinion about a work. Some contribute to it, some refuse to contribute to it. In such cases one must examine who is contributing and who is refusing. One can then say that it is a work of art to those who contribute to it and that it is not to those who refuse to contribute to it.

Criticism is some sort of index of degree of contribution. There are, roughly, two types of criticism: one can be called "invalidative criticism," the other "constructive criticism."

Invalidative criticism is all too prevalent in the arts for there exist such things as "individual taste," contemporary standards and, unfortunately, even envy or jealousy. Too often, criticism is simply an individual refusal to contribute. One could also state that "those who destructively criticize can't do."

"Constructive criticism" is a term which is often used but seldom defined. But it has use. It could probably be best defined as criticism which "indicates a better way to do," at least in the opinion of the critic. Those who simply find fault and never suggest a practical means of doing it better rather forfeit their right to criticize.

Art is probably the most uncodified and least organized of all fields. It therefore acquires to itself the most "authorities." Usually nothing is required of an "authority" except to say what is right, wrong, good, bad, acceptable or unacceptable. Too often the sole qualification of the authority (as in poor teaching of some subjects) is a memorized list of objects and their creators and dates with some hazy idea of what the work was. An "authority" could considerably improve his status by using rather precise definitions of his terms. The modern trend of seeking the significance in what the artist meant is of course not likely to advance the arts very much.

Viewing and experiencing art on the basis of what one is contributing to it and what others contribute to it is a workable approach. And it would result in improved art and improved appreciation.

Such a viewpoint, interestingly, also includes some things into the field of art not previously so viewed.

Jacob's Ladder
by
Shayne Bell

About the Author

Shayne Bell was born in 1957 in Rexburg, Idaho.
He grew up on the family ranch outside of town, and even before he could read, his mother was reading science fiction to him. After high school, he served a two-year mission for the Church of Jesus Christ of Latter-Day Saints in the state of São Paulo, Brazil. Brazil has inspired many of his stories.

Returning to the U.S.A., he continued to work on his writing skills while obtaining bachelor's and master's degrees from Brigham Young University. His Master's thesis was a collection of his own science fiction and fantasy short stories. He then devoted years of development to his stories, plays, poems and novels before winning First Prize in the second Quarter of the Contest, and since then has gone on to sell other fiction. After reading "Jacob's Ladder," we doubt that you'll doubt the brightness of his future as a writer.

We're very pleased to help him launch his professional career. . . .

The angel's wings had been broken.
"I saw three wings by stairs," Marcio said.
"I go. Two knocks, let me in."

He left the dressing room in a hurry, but quiet. I locked the door behind him. Marcio's a reporter for the *Estado de Pará*, so it was better that he go. Besides speaking Portuguese, he had pulled on a dead worker's overalls so he could maybe talk his way out of getting thrown over if he got caught. Maybe. Sandra and I couldn't even try that trick.

"Think he'll come back?"

I looked at Sandra. "Where would he go?"

"Turn us in. Get on their good sides. Stay alive."

"He'll come back." Marcio was Brazilian, but that made no difference to the terrorists.

I opened a locker, found a 120-foot rope. Sandra was trying on the construction workers' outsuits. She didn't have much trouble finding one that fit, but it took me a while. Most were too small. Most weren't built for American men. Sandra pulled on a suit and hung the camera around her neck.

"You're taking it?"

"Damn right. And if they catch us, I'll stomp it. No

one's going to film my death with my own camera."

They'd been doing that: taking pictures of the news-men they killed with the newsmen's own cameras—a final insult.

Two soft taps on the door: Marcio. He was shaking. The angel's wings clanged against the door frame. Marcio had to back up and hand them to me one at a time. Angel's wings look like a man-sized capital I: solar battery, gears, and levers at the top; narrow pole down the middle; foot clamps at the bottom that catch on doorjambs. Marcio came through with the last set of wings. Sandra locked the door. I set my wings on the floor. They didn't weigh much, and they looked flimsy —little more than aluminum poles to hang on to: not much to ride five hundred miles on.

"The place crawls with our amigos—I had to club one," Marcio said. One wing had blood on it. "I hope I kill him. If he wake up and remember me taking wings. . . ."

He didn't finish. But Sandra and I understood. They'd cut the cable.

Marcio pulled on an outsuit. "The vid? —videos are on," he said.

The one in the dressing room had been shot up.

"They are throwing over all the people they catch."

"Workers, too?" Sandra asked.

"Sim. Workers."

And videotaping it for everyone down in Macapá. Let Ground Floor know they were serious, that their deadlines were real. I wondered how long "We don't negotiate with terrorists" would last when it came to seeing the celebs Up Top murdered.

We'd been coming up in the second to the last car for newsmen—neither of Salt Lake's papers had the pull of

CBS, *Newsweek,* or The *New York Times.* We crammed
into the car with reporters from Vancouver, Lima, and
Sapporo—impatient, of course. Seventy-six presidents,
prime ministers and dictators were Up Top, with members of twelve royal families, the São Paulo Symphony,
actors from all seven continents, and twenty-three science fiction writers flown to Macapá to inaugurate the
story of the century: the elevator to space. Man's ladder
to the stars. Jacob's ladder to Heaven, as it was called.

It's location at the mouth of the Amazon gave the
elevator easy access to the world's shipping, and the
world easy access to the wealth beyond the gravity-well.
Spaceships could load and unload cargo at Up Top
station that had been built in geosynchronous orbit or at
any of the forty-four partway stations stretching down
the cables. Instead of fifteen hundred dollars a pound to
shuttle materials up from Earth, the elevator would lift
thousands of pounds an hour for twenty-five cents a
pound.

Flying to the Moon would be as cheap as flying from
Salt Lake to Toronto, Mars as cheap as Salt Lake to
Jerusalem.

Security for the opening had been the tightest I'd
seen. They checked everything and everybody everywhere. But I knew somebody'd failed or been bribed or
killed when "workers" at Partway-1 pulled guns.

The terrorists shoved two reporters from Montevideo
away from the rest of us, and five terrorists aimed guns
at their heads. "I have a mother and a sister to support,"
one Uruguayan said. "Please."

They shot him. Then they shot the other, kicked the
bodies over the side. "We do not joke," one terrorist
said.

They kept us at Partway-1 for three days, making

demands, getting nowhere. They threatened to blow the whole elevator, which must have pleased the Russians who were just starting to build theirs in an African minion's equatorial swamp.

The terrorists set a deadline, said they'd throw the newsmen (not the workers) at Partway-1 over the side. Nobody thought they'd do it.

They did.

When the deadline passed, they shot up the cars docked at Partway-1 and started hunting newsmen. Sandra and I hid in a meat locker till it got too cold. I'd been at Partway-1 before and knew a possible way down. Sandra was willing to try it; we were dead if we stayed. We ran into Marcio while looking for the construction site.

"These wings be enough?" Marcio asked, pointing at the three he'd brought in.

I didn't know. "Sure, of course," I said.

Had to be enough: there weren't any more.

Sandra picked one up. "Built for low G, weren't they?"

She saw right through me. "They have good brakes," I said.

"Japanese brakes," Marcio said.

"Ever use one, Marcio?" I asked.

"No. No, never."

That surprised me—his being Brazilian and so close to Macapá. I'd flown from Salt Lake to ride a pair of angel's wings up and down one of the cables with the workers. It hadn't been too bad. But I'd only had to ease my wings up a few thousand feet and then back down. Now, the Japanese brakes had to be good enough to ease three of us down to Macapá: five hundred miles.

Illustrated by Greg Petan

We heard a gunshot and a scuffle in the hall.

Without a word, we suited up. I led the way to the depressurization chamber. Once inside I checked everyone's air supply: twelve hours each. We'd have to cover forty-two miles an hour. I figured we could move along at twice that speed and make Macapá with half our air to spare.

I looked at my watch. 5:00 P.M. No supper. Not much food of any kind for three days. But all we had to do, I hoped, was hang on and pray. There'd be food in Macapá.

The workers had left tools lying about. I picked up a hammer and smashed the chamber's receiver. I left the transmitter alone so we could hear anyone coming through DP after us.

The lights on the outer door turned green. I opened the door. We stepped out.

No air in the open construction. Six unfinished docks there, cables stretching straight down to Macapá. Not a bad place to hide if we'd had plenty of air and could have believed our friends wouldn't eventually notice missing suits and come looking.

I turned on my intersuit com link and motioned for Sandra and Marcio to do the same. "Air all right?" I asked. It was.

I stood up my angel's wings and showed Sandra and Marcio the magnetic clamps top and bottom that hold wings to a cable; how you strap your feet in the foot clamps; where you hook your suit to the aluminum pole; which lever above your head increased and decreased speed, which was the emergency brake. Simple things, really.

"How long will the batteries last?" Sandra asked.

"Two hours," I said. "They'll recharge in half that

time. We should always have two units at full power. We'll drop with gravity. The power will keep us at a constant speed."

"West Germans made the batteries," Marcio said.

"What do *we* have in them?" Sandra asked, looking at me.

"The idea," I said.

"I *thought* America would have the defective part."

Marcio smiled. Sandra was good for a joke in tight spots.

I opened the toolbox welded at waist height to my wing's pole, told Sandra and Marcio to open theirs. The clamps were inside. "We'll hook our angel's wings together with these so we can travel as one unit," I said. I tossed my clamp back and looked to see what else the toolbox held: not much—a few wrenches, a belt with a magnetic clamp on it in case your wings failed and you had to go out on the cable. I closed the lid.

We walked to the nearest cable. I held my wings next to the cable, and the magnetic clamps sealed around it.

Then I looked down. I'd kept from doing that as long as possible. The escape plan was my idea. I felt responsible for the others, even though they chose to come and it was the only chance we had. But if I lost *my* nerve—

The Amazon looked big even from five hundred miles up: big and roiling east over the Atlantic that stretched into darkness where I could see stars—no, lights maybe? Monrovia? Dakar?—while below my feet the world was green and bright. Sunlight glistened on the rivers and the sea, and Macapá was invisible in the forests of Amapá.

I could not see the bottom of the cable. It disappeared from sight long before clouds down in the air cut across its vanishing point.

"I can't do it," Marcio said. He and Sandra were looking over the side.

I put my hand on his shoulder. "Just don't look down."

"I'm afraid of heights. I can't do it."

"Would you rather go down with or without angel's wings?"

He looked away, breathing hard.

Sandra led him from the edge and made him sit on a box. "Don't hyperventilate till we get you strapped on," she said.

"The cable disappears. Is it cut?"

I pushed on the cable. It didn't move. "Cable's solid," I said.

"You couldn't move a cable five hundred miles long."

"If it were cut, we'd see the end dancing below us." *Listen to me,* I thought, *talking as if I'm some kind of expert, someone who knows these things.*

I picked up the rope. "Sandra," I said, "You come last. We'll put Marcio between us."

She nodded.

I took hold of my angel's wings with both hands and stepped out. I did not look down, not then. I just stood for a minute with my feet in the clamps trying not to shake. When I had hold of myself, I strapped down my feet. Tight. Then I hooked my suit to the pole, reached up, switched on the power. My wings came on with a slight tremor. The light showed green. I took hold of the down lever and dropped six feet, enough so Marcio could put his wings on top of mine.

"You all right?" Sandra asked.

I'd been breathing hard, sounding nervous. Not good.

"Fine," I answered with as much confidence as I

could muster. "View's a bit breathtaking."

"Damn it, Nick, admit you're scared like the rest of us."

"I'm okay. Send Marcio over."

Marcio picked up his angel's wings and walked to the side. "I'm going to be sick," he said. "What happens if you get sick inside your suit?"

"We're at three quarters G," Sandra said. "Vomit will settle to the bottom. Smell bad, that's all."

I heard a clank over my suit com.

"Someone's in DP," Sandra said. "Get going, Marcio!"

Marcio shoved his angel's wings against the cable. They sealed around it. He stepped out, breathing hard, and strapped down his feet, taking less time than I had. He hooked his suit to the pole. We powered down. Sandra started out.

I snugged my wings up against Marcio's and screwed the clamp into place. "Get your clamp, Marcio," I said. "We've got to hook these things together."

Sandra had her feet strapped down.

"We're too far apart," Marcio said. "My clamp won't reach Sandra's wings."

I ran us up the few inches between Marcio's unit and Sandra's. We hit with a bump.

"Nick! I'm not hooked on!"

Now Sandra was breathing hard. She hooked on her suit, fast.

"Power up, Sandra."

She flicked on her unit.

I tied the rope around my waist and played out fifty-five feet through my hands.

"Clamp's on," Marcio said.

"Get us out of here, Sandra."

She pulled hard on the down lever, and we fell away from Partway-1.

I grabbed the pole, closed my eyes, tried to keep my stomach away from my chin. "Mãe de Deus," Marcio kept saying, trying to pray, not getting farther than the first words.

A speedometer and odometer unit was built into the pole on level with my neck. I forced my eyes open. Ninety per, and climbing.

"Keep it there, Sandra," I said.

"They can see us, Nick."

"They can see us in Macapá if they look with the right things."

She leveled off at ninety-six per.

"Any sign of them?" I asked.

"Nothing. The depressurization light wasn't on—red, isn't it? Maybe no one was coming through. We just won't know, will we?"

Not till the cable drops away with us on it, I thought. Sandra was probably thinking that, too.

Marcio hadn't said anything besides *Mãe de Deus.* "Power off, Marcio. We'll use your wings in a couple hours."

I turned off my own.

Marcio just kept repeating *Mãe de Deus* over and over again.

I reached up and tapped his leg with the rope.

He screamed.

"Damn," I said, and turned down my suit com volume.

"Can they hear us?" Sandra asked.

I looked at the odometer. We had dropped over eight miles in five minutes. "Suit units at Partway-1 can't pick us up now," I said, and I did know that. A suit com had a mile's range. "Partway-1 and Up Top stations can hear us, but they killed the folks at Partway-1 who knew how to listen in."

"Let's hope Up Top doesn't report us. Do we have a chance, Nick?"

"More than we had at Partway."

Marcio was muttering full sentences now, in Portuguese. I imagined he was promising to be quite a saint if he lived to walk the blessed earth.

"Marcio," I said. "Power off!"

He reached up and shut off his angel's wings. Coherent now, at least. "Take this rope, Marcio," I said. "Tie it around your waist and hand the end up to Sandra."

He took the rope.

"What's this?" Sandra asked.

"Safety backup." Backup I hoped we'd never use.

I looked at my watch. 5:35. We'd dropped for fourteen minutes. Twenty-two point four miles. Not bad time. I let us drop another sixteen minutes. At forty-eight miles down we were out of casual observation from Partway-1.

"Ease up on the speed, Sandra," I said. "We need to find out how these things handle so we'll know what to expect in Macapá."

"Good idea."

She pulled down her lever. We lost speed slowly: 90, 83, 78, 73—it leveled off at seventy-three per. "Keep slowing up," I said.

"Lever's pulled straight down, Nick."

We should have stopped.

"Thing's heating up. Red lights on some units—the battery."

Not only that, we were gaining speed again, fast.

"Power off, Sandra."

She switched off.

The speedometer was spinning in a blur.

"Hang on! I'm pulling my emergency brake."

I pulled it.

The brake caught with a jerk, let go, caught again. We ground to a stop that would have knocked us all off if we hadn't had our suits hooked to the pole. My brake unit heated up bad—red lights steady, not even blinking. I didn't know if it would work if I tried it again.

"So we're going to die," Marcio said, first.

"Not yet," I said, looking down at the green of Amapá and the long, bright Amazon: 448 miles away.

We had dropped four miles in that last minute.

"Well, at least the Japanese brakes work," Sandra said.

We all laughed. It felt good to laugh, we were so nervous.

"Who built the drive?" I asked.

"We did," Marcio said.

"What a team," Sandra quipped. "Our idea and your high tech. We should have known better than to climb onto these things."

"You still have a red light, Sandra?"

"No. It's cooled off."

"Can the batteries blow up?" Marcio asked.

"I don't know."

"Honesty at last," Sandra said.

"I don't know what holds from now on. You may just have bad angel's wings. Or it may be—who knows?"

"At least it seems we can keep a constant speed," Sandra said. "And we *can* stop."

"Unless these things aren't built to take dropping down into the gravity-well. We might get too heavy for them to handle."

"Cheery thought."

"So we'll probably die," Marcio said.

"Then again, they may hold up," I said.

"And in the meantime, our friends at Partway-1 may cut this cable," Sandra said. "Let's do something."

"Power on, Marcio. We'll start down with your drive."

He flicked on the switch. Green light.

"Push up your lever, easy."

He grabbed the lever. When he started to push up on it, I jerked off my emergency brake. We dropped away. Marcio's wings caught hold just fine. I had him level off at 102—figured the sooner we got down, the better.

We stayed pretty quiet after that, watching the night advance across the Atlantic.

"I can't see it," Sandra said, suddenly, an hour later.

"See what?"

"Partway."

I looked up. It was out of sight—had been for some time, I imagined. We were 154 miles down.

"I'd been watching it," she said. "I wanted a picture when it was just a bump on the cable." She looked down at me and took a picture. "I've gotten some good shots: you and Marcio below me, pictures of us back at Partway-1 setting up."

"Good for the grandkids."

"You'll have to get married to get those."

"Too young for that."

"To get married, or to have grandkids?"

"Both."

"I will get married in the Spring," Marcio said.

Which meant September or October south of the Equator. "Nice girl?" I asked.

"The best. She will have a baby four months after our wedding—a boy."

I looked up and saw a red light on Marcio's battery. "Marcio, what's that?" I asked.

He looked up, paused. "The *power is low* light," he said.

His battery had lasted for little over an hour. It should have lasted twice that long, easy. I switched on my power and brought up my lever to match Marcio's. "Power off, Marcio," I said. "My wings'll take over."

He turned off his power.

At that moment, night caught us. Its dark line flowed fast across the tip of Brazil, rushed towards us, engulfed us in darkness, sped west up the Amazon towards the Andes.

Lights gleamed in the black: Macapá, down; Belém, São Luis, south; Paramaribo, north; Manaus, west.

We dropped, quiet, for an hour. I turned on my helmet light and looked at the odometer: 256 miles.

"We've passed halfway," I said. Halfway to what, I didn't know.

"Going to have enough power?" Sandra asked quietly.

We were too heavy. The power wasn't holding up as it should, and now, without sunlight—"Open your tool boxes," I said. "Throw out everything except the belts with magnetic clamps." I didn't need to explain why we might need those. And I kept one good wrench.

My battery lasted for another hour and ten minutes—119 miles, 375 down, 125 to go. "Power on, Marcio," I said. "Let's see if you can take it."

He was not at full power, but he could take it for a time—forty-five, thirty-five minutes?

"We're not going to make it with all this weight, are we?" Sandra said, more a statement than a question.

"Doesn't look like it."

"Let's throw over my angel's wings."

"What?" Marcio asked.

"It's dead weight—only good for the emergency brakes—and both of yours have those."

I didn't tell her what I thought about my brakes.

"I can climb down and stand with you, Nick."

I thought about it. "We could clamp-on one of your feet," I said.

"And I can hook onto your pole. Take my belt, Marcio."

She handed down her belt with the magnetic clamp. Marcio put it in his tool box. I handed Marcio the wrench so he could unscrew Sandra's angel's wings once Sandra was down.

"I've unhooked my suit from the pole," Sandra said. "I'm going to release the top magnetic clamp on my angel's wings. Get ready to—hell, I don't know. If I fall, I guess I've got this rope."

"It's a good Brazilian rope," Marcio said.

"That's all I needed to hear." She crouched down. "I'm getting my feet out of the straps."

"I'll help you over your foot clamps," Marcio said.

She started over. Marcio held her feet. "I'm releasing the bottom magnetic clamp," she said.

It snapped open. For some reason, the clamp holding Sandra's angel's wings to Marcio's broke in two. Her wings fell away. Sandra tumbled back. Marcio kept hold of one of her feet and pulled her in. She clutched the top of my angel's wings.

"Grab the rope around her waist," I shouted.

Marcio grabbed it with one hand.

"Let her swing down to me, slowly. I've got her arms."

He let go of her foot. She swung down sideways, hung onto me. I hooked her suit to the pole, put her hands on the pole. I released my suit, got my feet out of the clamps, put my right foot in the left clamp, her left in the right clamp, hooked my suit back to the pole. I put my arm around her—she still had her camera, tied into the rope around her waist. "Damned brave girl," I said.

She said nothing for seven miles. "I had a bad thought," she said, finally. "How do we know our friends don't control Ground Floor?"

We didn't. The terrorists had negotiated from Up Top—we assumed with Ground Floor. But it could have been with anywhere. "It's night," I said.

"Helmet lights off," Marcio suggested.

Marcio's battery lasted forty-four minutes—another seventy-five miles, which put us 450 miles down. Mine took over again, and though not at full power, we believed we could coax our way down going back and forth between units.

I let us drop at 102 for another twenty-three minutes —roughly forty miles. I figured that when we hit the upper troposphere we ought to start slowing down. We needed to compensate for being tired and hungry. Our reactions would be dulled. Handling angel's wings inside the atmosphere would be something we weren't used to. Sandra and I gathered the rope around us so it wouldn't get caught or tangled in full G—

When my battery went dead. No warning.

"It's sparking," Sandra said. "There's air out around us."

Ten miles to go.

Marcio brought up his unit, but it hadn't had time to recharge much at all.

It wasn't going to work.

"Damned West Germans," Sandra muttered.

I had Marcio slow us down to sixty per. "Toss over your helmets," I said. "Air tanks, too. We'll breathe like Bolivians."

I had mine off. A bitter wind blew loudly. "I've never been on the Altiplano," Sandra shouted after she tossed hers down.

"I have," Marcio yelled. "It's cold, like here."

But we were falling into thicker, warmer air. We dropped for four minutes—four miles: six to go—when Marcio's *power's low* light came on.

"Try your battery, Nick," he said.

I switched it on. My red *power's low* light came on and stayed on.

We could see individual streets in Macapá, the tiny lights of cars and trucks on the TransAmazonica. My *no power* light blinked on. We were going on what was left in Marcio's wings.

"Hang onto your emergency brake lever, Marcio," I yelled. "When this gives way. . . ." I didn't need to say we had to hang on tight after what we'd gone through half an hour out of Partway-1.

Five miles, four miles—

Marcio's red *no power* light flashed on. We dropped away.

"Pull up!" I jerked up on my emergency brake.

Nothing happened.

"Pull up, Marcio!"

"I am!"

We slowed down, gradually, grinding to a halt at

498.1 miles: nearly two miles to go.

I could see the lights of ships on the Amazon, individual buildings in Macapá.

So close.

A wind whipped around us, knocking the loops of the rope against my legs.

"This is sparking bad," Marcio said.

I looked up. His battery was sparking, and all the lights on his angel's wings were red.

"Power off," I said. We hung there, quiet.

"Get on your belts," I said. Marcio handed Sandra's down. The magnetic clamps on the belts were big enough to go around the cable.

Sandra had hers on. "I'm going over," she said.

She crouched down, unstrapped her foot, went over the foot clamps without a word.

"There's ice on the cable," she said.

That's why we had taken so long to stop.

"A lot?"

"Thin film. Enough to make it slippery. Magnetic clamps can still hold us—I think."

It took ten minutes to get Marcio onto my angel's wings, over the foot clamps, onto the cable above Sandra. Then I went. It was a sick feeling till you got yourself hooked to the slippery cable.

We started down.

Sandra would slide till she hit the bottom of her fifty-five foot section of rope where she clamped on. Marcio would slide down above her. Then I would come. It was slow progress. With the length of rope we had, we'd have to slide down roughly 191 times to finish the 1.9 miles.

"Will the magnetic clamps hold our angel's wings up there?" Marcio asked.

The burnt-out brakes wouldn't be much help. The wings could start sliding.

"With the ice between them and the cable?" Sandra added.

"Hurry," was all I could suggest.

We slid past the ice. Our movements became automatic, hard. We were exhausted—physically and nervously—with two angel's wings above our heads that might not hold.

One hour downcable—probably eight hundred feet up—a floodlight was trained on us.

"Ground Floor must have picked up our suit-com talk before we threw over the helmets," I said.

"And they must be friends," Marcio said, "or they wouldn't give us light."

"Why didn't they talk?" Sandra asked.

"Up Top could hear—cut the cable."

More lights were turned on. We could see crowds of people waiting at the bottom of the cable, people running into the compound from all the buildings of Ground Floor.

They started putting foam on the ground, foam for us to fall into. We got low enough to hear the people, call to them. They cheered and clapped their hands.

Sandra dropped down again. "I'm only ten feet from the ground," she shouted as she clamped on. Marcio slid down to her. After I slid down to him, we felt a slight tremor in the cable.

"The angel's wings!" Marcio shouted.

"Jump!" Sandra yelled.

We unhooked and jumped.

The angel's wings slammed down the cable, hit the ground, broke apart.

I struggled up out of the foam. People hugged me,

held me up, got the ropes off from around me, talked to
me in a babble of languages.

"Mi hijo!" one old woman shouted.

But I was not her son.

She looked away and turned to run, but too many
people crowded around us. All she could do was stand
there, sobbing. Another old woman took hold of her
arm, pulled her off through the crowd. A dark haired,
pretty girl stepped up, spoke to me in English. "My
mother—she think you were my brother," she said. "We
come from Uruguay when we hear what happened. My
brother is reporter for paper in Montevideo. Do you
know him? He speaks good English. He is your age,
black hair—"

I thought of the Montevideans they had shot the first
day.

She saw my face. She stepped back. "Did you see him
die, then?"

I nodded.

"How?"

"First day. They shot him. He wasn't thrown over till
he was dead."

"But how did he die?"

I understood what she was asking. "He was very
brave," I said. "You would have been proud."

She turned away, held herself straight, walked back
to her mother, to tell her. To come all the way from
Uruguay to hear news like that—

Sandra put her arms around me. I held onto her.
"Let's go call home," she said.

And then Marcio was there, with his mother, fiancée,
and ten or fifteen relatives and friends, all smiles and
tears.

"They come stay with my aunt," he said proudly.

"You come stay in my aunt's house, too—not in bad Macapá hotel, not after this."

"Oh, no," Sandra murmured, looking up at me.

A woman who must have been the aunt took hold of our hands. "Food good, my house," she said in halting English. "Bed, soft. You very welcome stay my house." Marcio's mother hugged us and talked and talked to us in Portuguese. Marcio translated. " 'You saved my life,' she says. She knows I am afraid of heights. 'Come stay with us,' she says."

Government doctors took the three of us away. When they finished poking and probing, American and Brazilian military men questioned us until I, at least, couldn't stay awake any longer. So they let us go till morning. One of them told us that since the bodies thrown from Partway-1 couldn't be identified as individuals, they would be buried together east of Jacob's Ladder, in a memorial garden.

"Already planned," Sandra murmured.

"The price of the stars," one official said.

I thought of the Uruguayan mother and figured it was a high price.

Marcio's family was waiting for us. We went with them.

The food was good.

The Language
of The Sea
by
Carolyn Ives Gilman

About the Author

In person, Carolyn Ives Gilman is very quiet and charming. Like most writers, she does not at once strike you with the discovery that she is full of universes. But they're there.

She works at a history museum in the Twin Cities area, and has authored several books on the fur trade and American Indian history, but only one previous published work of fiction. Her story here was her fourth entry in the Contest; winning Second Place in the second Quarter.

She interacts with a local writer's group, and sees SF as "A logical form of rebellion." That it is, in some ways of looking at it. And in the story that follows, rebellion crops up again and again . . . in the characters and situations. The author just quietly moves them along, from flare-up to flare-up, as if she were totally in ultimate command. . . .

We did not deal with the problem of Ritchet until too late. It was typical of us. A-board the Vessel we had a saying, "A problem put off is a problem put right." The truth is, the collective could not make a prompt decision, any more than I could have gotten out of my chair and run around the main deck.

But the behavior Ritchet had brought back from his sojourn ashore grew more disruptive each day. He acted as if he had never left the depraved quayside bordellos, where brazenness is taken for courage. Many of us came to wish secretly that he would take to the land and never darken our decks again.

By the time we called him to an accounting, the list of his enemies was long. He also had some friends left; for even in his debauchery he had a kind of ruined charm, an afterglow of the seagull braggadocio that had lured him to land in the first place. But he made no attempt to call his friends to his defense. As a result, all his judges were his enemies.

All but one. I sat in the midst of them, though Ritchet had never given me offense. As if to show his disregard for us, he sauntered into the justice center wearing gray stevedores' pants torn off at the knee and a sweat-stained palampore. His jaw was unshaven and his hair slicked down to hide the touches of premature gray. He

Illustrated by Brian Murray

stood before us with thumbs hooked in his belt loops, sullen and impatient.

I could feel the surge of indignation on either side of me. The judges had discussed two courses of action: one harsh, one lenient. There was no longer any question which they would pursue.

Graban served as spokesman. With meticulous accuracy he listed each of Ritchet's offenses against the Vessel. The accused man listened passively, occasionally acknowledging the truth of a charge with a shrug. Once, he pretended to rub his chin to hide a smile. Some inebriates are penitent afterwards; not Ritchet.

His attitude goaded Graban into a rage. "There is no word contemptible enough for you. Your existence is an insult to us."

"Ah, the harmony of consensus," Ritchet said with sarcasm thick enough to caulk a dory.

"Animal!" Carche sprung up. "Don't you soil our Vessel with your sarcasm. Get back to the fleshpots of the mainland where you belong!"

"Be docile or be gone!" Ritchet mimicked her. "You're all a pile of puppets, scared of life. Where's the one of you that would stand up straight in a storm? You'd all be shitting in your pants for fear."

"And you would be vomiting your liquor!" Carche snapped.

I caught Graban's eye to let him know I thought this had gone far enough. With difficulty, he spoke in an even tone. "Ritchet, we have an accounting to offer you. It is your choice: either consent to confinement for a year's work in the heart room, or take the sloop tomorrow for the mainland and never return."

The hook was shrewdly baited. To confine Ritchet in the heat and roar of the heart room was to clip a seagull's wings. The accounting only had the semblance of fairness. It was banishment either way.

Ritchet saw it, too; I could tell from the wild-wary glance he shot at Graban. But there was something heavy in his look as well, as if the hook had snagged him long ago, and he had carried it with him into the room. All this time he had avoided my eyes; but now he stood before me, and could not look away. Our eyes met, and I understood.

His flight to the mainland had not been one to freedom. His wanderings had only exposed the boundaries of his prison. Contempt, loathing, defeat—no word Graban used could come close to what Ritchet's pitilessly clear eyes saw in the mirror of their own honesty.

In the instant that I understood, I knew he must not leave, or he would never be free. His eyes widened in surprise as he saw my understanding, narrowed again as he realized what I would want him to do.

"All right," he said slowly, never taking his eyes from me. "It will do no good, but I will let you see that. Give me the keys to the heart room."

The others said nothing after he left. They were not angry at me, but a little angry at themselves for not foreseeing what I would do. Graban collected their judicial robes to throw back into the chest, transforming them into ordinary citizens again. He came to me last, kneeling down to unfasten the robe at my throat.

"I assume you have a reason," he murmured.

"Yes," I answered.

But I couldn't have said what it was.

An hour later I lay on my face in the natatorium with Geal massaging my knotted muscles. Ordinarily it was a pleasant experience; today for some reason every pass of his hands was like a knife twisting among my weary tendons.

"You're tense today," he said.

My teeth were clenched too tight to let me answer.

He paused to apply sweet-smelling oil to his hands. "So you foiled their little plot to get rid of Ritchet," he said.

"Mmm," I acknowledged.

"Why?"

I had difficulty speaking from a prone position. He waited patiently until I said, "I like him."

Geal's low laugh was a comfortable sound, like waves rippling against the hull. "Good for you," he said. "I like him, too. I only wish he liked himself better."

So Geal understood. I should have known. He worked in silence for a while, then finally turned me over. "Want to try the pool today?" he asked.

I shook my head. "I want . . . to go. . . ."

He saw I was having trouble, so he helped me sit up. "Where do you want to go?"

"The grove."

"Oh, no, you don't. It's raining."

"I don't care."

"You'll get arthritis."

"Not with you there."

Sighing, he brought my chair and wrapped my arm around his neck to lift me in. It always amazed me that a man of Geal's age could have such strength in his spindly limbs.

He dressed both of us warmly, with an outer layer of storm gear. As he rolled me out through the corridors, the glances of passers-by were sharp with curiosity. Word of what had happened in the justice center had spread fast.

While we were passing the playground, two children persuaded Geal to let them push my chair as another rode on the arm. It was all I could do to keep them from breaking their skulls and mine. I was mildly grateful when Geal finally shooed them away.

Despite Geal's prediction, it was not raining when we emerged into the soggy sunbean fields amidships. The squall was departing like a mourner in a veil of gray. It was still blustery, and none of the horticulturists were at work. Far off toward the hilly pastureland of the bow, we could see a lone herdsman rounding up a flock of sheep that had strayed too near the gray cliff-edge of the hull.

We headed astern through muddy grain fields. The Path grew steeper and more rocky as we climbed through the orchard, until at last we left the cultivated area. There was a steep rock escarpment which we skirted on a path silent with pine needles. Then at last we were atop it, among the sighing firs, with all the landscape of the Vessel spread below.

I surveyed the entire world as I knew it in that moment atop the Vessel's tree-bearded spine. I had never been aboard another Vessel, and the land was merely a rumor to me. I believed it did exist, of course . . . a brief blemish on the glistening globe.

The sea was dark and froth-scarred, but we could scarcely feel its swells as the Vessel, athwart the wind, rode south. It was feeding now, its mammoth jaws open to suck plankton into the processing chambers, from which the waste water discharged in two white gushers beneath the Vessel's bulging sides. We were close to Antarctic waters, but there was still no sign of ice floes on the sea. When they appeared, we would start the summer harvest in the colonies of krill, stocking our

Vessel's belly full for the return trip north, where we would sell our sea-crops to feed the wasted land.

The sun was struggling with a scowling mob of clouds in the west. At last it broke free and gilded a path across the waves. I stared at the black mote outlined on its edge; and so I became first to see the invaders.

"A boat," I said in some surprise. It had taken me several moments to come to that conclusion. It was so laughably small.

Geal had wandered off into the forest; but he came back at the sound of my voice. I pointed the boat out to him.

He squinted into the sun. "A landsman's craft. A long way from home."

The radio antenna on our forecastle swiveled till it pointed its dish toward the black fleck on the water. Someone inside had picked up a transmission.

"What land?" I asked Geal.

"There's a coast some fifty leagues west of us," he said. "I never heard if it was inhabited."

We started back down the rust-carpeted path. The sun surrendered to the clouds again.

As Geal propelled me down the cochlear spiral of the Vessel's ear complex, we felt the subtle shift of a change in speed underfoot. When we entered the inner ear, Doreal looked up from the radio receiver and made a motion of greeting. I raised my eyebrows in question.

"A distress signal," he explained. "A boat of landsmen in trouble. They want us to let them on board. Tat and I decided we ought to do it."

A message on his earphones interrupted him. He paused to listen, then responded, "All right, I'll tell them." He switched over to broadcast and intoned,

"Flotsam, Flotsam, this is Leviathan. You are cleared to enter the starboard cargo dock. We will cut speed to match you in 60 seconds. Over."

A second tremor passed through the bulkheads as the Vessel lost more speed. I tried to look at Geal's face, but he was behind me. Doreal turned back to us. "Landsmen! They're a menace to themselves. They have been traveling for three weeks and are almost out of supplies. They were lucky we came along."

Traveling to where? I wondered. If they were looking for land, they were 150 miles off course.

"We'll find out more soon," Doreal said. "Porchet was going to bring them to the Ganglion."

The Ganglion was not so much a room as a node formed by the intersection of a webwork of passages. From any one point it was impossible to see how many people watched from the nooks and embolisms of the free-formed metal; but as Geal and I entered, I sensed there were many.

Five citizens had volunteered to act as delegates; they were still shrugging on their robes as Geal pushed me up onto the dais. He did not have time to fetch my robe before the strangers were shown into the chamber.

They were all men, tired and weather-worn. As they came forward, they craned in wonder at the walls; I later learned it was because metals are rare and precious in their homeland. There were less than a score of them, but their leader walked as if they were an army.

He seemed larger than other men in the room, though in fact he was small, stocky as a wrestler, with tightly curled black hair and beard. His eyes were fixed, not glancing as most people's are, and too much of the whites showed. Yet they had a persuasive quality, too. It was hard to look away from him. The intensity of a hurricane seemed compressed into his frame.

He took charge of the situation immediately, and none of us had the wit or assertiveness to stop him.

"Lords of Leviathan!" he addressed us with dramatic courtesy. "I am Barone, of the Crusade of the Eastern Warriors. Our small party set out from Bashin three weeks ago, searching for you; we wandered over a hundred leagues of empty sea. It was God's will that brought us here together."

He paused, but no one offered to answer him, so he went on, setting one foot upon the dais as if about to mount it. "Your vast riches and powers are only legend on the mainland; we have made this pilgrimage to see their truth. We come in peace; you may search my mind if you doubt me." He closed his eyes and stood still for several moments. The delegates exchanged puzzled glances; this mainland custom was new to us.

"You are welcome to the Vessel," stately Raen replied. "We do not deal with landsmen much, so you must forgive us if we fail to know your ways."

His eyes opened again, and for an instant they held a spark of triumph that made me wonder. He turned to look around the Ganglion. I saw him take in the dome, dripping metal stalactites; the arched, irregular openings crowded with spectators; the pillared superstructure of aluminum and steel.

"Rumor has not done you justice," he said at last. "You are rich beyond the wildest dreams of the land-born."

"We try to nourish our Vessel," Raen replied.

"Who is your leader?"

"We are all leaders."

"But who is supreme above you all?"

After a moment's hesitation, Raen turned to me. "This is our Given."

The landsman's eyes upon me were opaque and indurate as agate. A slight smile shadowed his face, and it gave me a chill. For an instant I saw myself as he saw me—a huddle of thin, misshapen limbs, of no more consequence than the chair I sat in. It was a shock, for I had never known contempt before.

"This is your commander?" he asked with a gentleness that lied.

"No," Raen said patiently, "he is our Given."

Barone turned away. "We are eager to see the marvels of your Vessel. But it is knowledge we seek above all else. Your sciences are fabled far and wide. The psychic arts are forgotten on the mainland."

He made this strange statement with an air of forced casualness, like the boy who tries to see how outrageous he can be before someone will stop him.

I grappled down my doubt: I could not be sure it was founded in truth, and not in envy. When I looked at him, so commanding, so controlled, I could not help but wonder about myself. As I sat silent, Raen answered with a laugh, "They are forgotten here as well, if such arts exist. But we will show you what we can. I fear we cannot return you to your homeland soon, for we are bound south for the harvest."

"Nothing could suit me better," Barone said.

He continued asking questions until I reached a resolve. Raen's attention was fixed on him, and I was forced to say her name.

It was Barone who turned to me, all seeming concern. "I fear your Given is ill," he said.

Raen bent down beside me. I did not wish to explain

my fears before the man, but my expression said enough:
I did not trust him.

"Why not?" she asked softly.

I shook my head. "I . . . don't know."

When she rose to resume her conversation, she was
more guarded. He looked at me, more surprised than
angry, I thought. When Raen had assigned them rooms
and hours, I glanced at Geal to come take me away. But
Barone stepped in his path with a great show of courtesy
and said, "Let me."

He wheeled me out through the curious crowd. I
could see the effect his kindly gesture had upon the
onlookers. As we passed, Barone nodded to them with
unassuming dignity; but I was sunk deep in thought.

In the next week, it seemed that Barone's men were
everywhere: exploring, observing, and listening. The
people were patient with them, since they were uncouth
landsmen who knew no better; but it became hard to
have a private conversation.

I avoided Barone myself. Whenever I saw him, all my
failings seemed thrown into harsh relief, and I doubted
my own fitness. Nevertheless, I heard much of him. The
man was a dynamo. He seemed to be everywhere at
once. He asked many questions, but never the same one
twice. Processes that had taken us years to learn, he
grasped in a few short hours, and never forgot a detail. I
cannot say that people liked him; he seemed to hold
himself above us. But they admired him.

He had one odd trait: he was obsessed with what
he called the "psychic arts." At first he could not believe
what Raen had told him honestly, that we had no knowledge of any such arts. After many others had echoed
her, he stopped asking openly, but came at the subject

obliquely, as if to trick us into revealing something.

I overheard one such conversation on a day when Geal had left me alone in the conservatory. I was supposed to be reading a proposal on phytoplankton processing that was coming up for discussion at the next roundtable; but I was distracted by the sound of voices on the path beyond the fragrant screen of tomato plants. It was Barone and Carche.

"I have been here a week, and never yet seen anyone give an order," Barone was saying.

Carche laughed. Her normally acerbic manner was respectful.

"Are they given in some way I cannot see?" Barone pressed.

"No," she answered. "They just aren't given."

I could practically hear the frown on his face. "How do the workers know what jobs to do?"

"They just see what needs to be done, and do it."

"No supervision? No discipline?"

"If you're not working well, everyone knows it."

She hadn't really answered his question, but he did not pursue it. Instead, after a short silence, he asked, "Then who makes the large decisions?"

"The community."

"Through majority vote?"

"No, through consensus."

"And how do you reach consensus?"

"We argue the issue through. In the conscience center."

"And what happens if you disagree?"

She laughed again. She was being uncharacteristically patient with him. "We always do."

"Then who prevails? The most powerful, or the most numerous?"

"The most stubborn," she said.

The report slid off my lap onto the gravel. At the sound, their voices ceased and I heard a rustle among the rhododendrons, then their footsteps receding. There was no one to pick up the paper for me, but I did not care.

There was too much else to think on.

We might have paid more attention to Barone and his crew if it had not been a busy time. We had come into Antarctic waters. Night was falling behind as we sped south toward the pole, and the harvest workers were preparing to start continual shifts in the unending light of summer. The other Vessels had not arrived yet, so we set about the search for the richest beds of krill alone.

I was on rest shift when the crisis came. I woke suddenly from a sound sleep, wondering what had disturbed me. Staring through the dim light at the rubbly metal wall, I at last realized what was wrong: the silence. The rumble of the Vessel's digestion, which had been continual for weeks now, was gone. The Vessel was no longer feeding.

I pressed the buzzer for Geal until he shuffled grumpily into my cell, cross at having been wakened. When I told him what I had noticed, he immediately called the brain room. When there was no response, we knew something was wrong.

Hastily, Geal threw some clothes on us both and we set out. At first the corridors were strangely empty. But as we neared our destination, we found a crowd around the entrance to the brain room, listening silently to something within. No one spoke as we approached, but they moved aside to let us pass through, and their faces were grave.

The room was packed. When we broke through to the front, I saw what was afoot. Barone was speaking from the raised deck where the second tier of navigational instruments lay. He was flanked by three of his companions. All held ugly black machines that made my skin crawl. I had never seen such things before, but instinct told me they were weapons.

When Barone saw me, he paused. Geal spoke up forcefully. "The Given wants to know what is going on."

"I have taken command of this ship," Barone answered in a voice like law. "The Vessel is rededicated to the Crusade of the Eastern Warriors. You will all be serving the great cause by following my orders absolutely. My men are stationed at every key point; they will give you your assignments."

By his voice I knew we were no more to him than motes, details. He had measured us as adversaries and found us lacking. As I looked around the room, I could see why. Nothing but confusion, fear, and apprehension met my eyes. Inside me, anger surged: Did they need a consensus meeting to know that this was wrong? I looked up at Geal and jerked my head in a swift, uncompromising negative.

"The Given does not agree," Geal announced. "You do not have consensus."

A slow smile spread across Barone's bearded face. "Then let him stop me," he said.

There was a silence. Geal looked at me for guidance. Strands of his white hair were stuck to his forehead with perspiration.

Mistaking our silence for defeat, Barone gave a thundering laugh. "You call this a leader?" he mocked the crowd. "This palsied cripple? If he wishes to command, let him take this gun from me!"

I gave Geal the signal with my eyes. "Very well, we shall!" he said, and started forward. At his back, the crowd surged up like a monsoon wave, all confusion suddenly gone.

An explosion stunned us. With startled cries, the crowd pulled back. Before me, a red flower bloomed upon Geal's back. He fell slowly, first onto a knee, then crumpling with a terrible bubbling gasp.

Barone stood on the deck, his weapon still breathing smoke. Into the silence he said, "Does anyone else oppose me?"

On the floor, Geal's body quivered once, as if the stubborn nerves rebelled against the failed heart; then it stiffened from the center outward. Everyone had drawn away, leaving him alone, like a pile of discarded laundry. I wanted to go to him, but no one came to move me.

With a peremptory gesture, Barone ordered us to disperse. Someone jerked my chair around and was about to push me quickly out of the room. Stunned by what I had done, I would have submitted passively, but a disturbance at the door wrenched me back to my senses.

Someone was trying to force his way in as all the others were leaving. There were arguing voices—hushed and angry on one side, loud and belligerent on the other.

The woman beside me bent down to hear what I wanted to say. "Let him in," I ordered.

The word passed quickly through the crowd, and they stepped back to let Ritchet in.

He was drunk. His gait was unstable, his face flabby as an undercooked pudding. But it took him only a glance at the room to understand all that had happened. His gaze rose from the body on the floor behind me to Barone, and then down again to me. His eyes would only have grazed me, but I caught and held them. Against his will he shared a moment of understanding with me. His head jerked in an automatic negative, denying he realized what I was thinking. But I gestured to him, demanding, desperate. Slowly he came forward.

I signaled the others away. There was a stir when the people nearby realized what I intended. But with Barone watching, no one dared protest. Without opposition, Ritchet took Geal's place behind my chair.

The sight of Geal's unmade bed was almost too much to bear. Ritchet had brought me back to the cell that was now his as well as mine, and left me sitting in the nucleus as he rummaged in a cupboard for a stimulant. Through the door Geal had left ajar I could see the orderliness of his room, disturbed only by the crumpled covers he had left at my call. I wondered if they were still warm.

Gentle, cranky, devoted Geal. How many nights had he given up his sleep for my sake? He had lived a taken-for-granted life—not unappreciated, but unpraised. I could only hope he had known he was loved.

Ritchet slumped into a chair in front of me, legs spread haphazardly. He had settled for a cup of hot drink. He was sobering fast. His eyes now lanced around the room suspiciously.

"Nice try," he said sardonically. He waved his hand at the simple luxuries that surrounded us. "Private bath, separate heating, carpet, communications, status, deference, power—" His voice rose with each word, and he capped them off with a landsman's oath. "You must think I'm an imbecile to fall into this trap."

I didn't need to answer; he knew it was untrue. After all, I was putting my life in his hands.

My silence only made him angry. "You can't fool me.

You're no better than Graban and his crew, just craftier. Not one of you can bear a free mind in your midst. They tried to tame me with punishment, you try rewards. It's all the same."

His self-centeredness almost made me lose my temper. How could he imagine I had been thinking of him at the moment of Geal's death? But I controlled myself. "We need you," I said.

He gave a bitter bark of laughter. "That's true. You've needed me ever since that barracuda Barone came on board. Why didn't you ask me? I could have told you what an Eastern Warrior was."

He didn't have to remind me. It had been a fatal mistake. But my answer was obvious: I was asking him now. When he realized it, he flushed and rose, running his hand across his thinning hair. "What makes you think I'll help you?" he demanded abrasively. "I happen to be attached to my own skin, and I know the sort of man Barone is. I wouldn't go athwart him for a hundred Vessels."

He was trying to shock me into denouncing him so that he would have an excuse for returning the favor. But I wasn't the sort of fool Graban was. Frustrated, he grew even more outrageous. "Perhaps I'll just join up with Barone and help myself to some of the spoils. Maybe he'll set me up in business if I give him the information he needs, if I tell him who his real enemies are."

"Then turn me in," I said.

He stared, remembering too late that I saw through him. His lip curled; he hated me for reminding him that he had some integrity left.

"No," he said, "I'm not going to do you the favor of ruining your Vessel. You can do it all by yourself. I don't

give a damn who loses, who wins. You'll have to make
your own mistakes." He crossed the distance to the door
like a man in flight. "You can find me in the heart
room," he said, and slammed the door behind him.

I waited for him to return all that day, and all the next
night. He had left me sitting in the center of the room, so
I could not move my chair by grasping onto furniture or
walls. With great effort I might have pushed my way to
the door to summon help, but I decided not to. I did not
want just anyone's help.

I spent the time trying to understand how I could
have misjudged Barone so disastrously. All the moral
forces that controlled our minds like the laws of physics
control the atoms were missing from Barone. He existed
in another universe, able to harm us but safe from harm
himself.

Yet there had to be laws even in his alternate world.
There had to be limits he would respect. I needed Ritchet desperately. There was no way to fight Barone
without stepping into his world. Ritchet, with one foot
permanently planted in each sphere, was the gateway I
must use.

But first I had to conquer Ritchet. I followed him in
my imagination, gauging the moment when he must
realize he had left me helpless at the worst possible time,
tracing him through excuses, rationalizations. I marked
the time when he would start asking after me, then his
stubborn refusal to care.

In the moments when I grew weary of waiting, I idly
tallied up the insurmountable obstacles that surrounded
me in the shape of simple things like beds, cups, and
bathrooms. Without Geal's patient presence, my familiar home was like the fabled torture chambers where

prisoners were starved in sight of banquets, or frozen in sight of crackling fires.

Hunger was the first thing that began to trouble me, for I had not eaten since the previous day. Then my back and chest began to ache from sitting upright, and I slumped down till it grew difficult to breathe. Toward evening, shooting pains in my thighs kept sleep from coming. Hour after hour I sat awake, Geal's ghost my only companion.

Once, when it seemed as if the old man stood before me, I asked if he thought I had killed him. He frowned testily at my question. "I would have left you sometime anyway," he said. How like Geal that answer was.

By the time I heard the door open and saw Ritchet in front of me, I no longer cared that I had won. I only cared about myself. It was not until he lowered me into a steaming bath that I began to come alive again. Later, as he was helping me eat, he asked half resentfully, "What would you have done if I hadn't come? Sat and starved to death?" I smiled at him through a mouthful of spoon. "Stubborn!" he exclaimed violently under his breath.

I was asleep almost before he put me to bed. The luxury of lying prone had never seemed so close to heaven before. I did not even dream of guns or death.

When I woke, I lay for a time listening to Ritchet moving around in Geal's room next door. I reached for the buzzer to summon him, but he came to the door before I had a chance to press it. It was strange; Geal had had that trick as well.

He was still unshaven and disreputably dressed. His eyes had the self-accusatory resentment of a man who has been the butt of a joke and doesn't like it. I did not wholly have him yet. But I could not wait. I gestured him over. Our business was just beginning.

"Tell me about Barone's world," I said.

The consensus meeting was held in the conscience center, as usual. When Ritchet rolled me in, my heart fell to see how many people had come. I could not blame them; of course they were concerned about what was going on. But if they had stayed away, we might have reached consensus sooner.

People were still filing in when Graban rose and addressed me.

"Given, I cannot accept this drunken ruffian as your speaker. Many others feel the same. You must choose another."

Ritchet was leaning casually against my chair, one leg bent. "Do you really think this is the time to be quarreling amongst ourselves, Graban?" he asked.

"I was addressing myself to the Given," Graban said formally.

I stared stonily at him. Graban was not stupid; but ambition had tamed him. Ritchet was a living mockery of all men who lived by self-discipline.

Glancing down at me, Ritchet said, "I think the Given has answered you. Satisfied?" He whirled me unceremoniously around and planted my chair near the center of the circle of seats.

"You're drunk," Graban hissed, outraged.

"Perceptive," Ritchet grinned, though I knew he hadn't touched a drop.

"You bring disgrace to this Vessel."

I brought my hand down forcefully on the arm of my chair to shut them both up. Graban subsided, smoldering. Ritchet propped his feet up on a nearby chair and began to trim his fingernails with a pocket knife.

I signaled Dilja to start the meeting. Composed as always, she stood to summarize the situation.

We were no longer heading south for the rendezvous and summer harvest. Barone had ordered the Vessel around, and now we traveled northwest at top speed. We were due to make landfall in 48 hours, somewhere along an isolated stretch of coast south of the inhabited lands. At my side, Ritchet nodded grimly; the news confirmed a conjecture of his.

"Barone must be made to understand that he does not have the consensus of the Vessel," said Donall, one of the elder citizens.

"I have spoken to him," Graban said. "His reply was, 'I need no consensus but fear.' And he himself fears nothing."

"Then perhaps we may bribe him," Faro suggested. She had been working in the digestive system, and her coveralls were stained with green protein. "Our winter harvest lies in the hold. The landsmen would find it valuable."

There was heated discussion of whether this was an appropriate use for our harvest. Ritchet and I exchanged a look. At last he broke in, "And what makes you think the harvest is ours any longer?"

No one answered. They stared at him, uncomprehending.

"If Barone controls the Vessel, he controls all the Vessel holds."

"You mean he would simply take it?" someone asked.

Ritchet grinned. "That's how landsmen act."

A divisive series of recriminations began. "Why did you let him make you change the Vessel's course?" Dylaka demanded of the brain room workers.

"He puts a gun at your head and threatens to kill

you," one exclaimed. "It would do no good to defy him.
All he needs is twenty people more afraid of death than
of obedience, and he would win, though hundreds of us
died."

We were learning Barone's lessons fast.

At last Graban spoke up. "We outnumber these
landsmen many times. Why cannot we use violence and
fear as well as they?"

I signaled Ritchet, and he rose. "Would you like to
hear the Given's plan?" he drawled, scratching his jaw.
Graban turned angrily to protest, but I caught his eye
with a warning glance. The plan Ritchet and I had
concocted would need absolute consensus.

Slowly, eyes locked on mine, Graban sank into his
chair again. Ritchet was about to speak; but from the
balcony above us, a stony voice fell into the silence.

"I have seen enough." Barone came to the edge of the
balcony railing. He gave an order, and four armed men
entered the room.

"This meeting is treason against the Crusade," Barone
addressed us from above. "I have marked you, every
one. From now on you will be watched, sleeping and
waking. No word you breathe will escape my knowledge. Now disperse to your jobs, and think twice before
angering me again!" He turned to his men. "Clear the
room. I want that one only."

He waved his hand, and for a moment of sheer panic
I thought he meant Ritchet. But as I looked up, Ritchet
was no longer at my side. As Dilja passed me, I caught
at her hand. "Ritchet knows my mind," I said. She gazed
at me, consternation and worry battling for the upper
hand. The words I had uttered virtually delegated to
Ritchet my place as Given of the Vessel.

"Given, he fled," she said. "He has deserted you."

One of Barone's ruffians shoved her away and wheeled my chair over to where another guard stood. Only then did I realize that I was the one Barone had singled out.

When the room was empty Barone entered, having descended from the balcony. His gait was slow, but his shoulders held stored tension like a spring.

He did not turn to me at once. Instead he looked to the guard at my side. "What did you think of that, Jerro?"

"I think you should get rid of that Graban," the man said. "He's a ringleader."

Barone's smile showed teeth like a serrated knife amid the sheath of beard. "I think not. I think he has no courage. He was being goaded." He finally looked at me. "The algies told us who their ringleader was, only we didn't believe them. We thought our mission had failed, Jerro. It hasn't. God has given us what we wanted."

With cautious disbelief, Jerro looked at me, then at Barone. "You mean this cripple?" he asked.

"They didn't read our minds when we came, so when they said they had no psychic powers, we believed them. And they were right, in a way: the algies are not telepaths, as the stories say. There is only one telepath on board: this one."

I waited for Jerro to hoot him to shame. The idea was so wild, so ludicrous. But Jerro only gave a thoughtful grunt. Barone continued unchecked.

"He was the only one to suspect us from the beginning. When we took over, the algies were as docile as kittens—until he showed up. He's able to give commands without leaving that chair or even talking. Who knows? He may control everyone aboard." He turned to me, reveling in his delusion. "Only you can't control *us,* can you? Your powers have their boundaries."

Under other circumstances I would have laughed. I looked at Jerro's battered, unimaginative face, wondering why he didn't see reason.

"How can we be sure?" he asked stolidly. "We've never heard his thoughts."

"No; he's able to hide them from us, to pass for normal—or subnormal. A useful talent. If the Consortium had known of him, they would have seized him long ago. But they were slow and unimaginative, as usual. Once more God has aided the quick and crafty."

I was growing afraid.

Barone drew up a chair in front of me, so close his knees almost touched mine. "It's time for you to cooperate."

It was like sitting before a furnace: he radiated monomania. At such close range, the force of his personality and my hatred were like the poles of two magnets forced together. I had to look away. As my eyes moved to Jerro, the soldier stepped back, shielding his face. Hearing the movement, Barone whipped around, a pistol suddenly in his hand.

"Damn it, Jerro, get behind him, where I can see you," he snapped. The soldier obeyed. "Watch out, in case he attacks."

Barone's eyes were narrow on my face. "Now tell me what I'm thinking," he said.

I searched feverishly for some response. Nothing Ritchet had said had prepared me for this. After a silence, Barone asked roughly, "What's the matter, can't you talk?"

"I . . . I can talk," I stammered. My neck muscles were twitching with tension.

"You just don't need to very much, right?"

It *was* right, but not for the reasons he thought. "I'm no telepath," I said.

"I don't have to tell you how short my patience is," he said. It was true; he was like a forest branch bent and ready to snap back in my face. "I have to know the nature of your power."

And I had to know the nature of his. Gathering my resolve, I looked him in the eye. But there was nothing to see. There was no crack in the wall of obsession. I only sensed one thing: if he was a closed door to me, I was the same to him. To him, I existed only as a reflection of the driving idea he had followed across the ocean. And if ever I ceased to reflect his thoughts back to him, he would forget me or see me killed with equal unconcern.

I had no choice but to lure him on into the morass of his own delusions. The alien landscape of his mind was my only weapon.

"I will not show you," I said.

A slow smile spread across his face. "So I am right," he said. "You admit that."

He read my silence as one of frustration and defeat. In a way, it was: but it was a calculated defeat. I had to entice him on, to buy time. Forty-eight hours, to be precise.

"You *will* show me, and you will serve me." He watched me with a predatory triumph. "When I return to the White Chamber with you, I will know the traitors, the hidden plots, the strategies of my enemies. There will be no stopping me." His eyes flashed to Jerro, and his

hand jerked in a command I did not understand. But
Jerro did. Seizing hold of my chair, he wheeled me back
and toward the door. Barone was laughing softly as we
left.

Over the next two days, I became a pilgrim in the
strange land of Barone's fantasies. He started by telling
me a heady tale of the future. Big words like "conquest"
and "retribution" filled the small room to bursting. I
would be at his side, he said, a shadowy counselor and
confidant. All he accomplished would be mine as well.

Gradually he revealed how he hoped to use me. We
started with experiments. One of his henchmen stood
outside the door, and Barone called upon me to read the
man's mind and relay the information telepathically to
him.

I pretended to resist. My deception was delicate: to
make him believe he was on the right path, to hold his
attention without letting him guess I could never give
him what he wanted.

He tried tricks aimed at forcing my hand. Once, Jerro
burst into the room with a gun, threatening to shoot me.
Afterwards, Barone asked why I hadn't tried to stop
him. "I knew he wouldn't do it," I said. There was
always an answer like that: telepathy, like precognition,
lends itself to tautological explanations.

But Barone was no fool. To convince him I almost
had to convince myself. The multiple layers of my ruse
began to blur after a while. What was I really trying to
hide? I was no longer sure.

Worse, as the long hours passed, I was no longer sure
he was wrong. Once, when he left me alone for a while, I
closed my eyes and tried to send my people a thought to
rise and rescue me. I listened feverishly for voices in my

brain that would bring an answer. But there were no
voices, and no one came. When I came to my senses, I
realized how nearly the trapper had become the trapped.
My footing was treacherous: if I forgot for an instant
who I was, then I would start to share his delusion.

At the same time, I became aware of a hidden stra-
tum of communication between Barone and his men.
They were so intent on him that they knew his purposes
and needs before he had to voice them. Often, an order
was no more than a glance, a movement of the head, an
expression of the eyes. I felt like shouting out that
Barone's telepaths were right under his nose.

More than forty-six hours passed before Ritchet
made his move. Barone was with me when tumult arose
in the artery outside and a soldier burst into the cell,
asking to see his commander. It was as well they did
not see the expression on my face, or they would have
thought me telepathic indeed.

They left me alone for almost an hour. I listened in
suspense to the hurried footsteps passing outside my cell
door, the series of odd clanks and thumps propagated
through the bulkheads. At last one of Barone's men
came to fetch me to the brain room. When we entered,
Barone and three others were bent over a chart, talking
heatedly. Around the controls, technicians stood anx-
iously monitoring speed, course, and fuel consumption.
When the men at the chart table looked up, I was
shocked to see Graban was one of them.

"Given, the Vessel is in danger!" he exclaimed, stung
by my accusatory look. "We have to put our differences
aside, or we will all be destroyed."

"One of your people has gone berserk," Barone explained shortly. "He disconnected the main navigational
controls and barricaded himself in the engine room.

We're traveling at twenty knots straight toward land. Unless we can get past him to shut off the engines, this Vessel will run aground in minutes."

The brain room workers were watching Barone with desperate trust. In their uncertainty, they needed to believe he could save the Vessel.

"This is all Ritchet's doing!" Graban exclaimed bitterly. "He has seized this moment to have his revenge on us all. He does not care if he must commit suicide, as long as he can harm the Vessel and all it stands for."

Barone had come around the table and now stood in front of me. There were beads of sweat on his forehead, but his control was tight as the jaws of a wrench. "This saboteur has cut off all communication into the engine area. There is no way for us to talk to him. No way but one." He bent down, placing one fist on either arm of my chair. His face was inches from mine. "I have seen what you can do. Now you must do it to save your Vessel. You must enter this madman's mind, and control him."

In two days I had seen his every expression. Now I used one I knew well: his smirk of secret control.

"I already have," I said.

More than the words, he understood the expression. He jerked back as if I had stabbed him.

"So you are behind this?"

I smiled. His own expression again. It was frighteningly easy.

There was a dangerous dance of fear in his eyes. He spoke slowly, through his teeth: "You will stop this madness, you twisted cretin. If not for your Vessel, then to save your own skin."

He seized my chair and pushed me out into the artery, setting a fast pace toward the lift.

The noise struck us like a blow when the lift door opened onto the main artery leading to the heart complex. The engines were working near top speed, and the vibrations shook the floor. As we rounded the corner, I saw that Ritchet had closed the great sliding fire door across the artery, sealing the heart room off. A team of workers was cutting at the door with blowtorches. It was a hopeless job; the honeycomb structure was built to withstand explosions.

Barone shouted a question into the deafening noise. The men with the blowtorches answered in signals. I wondered what it must be like beyond the door, where Ritchet was. By cutting off the artery he had cut off the main ventilation. The heart room would be an inferno by now. How long could he survive?

Barone leaned over me. I refused to look at him until he took my face in his hand and forced me. "Now," he shouted, "make him open the door."

At last I allowed myself to laugh at him.

He hit me hard across the face, knocking my head against the chair back. "Do it," he roared.

I shook my head.

He hit me again. His rage was building. I realized with a cold clarity that he might kill me, and there was nothing I could do to stop him. By now, he would not even believe the truth.

His hand rose to batter me again. A shudder ran through the hull; then the floor beneath us lurched. Stressed metal screamed. My chair teetered and toppled over on its side, throwing me to the floor. I slid as the deck tilted crazily, and unsecured tools and furniture went flying. With a groan, the Vessel shuddered to a halt.

And suddenly there was silence. Complete silence.

The Vessel's great heart, never still within my lifetime, was beating no more.

Gradually, the men around me started picking themselves up. None of them paid the slightest attention to me. Barone was on his feet, sending men off in several directions to assess damage. Already he had put himself in charge.

He left me lying like a discarded tool. I was glad to be ignored until they all left. I lay still on the strangely angled floor. My chair was on its side ten feet away, looking forlorn and alone. And now, through Ritchet's and my handiwork, the Vessel too was crippled, lying helpless aground on the sand flats of Tuamo.

There was a hiss as the hydraulic mechanism drew back the heart room fire door. Steam and heat burst out. A figure staggered through the opening into the artery. He swayed, taking in the scene around him. Then his eyes fell on me. He made his way over and collapsed on his knees in front of me. His clothes and hair were drenched, but he was grinning.

We said nothing. We didn't need to. Our eyes shared our victory.

At last Ritchet's attention focused and he bent over me. "What did he do to you?"

He helped me to a sitting position, feeling for broken bones. I was a mass of bruises, but nothing worse. He fetched my chair and hefted me into it. The left front wheel wobbled as he pushed me to the lift.

We emerged into the daylight of late afternoon before anyone else. But by the time we reached the overlook, the fields below were dotted with people out staring at a sight not they nor their grandparents nor *their* grandparents had ever seen. The gray glistening prow of the Vessel lay beached in about thirty feet of water. We were still far from land, for here the coast subsided gently into the water in gradual hills of sand. Around us, long combers coasted shoreward over the shallow water. A pinwheel of seabirds circled the stranded giant. The tide would just be starting to fall, if Ritchet's calculations had been correct. The tilt of the deck would grow as the stern sank with the sea.

We stayed in the grove until stars began to bloom in the east. Ritchet sat with his back to a tree, smoking a pipe he had somehow carried in his pocket through it all. As the sun sank, his profile was outlined in black against the sky.

"He thought I was controlling you," I said.

Ritchet chuckled softly. "I figured he'd see that." The smoke drifted up around his head. "Of course, he was right."

I stared at him, dumbfounded.

"Well, what did you *think* was happening?" His tone was on the edge between laughter and resentment. "You might as well have held a gun to my head. You did the next best thing: you trusted me."

"You deserved it!" I protested.

"Don't give me that," he growled. "No one deserves trust: they let it happen to them. 'Trust,' 'consensus,' 'love,' they're all different names for the same thing. I figured it out, there in the heart room. Lots of things came clear."

I didn't have the faintest idea what he was talking about. He went on: "It used to drive me crazy, you were all so predictable. I could tell what a Vessel person was going to say before he said it; everyone knew what jobs the others would want to do, and which girls each fellow went for. It was like living with a horde of peeping Toms. I never thought there could be an explanation."

Now I saw where his mind was going. "Telepathy?" I scoffed. He was as bad as Barone.

"You expect telepathy to be something unsubtle, like voices speaking in your head. But if that were possible, people would never have learned to speak—or to lie. No, it has to be meant for a totally different kind of information."

I told him then how Barone had tried to make me exercise my supposed occult powers. If I had had the slightest trace of telepathy, I would have used it to save myself.

Ritchet only smiled. "Maybe telepathy doesn't work that way. Maybe it only works in quiet ways we scarcely notice. Maybe you didn't know you were using it on him because you do it every day."

The breeze insinuated cold fingers down my neck, and I shivered. Seeing my discomfort, Ritchet rose, knocking his pipe against the tree trunk. "Shall we go back down?" he asked.

"We have to stop them," I said.

"Stop them from what?"

"Helping Barone."

Ritchet smiled and slipped his pipe into his soiled pocket. "I'll make a wager with you. I'll bet by the time we get back down, every person in the Vessel will have figured out what you and I were up to. As if the idea had spread through the air. Want to shake on it?"

We did. But I should have known better; he was an old hand at wagering.

Dylaka was waiting at the lift entrance. She came forward to warn us. "Barone's in a rage. He wants your head, Ritchet. And you, Given—" I nodded, knowing he wanted my head as well, but in a different sense. "We

have a way to hide you," she went on, "but we'll have to
be quick and quiet."

As she turned to lead us, I caught her hand. "We
must not help him."

She stared. "Of course not!"

"He means help him free the ship," Ritchet put in.

Dylaka smiled slyly. "We're not idiots, Given. We
have figured out that a grounded Vessel is not what he
wants."

But Barone did not give up. His mission was like a
hook stuck in his throat; he could not loose it.

For a whole day he tried to whip the Vessel into
freeing itself. When the tide rose, he ordered the engines
started up and tried to work loose of the imprisoning
sand. Our people obeyed his every command, but nothing more. He never imagined there was more to do.

The stubborn thing refused to budge. Though the
stern still floated, the bow was firmly grounded on the
crest of an underwater hill of sand. At day's end he
finally allowed the efforts to cease.

It was then I made my appearance. As Dylaka
wheeled me to the head room, we heard raised voices
from within: Jerro and his commander were quarreling.
They ceased as I entered.

Barone rose from his seat at the chart table. People
said he had not slept in twenty-four hours, but he did
not show it. Except for one thing: when his eyes first
rested on me, I saw a flicker of fear.

"So they found you," he growled.

"No," Dylaka answered as we had arranged. "The
Given has come to bid you to leave. The Vessel cannot
be freed. We are no further use to you. You must go
home now."

"Is that a threat?" he sneered.

"Yes," I said softly.

This time it was he who looked away.

"What happened to the madman?" he demanded of Dylaka.

"Ritchet is no more," she said with a trace of regret. "We tried to help him, but he broke away and threw himself from the cliff. He was crazed."

Barone never questioned the story. He turned to me again, his face dark with superstition. "That is the second man I have seen you drive to death," he said.

"Yes," I answered again. I looked from Barone to Jerro; the soldier flinched back, raising his gun instinctively. I smiled.

Dylaka spoke calmly. "There is nothing more for you here. You should make your escape while you can."

From the look Jerro cast at Barone I knew this was what they had been arguing about.

He gave a loud laugh. "There is much for us here. Your Vessel will be cut apart for the metal. Your harvest will be shipped north to feed my warriors. We will scavenge this corpse for every scrap of value in it."

His profanity made my blood boil. For once, I felt able to talk with perfect clarity. "Touch this Vessel," I said, "and I will drive you mad."

There was total silence. "You cannot touch us," Barone said.

"I have not tried."

"You will not if you know such a thing as fear," he declared too loudly. "You are no devil's spawn. You can be hurt like other mortals."

The threat was still on his lips when there was a noise behind him. He whirled around, every nerve on edge. The door at his back was flung against the wall and a man with a gun appeared in the opening. Barone's pistol flew into his hand from nowhere. Jerro shouted a warning. There was a deafening explosion. The intruder stopped, an expression of astonishment on his face, then crumpled forward.

"It's Dack!" Jerro shouted. In an instant he was at the fallen man's side. When he looked up, his face was white. "You killed him."

"Another second and he would have killed me!" Barone roared. "He was mad. The mind-reader was controlling him."

"You're the mad one!" Jerro rose, shaking with fury. "Dack wasn't attacking, anyone could see that. If you thought so, you were seeing shadows. *You* were controlled."

Barone's whole body seemed to waver as a terrible uncertainty washed over him. He raised his hand to his head. "No!" he cried. "I didn't feel anything."

"What did you expect to feel?" Jerro seethed. Dropping to his knees again, he said, "Oh, God help us. Poor Dack."

Barone turned to me, and I heard Dylaka gasp. I was looking down the barrel of his pistol. The bullet would come straight into my left eye. I wondered if I would see it.

But he did not fire. "Get out," he said in a strangled voice. "Out of my sight."

Dylaka obeyed. My chair had never traveled more swiftly. Once safely around the corner, she stopped and knelt before me. Her face looked rubbery with shock. Mine must have been like a mirror. "Given," she asked urgently, "was it true? Did you do that?"

I couldn't answer. Barone had never needed help from me before. Violence surrounded him, bred in his

every action. But at the same time, I wished desperately
that Ritchet had never told me his theories.

They left that night. Secretly, so that none of us
would know. But of course, we did.

As soon as Barone's ship was out of radio range, we
set to work. Every spare hand reported to the hold to
move our cargo from the bow to the stern. To lighten the
ship, we cast much of our harvest overboard. Barone
would have been horrified to see his treasure bobbing
shoreward on the waves.

At daybreak we lowered the four great anchors into
motor dories, hauled them seaward, and set them fast
in the sandy bottom. Then we started the engines in
earnest. This time we did not just use the main stern
propellers. The transverse screws came into play. We
rocked the stern over to starboard first, pivoting on the
grounded bow. Then back to port, then the anchor
winches attempting to pull the Vessel outward.

To and fro but not sternward we went. After a few
hours, people began tossing more things out to lighten
the Vessel: rusty stoves and bedsprings, the complete
equipment of an old bowling alley. It probably did not
help much, but the closets had never been cleaner. What
did help was a strong offshore wind and current that
pushed and tugged as if the sea itself wanted us back.

We broke free just twenty-four hours after Barone
had left. Within an hour we were out of sight of the
cursed shoreline of Tuamo, heading south with only the
sea before us.

The people held a great celebration in the dining hall.
I did not want to go; Dylaka persuaded me I had to. But
first I insisted she take me to the conservatory and leave
me alone for a while. It was there that Ritchet found me.

He was not well dressed, but better than I had ever seen him. He was clean-shaven and frighteningly sober. Sitting down on a bench by me, he said, "They're calling for you in the dining hall."

I did not reply. I had no taste for revelries, not with Geal gone.

Ritchet cleared his throat. "Given, I've decided to leave."

I looked at him in astonishment.

"I'm going back to shore. Someone needs to spread the word of what happened to Barone. Unless the landsmen know the story, they may try again."

It sounded good, but of course it wasn't the real reason.

"You will have to find another speaker," he said.

"I want you."

He looked down at his hands, then laughed softly. "No, you don't. I'm too disreputable. I couldn't keep it up. You need someone to depend on."

It would have been fine and romantic to deny his words, but in sober truth he was right. He would rebel against any prison I constructed for him, even if it were built of that type of mind control called 'love.'

"Will you come back?" I asked.

"I suppose I will." He scratched his head, then turned to look at me sideways. "Yes. I will."

"We owe you," I said.

"Hell, no. I owe you, Given. Besides, you did all the hard part. Everyone else believed what Barone thought about them, just like I believed what Graban thought about me. When he thought we were helpless, we were. When he thought we were docile, we acted that way. He must have been a pretty powerful telepath himself."

I groaned. Not that again.

Ritchet was grinning at me. "You still don't believe it, do you? Want to make another wager? I'll bet the minute I take you into that dining hall, you'll lose that moping face and be as happy as all the rest of them. Want to shake?"

This time, I knew better.

Living in the Jungle
by
Martha Soukup

About the Author

Many W.O.T.F. judges also teach at various facilities attended by promising apprentices. When one of the anonymous manuscripts circulated to us by the Contest adminstration turns out to be the work of a former student, there's always a glow. And the (unrealistic) hope that one was the teacher, among so many in an aspiring writer's progress, who made the difference. (It's the student who makes the difference.)

Martha Soukup has studied at the Michigan State University Clarion workshop, like two other writers in this book. She also was a high finalist in an early Contest quarter. She was then invited to study at the first W.O.T.F. workshop. For a week in early 1986, she helped as Frederik Pohl, Jack Williamson, Gene Wolfe, and I applied the baselines for the now-continuing W.O.T.F. workshop program. So when Martha later proved to be a First Place winner in the third Quarter, our glow was a particularly warm one.

But it was still Martha who made the difference. Her interest in theater arts is reflected in "Dress Rehearsal," a story published in Universe 16, and she has continued to sell since then. As for her depiction of what it's like to be young, bright, and one's own emerging person, turn the page. . . .

For Michael, with love.

I don't want to leave the Jungle.

They're trying to take me out, of course. Just this morning, before dawn, they sent in another robot. It was the kind that's slung very low and articulated into twenty sections, each with a separate tread and retractible legs. I took it out with a coconut. If you sneak up alongside them it takes three or four seconds for them to sense you, and while the front sensory segment is whipping around to get a fix on you, you can take the half shells in each hand and scoop them in and under the oval front plate. The milky meat provides just enough lubrication. There's a lot of resistance when the shell meets the cabling, but you don't have to break it completely—something in there is fragile enough to make its input go blooey. That's the start.

Then the rear end starts to whip around to get a fix on you instead, and its sensors won't tumble to the coconut system because they're on a flush immobile seamless panel, but on the other hand they're not so sensitive either. A handful of mud smeared across the plate will slow it down. Then while the thing starts to thrash a little you can give it enough of a kick to make it go belly-up. There's a lot of stuff down there, when you loosen the thumbscrews, that you can disable with your bare hands. A heavy stick is better. The whole thing takes maybe thirty seconds and then you've got a dead robot.

I don't know very much about robots or most machines, so while back learning this I scarred up my rib cage pretty badly and broke two fingers on my left hand, tore out a huge patch of hair and took some other minor damage. I suppose it's something I should've studied up on first. But I'll tell you that now there isn't anyone who knows so much about how to destroy something she understands so little.

"Whatcha doing, honey?"

She looked up, startled. She was reading, slowly and carefully, trying to figure out if Hegel was really an idiot or if perhaps she was.

The man was dressed like a jock, sweatshirt over a one-piece jogging suit, with incredibly new sports shoes. The baggy shirt didn't quite hide the fact that he was losing the figure of a jock. He was a complete stranger. She shook her head a little, trying to come into the real world.

"A quiet one, huh?" The book was snatched from her hands. "Whoa! Lookit this. Hegel!" He pronounced it Hee-gull. He mimed a great strain on his arm. "Awful heavy stuff for such a little girl." He winked at her. "Do you know what it's about?"

"Well," she began, "I don't know—"

"I didn't think so," he said. "A cute little thing like you."

When the robot had stopped twitching and I'd ripped out everything rippable and twisted and bent everything that wasn't, I went over it thoroughly. A lens out of the front section can start a fire by focusing sunlight on

Illustrated by Bob Eggleton

dead leaves. The last one I was using, I'd managed to drop in the river; there was no finding it in all those rocks and mud. An edge of the legs can be pried off to make a good skewer and a fair knife. They don't last long, so I always need more.

The power supply is something I like to take, although I've no idea what I'll do with them. They make an artistic stack in the corner of my lean-to. Wires are good for tying fowl while I'm cooking it, for holding my lean-to together, for holding my hair back in a ragged tail, for making traps, for a million things. There are only a few long useful pieces. I wrenched out those I could, braided them together, and strung it all through a loop of my pants. The pants are getting ragged, and I'll have to think about what to do when they wear out: they were my third and last pair. Everything else I bundled in a wrapping of banana leaves to take home with me.

Killing a robot is like a day at the market.

The groceries were too heavy to hold in one arm, and it had been a morning full of rain, making the ground too wet to set them down. She grunted the bags to one side, freeing one thumb and forefinger to work the latch. She got the door open, then turned quickly to hold it open with her back.

As she was backing into the lobby against the heavy door, it was pulled away from behind her. Clutching the bags, she toppled into the building and banged her head on the old tile floor.

The matronly woman holding the door above her looked chagrined. Then she pulled her face into a stern mother's expression.

"You should have your groceries delivered like a normal person," she scolded. "You see what happens?"

The Jungle isn't much, I suppose. I always used to picture long constricting snakes hanging from every tree and huge bands of monkeys and apes clambering in the trees with them, and lions staring up at you and leopards staring down with cool murder in their faces, and more kinds of giant insects than you could count in a year, and mongooses and parrots and elephants—killing and dying all the time, all making this wild musical shriek of noise all through the day and the night.

I don't know where I got it from—maybe an old Tarzan sound track—but the noise was the best part of the image. The jungles I imagined were places for whooping and shrieking. This Jungle is very quiet, and the few animals here seem to keep their thoughts to themselves.

By the time I'd finished scavenging, the sun had begun to light things up some. I left the robot's shell, littered with the bits and pieces I didn't think I'd need, and started back to my lean-to.

The beginning of the day is the best time to look at the Jungle, which is why I was up before dawn to start out with. When it's just getting light you can't tell the difference between the little, real trees, and the big, synthetic ones that loom overhead. The management made a small effort to make the big temporaries look real, but it doesn't stand up to full light.

In silhouette, though, they loom over my head as alive as any ghosts. Real vines dangle down from their plastete branches, and an occasional real parakeet or finch flits from limb to limb, not caring that they're not nature's own perches. Nor would the birds, seeing as they're such live-for-today types, care that the trees are designed to disintegrate over the next couple of decades, as the real trees grow up to replace them.

Nor do I care, as long as they're here for me now.

"You work in the government," she pleaded. "You could have them change this." She shook the letter at Marie like a cat trying to stun a mouse.

"I'm sorry, honey," her older sister said. "It's not my place to do that."

"But they want to take away my car!"

"And give you a better one," Marie said reasonably.

"And give me one that drives itself!"

"Most people like them. It gives you a chance to relax, read, watch some television. Is that so bad?"

"I *like* driving myself."

"Then you ought to have been more careful. If you hadn't broken traffic laws they wouldn't be making you trade in your old car towards a computer-driven one."

"Then you aren't going to help me fight this?"

Marie sighed."Nikkie, as far as I'm concerned, they were right when they had the original idea of just impounding violators' cars. I have a little boy. I don't want some dangerous driver threatening his life on the road when a computer can do it so much better." The younger woman would have smiled at the phrasing if she hadn't been so upset.

Marie tousled her sister's hair, as she had when they were small. "Cheer up! It's not the end of the world."

She watched Marie let herself out the front door, shook open the letter. It listed her lifetime infractions at the bottom: Running four red lights. Speeding, once, in Wisconsin. A broken tail-light. A missing muffler. Some parking tickets.

Eyes stinging, she crumpled up the notice and flung it at the wall.

I strolled back to my lean-to and got another surprise. It was collapsing.

I went through weeks of experimentation before I even found a shelter I liked. I didn't bring very much stuff with me—after all, I was only supposed to be a tourist and I was supposed to be staying in civilization—and, like a lot of things, I just hadn't thought through the living arrangement question.

I had brought, because they seemed vaguely useful and important, two clear plastic tarps.

The first night I was here, I ended up wrapping myself in one of the tarps, like it was a big plastic sleeping bag. The odds and ends I brought with me, which I also thought would be important and useful, I wrapped in the other. I used the lumpy second tarp as a pillow. There I camped, under the sky and everything.

In the middle of the night I woke up shouting from a vivid nightmare. I'd been naked and tied down in a steam bath, and the attendant kept hitting me with wet towels that were covered with little stingers. It was a relief, for two seconds, to open my eyes to darkness and not that horrible place.

Then I discovered I was still in that horrible place.

I was drenched in sweat from being wrapped in plastic. Better yet, I'd put myself right in the path of a colony of ants. I wasn't so tightly wrapped up that they couldn't find their way into my tarp, which is exactly what they did. As I've come to learn, nothing will stop a bunch of ants from being exactly where they want to be, and where they wanted to be was where I was. And since I was there, well hell, they might as well give me a taste. Or some good healthy stings to show they didn't appreciate me rolling over and crushing the life out of them.

It's very hard to get out of plastic mummy-wrappings when you're screaming, soaking, in pain and in panic. But I'll bet I looked funny.

I broke a bunch of the stuff I'd wrapped in my pillow. (Just as well—what did I really need my alarm clock for? I don't even use my little pinkie watch anymore. And shampoo I'd have had to learn to live without eventually. I wish the bottle hadn't broken, though. I was eating shampoo-flavored dried food and vitamin pills for weeks.)

That very day I started to devote serious attention to How to Build a Better Shelter.

It took, if I'm counting right, seventeen separate attempts before I got it the way I wanted it. Of course, the later incarnations were perfectionist fiddling. Only the first six or seven were complete flops, no better than sleeping out in the rain.

Not terribly far from my favorite river there were three plastete trees all in a row, pretty close together. Vines hung down between them. I ended up weaving leaves through the vines to fill in the gaps, a two-day project that resulted in a nicely wind- and rain-proof wall. Then, climbing the trees a little (*that's* not easy; you can pull yourself up on the vines just fine, but that rough plastete scrapes your skin raw), I attached a tarp to one end of my tree-and-vine wall, then to the other. The front I tacked to the ground.

Vines make mediocre ropes for tying that sort of thing, but by that time I'd experienced the thrill of my first robot kill. I'd just wanted to get as far from its body as possible after it happened, and it took me hours to relocate it, but the image of its wires and cables kept me looking. I was learning.

Ten modifications later, after I finished rigging up a

floor from bamboo slats on stones—keeps some of the insects from walking across your bed—I was just getting happy with my little home. But now I came into the clearing and found the right-hand tree disintegrating.

I set everything down carefully before panicking. Then I ran full tilt to the lean-to.

He stepped forward and neatly blocked her way. He wore a button that said "GIVE" in tasteful simulated wood. She avoided looking at him and tried to sidestep him, but somehow he had already guided her behind a table of leaflets.

"I know what you're thinking," he said. "Another dumb charity drive, and probably one you don't even support." She looked up into a broad, smiling face. "I can understand that reaction. So many good causes. So hard to choose between them. And so many of them just fall by the wayside, because nobody can spend all the time it would take to learn how to do the good they want to do. Leaving you feeling guilty about the good not done.

"And you do want to do good, don't you?" He paused, waiting for her response. She stared at him. "Of course you do. We all do.

"That's what GIVE is for. All we ask you to do is fill out one questionnaire. We take a complete psychological profile of you, we find out exactly what your own individual values are.

"And from then on, you have nothing to worry about! Your profile tells us what you want to give to each cause. Abused children, homeless kittens, the Lunar station, your church of choice, the gun lobby—they'll all get the fraction of your donation that your profile dictates. So if you'll just sign up now, we can run you through right away."

She shook her head.

"No time now? Give me your number and we'll call to work out an appointment." He smiled at her. He was sincere, concerned.

She turned and walked away.

"Would you care to leave a general donation to GIVE?" he called after her.

She tipped the table of leaflets as she passed.

The right-hand tree was indeed crumbling. Worse, it was collapsing toward the lean-to. For a moment I wondered if the tarp was heavy enough to pull the tree down.

Of course that couldn't be the case. So I calmed myself down and walked around the tree to get a better look at it.

It was coming down, losing its structure around the base. It looked like it was being eaten away from the inside. They were supposed to do that eventually, but this just had to be too early. I rapped my hand against it a few times, trying to decide if it was still sturdy enough to risk going inside. I decided to go inside anyway.

I had to keep punching the ceiling up out of my face, and finally I just stuck both hands up and held it off. It was a mess inside. All of my somewhat arranged piles of things were knocked askew by the collapsing plastic that draped over everything.

If I couldn't predict when the trees were going to wear out, how was I going to manage a stable home?

I went back outside and shoved the plastic under the floor stones on the right-hand side, straightening out the shelter's wall as much as possible. Then I took another look inside.

My pile of power packs had been directly in front of the falling tree, and had been knocked all over the floor by it. I vaguely remembered moving them before I went out, after I tripped on them trying to get to the door flap.

I shoved them back and started to pick up the rest of the stuff on the floor.

Something seemed off. I looked back and I could actually see the tree bending in toward me—

"Holy shit, the batteries!" I screamed. Don't ask me who else was around to care. I cared enough for triplets. Between the contacts of a couple power packs, where they touched the tree, the plastete was eroding merrily away.

I thought of moving the power packs, but decided it was the better part of valor to hit the floor—the left-hand side of the floor.

The tarp came crashing down around me.

She was curled on the sofa in his living room, her chin on her knee, watching him. He paced around the room.

"For God's sake, Nikkie," he said. "You quit your job?"

"It didn't mean anything."

"What the hell do you mean, it didn't mean anything? Do you really want to live on the dole level? Do you have something against eating well?"

She frowned and said nothing.

"I mean, if you need some help from me, okay. You can move in here—like I've asked you to do before, if you'd only listen to good ideas for once—but it's just stupid to give up your paycheck." He stopped pacing, stood over her and shook his head. "Jesus. It's not like shuffling papers six hours a day is going to kill you or anything. Everyone else does it."

"I'm not everyone else," she said, very quietly.

"Most people really *like* a little bit of security. It's no skin off your nose to follow the rules once in a while."

Her hand clenched at a sofa cushion. "I'm not most people."

"You're obviously just going to keep acting like a child—"

"I'm not a child!" she shouted. She wrenched up the sofa cushion and flung it at the wall. It didn't help. "I am not a fucking child and I don't have to be taken care of! If people would just leave me alone once I might even be able to accomplish something for a change!"

"Jesus, Nikkie!" He stared at her, uncomprehending. "What are you so hostile about all of a sudden? It's not like anyone's stopping you from doing anything. Stop being so paranoid, for Christ's sake."

She was on her feet. Every muscle in her body was knotted. It felt like every muscle had been knotted for years.

"Shit, you never even swear," he said. "I don't know what's wrong with you today."

"I guess you don't," she said. She went to the door. She took a deep breath, then turned to face him. Her voice was almost steady. "Why don't you just stop worrying about it? I doubt I'm worth your valuable concern."

The door slammed behind her.

My first impulse was to slash my way free with the dagger in my boot, but then I wouldn't have the tarp any more. I freed my face before my lungs burst and freed

the rest of my body in good time. I didn't get up for a
while, though. I just lay there and glowered.

The place was trashed. Two-trees-wide might make
an acceptable temporary shelter—better than I had the
first month I was here—but damned if I wanted all that
experimentation and work to go down the tubes. Ugly
visions of a full week of finding a new site and preparing
just a beginning lean-to filled my mind.

I cursed for about five minutes. Finally I got all
the vinegar out of my system, got up, and started to
untangle the tarp. There was only one rip in it, and it
was along an edge. Tough stuff.

I searched out my belongings and piled them up. The
batteries I put off to one side, and when I finished
picking up everything else, I spent a little time experi-
menting with the tree stump. The power from one battery caused a slow but visible breakdown of the plastete.
I walked over to a different plastete tree, a smaller one.
No apparent result. I scratched my head, then went back
to the rest of my stuff, got some wire, and hooked six
power packs up in series. Bingo. It started pulverizing
immediately and kept right on turning to powder. I
jumped out of the way just in time.

However it is the stuff ages, a good zap of electrical
current really speeds it up. I suppose there's a tiny little
battery at the heart of each tree, regulating how soon
it'll come down. Battery-operated trees. It wasn't in the
literature, but it's cute.

I'll have to keep this in mind next time there's a
lightning storm. I wonder if they thought of that when
they were designing the things.

Once again I stretched the tarp into some semblance
of shelter around the remaining two trees and the big
front rock. I put the power packs back in my clearing,

draped tarp over them, and went off in search of breakfast. The stuff I'd had ready to eat had been ground into the dirt.

"South America," she typed into the terminal. "Jungle." The computer narrowed down the possibilities of what she was looking for and gave her data. It was not much more than the fluff she had heard in the media: the death of the jungles around the world, the international effort to make an effort to save some remnant of them—although the oxygen problem had been solved—as a good-hearted gesture to the world that had birthed humanity. It was a good, knee-jerk issue, and did well on most people's computer voting profiles, as long as too much money wasn't spent on it.

It was a fake. But it cost relatively little to put together, once Brazil had consented to sacrifice the land.

Clones were taken from the small bunches of trees left in the few pockets of jungle remaining. Animals were donated from zoos. Artificial, biodegradable trees were adapted from existing technology to fill the gaps until the imported plant life grew to maturity. All this was put onto land fenced off and renewed at fair expense.

The computer assured her that it would be a good climax jungle in a matter of decades, albeit a mixed, homogenous one. It also assured her that everyone was satisfied with the effort.

People were not allowed in the Jungle. It was not controlled for human habitation, and human interference could nullify the pure scientific aspect which put the project a little higher on many voters' profiles.

"Brasilia, Brazil," she typed. "Airfare."

Bananas. Grubs. A big turtle which I decided to save for dinner. Then I took a muddy swim in the river, thought about my next home, dripped dry, dressed, went back to the clearing and discovered the man.

He had a weapon at his side, but he didn't look like he thought he'd need to use it. He was dressed in pressed jungle khaki.

I just looked at him. I didn't know what to do.

He was sweating and looked uncomfortable. "This isn't my job," he said. He sounded upset.

"Why don't you go do your job, then?"

"Public opinion is that you shouldn't be allowed to stay."

I walked carefully into the clearing, keeping an eye on him. He kept facing me, and he didn't take his hand from his weapon.

"Does everyone know I'm here, then?" The thought surprised me.

"No. But they've run projections. The longer you're here, the less likely it is we can keep a lid on it. Public opinion will be bad when it comes out. So you've got to go."

Even killing robots made me feel guilty at first, since I knew they were just trying to disable me and take me out of the Jungle. I didn't think I could bring myself to kill this person—even if he'd had no gun. I moved slowly, so as not to make him panic, past him into the center of the clearing. His eyes darted away now and again, as an insect flew close or a plant rustled, but came back quickly to fix on me.

"How do you know what people will really think, if you don't let them make the decision?" I could throw a dagger at him, maybe even hit, although I've never had much luck with that. But if I didn't kill him or completely disable him, he was the one with the gun.

"Grow up," he said in an irritated voice. "Live in the world."

"I'm trying," I said. He wiped sweat from his jaw, a fastidious movement, and suddenly I could see what I looked like to him: mud-grayed skin, a wild tangle of partly tied-back hair, rags of a once-trendy shirt and pants. More muscled than I'd ever been. An animal.

"Will you come back without fighting?" he asked, using the tone reserved for small children and unstable people. "There's plenty of help waiting for you outside."

"All right," I said. "Let me get a few things."

She stood at the border of the Jungle. She could barely see anything past the fence in the dark.

She had to decide now. Was she a tourist taking a spicy, forbidden look at an off-limits site? Had she indulged in a fantasy when she bought camping odds-and-ends at the approved camping grounds and brought them with her? She could get past the electrified fence, but it would be painful.

Her legs ached. This was not a part of any route her rental car would drive her to. She'd abandoned it a dozen kilometers back, at the nearest point the computer would drive the car. It was probably already relaying the alarm at her absence.

She looked down at the key card that operated the car. Her name and picture were on it. She'd always hated the name Nikkie. There was a long ID number after the name.

She ripped it up and picked up her sack.

I smiled at him, picked up the tarp in the clearing,

and went into the lean-to. He watched me go in.

I put the contents of the tarp against the left-hand tree, careful to position it just right. Then I picked up a couple of things, including my dinner, and went back outside.

"Can I just look around for a few moments?" He was about to respond when I yelled "Look out!" and the tree came crashing to our left. I was on the right. While he gaped at the huge plummeting tree, I brought my nice turtle dinner, still in the shell, square down on his skull.

He wasn't badly hurt, although the turtle was ruined. I bandaged his head with his shirt, then dragged him in a fireman's carry toward the nearest perimeter. I found a pen in his pocket, and I wrote on his forearm:

"Out is toward the banana bush and straight from there. So long. Don't call."

He was beginning to stir when I slipped off.

The gun should come in handy for protection while I'm building the next shelter. I've got some pretty good ideas for it. I suppose it's too much to ask that the next guy bring an axe. I sure could use one.

How to Impress an Editor
by
Frederik Pohl

About the Author

A notable SF author since before World War II, Frederik Pohl has also been an editor of great influence throughout his career, starting at Astonishing and Super Science and going on to Galaxy, IF, and elsewhere. He is the discoverer of Ray Bradbury, R.A. Lafferty, Keith Laumer and Larry Niven, among scores of other well-known names. Thirty-five years ago, he created the Star series, setting the pattern that other editors still follow for anthologies of original SF short fiction. He has also been a novels editor at several prestigious publishing houses, has served as an instructor within and outside of the W.O.T.F. program, and of course is a Contest judge.

His own work in fiction includes "Day Million" and "The Gold at the Starbow's End," The Space Merchants, Man Plus, and Gateway, which have garnered a thicket of awards. But those symbols of expertise are equalled in number by the trophies he's won as an editor. One year, IF won the Hugos in every eligible category.

What goes through his mind when he reads a story by an aspiring writer? He is about to tell you. . . .

I don't advise writers to *write* with editors in mind. An editor is really only a middleman; his job is to try to guess what readers will like, and it is the ultimate reader who will in the long run decide who succeeds in writing.

However, it's important to *impress* an editor—especially if he has no idea of how well you write. It is the editor who makes the decision on what gets into print, so he can't be ignored. Moreover, there are things to be learned from editors, if only because the editors have had to learn them themselves. At least half of the workmanship skills and techniques of writing are things I learned over the thirty-nine years from my first professional editorial job to my last. These form a major part of how I appraise a story from someone I've never read before . . . and a good part of how I do all my reading.

What editors learn about writing comes largely from the things that writers do wrong. It's easier to see where somebody else has gone wrong than it is when it's your own work, and then you can look at your own with a more knowing eye. That's a big plus, for anyone who wants not only to "be a writer" but to write well. Unfortunately, becoming an editor is not an option open to everyone who wants to write; there simply are not that many editorial jobs.

What you can do, however, is what Albert Einstein called a "thought experiment." Put yourself in an editor's place for a moment, and see how you look to him as he goes through the process of deciding whether what you will subsequently find in your mailbox is going to be a rejection slip, or a check, or something in between.

I'm going first to spend some time discussing manuscript preparation because that's what makes the first impression for your story.

Your first contact with an editor (not necessarily *the* editor, but we'll come to that later) occurs when the mailman drops your manuscript on his desk. (It may well be "her" desk, rather than "his." In fact, these days it is more likely to be a her than a him—but forgive me if I don't keep saying "his or her.")

You can lose the whole game right here if your manuscript is handwritten, or otherwise illegible. You can also stack the cards against you, though not *always* lethally, in a lot of lesser ways, and a lot of them come under the general heading of "neatness."

You see, what you don't want to do is make it hard for an editor to like your work. His eyes take enough punishment. Pica type (also known as 12-point in printers' measure, or 10-strike in IBM's loopy dialect) is usually better than the smaller elite or "12-strike"—but don't go overboard and use one of the giant sizes available with some computers. Type as neatly as you can, and make sure that your black typewriter ribbon prints *black* and your standard-size white paper is *white*. George O. Smith, one of John W. Campbell's stalwarts in the Golden Age of *Astounding,* claimed that he never had a story rejected for a weak ending. The reason, George said, was that he was always careful to punch up his endings by using a new typewriter ribbon on the last few pages . . . but it's my personal opinion that he would have done even better if he'd started his manuscript with one.

Although neatness counts, you don't have to be fanatical. If you mistype a letter here and there, you can correct the mistake with a black pencil or pen; but do it legibly, and if you make very many corrections, you should learn a standard copy-editors' marking system so that the editor (and, hopefully, the typesetter after him) will know what you mean. Ask the reference-desk clerk at your local library for a source of this information, or check the back pages of Webster's Collegiate Dictionary, which used to have an excellent short description.

You should, (1) enclose an adequately stamped, self-addressed return envelope in case of need; (2) put enough stamps on the manuscript mailing envelope so it doesn't arrive postage-due; (3) *put your name and address on the manuscript.* The right place for your name and address is in the upper left-hand corner of the first page, but at least get it on there somewhere. If you want to use a pen-name on the story you can, but put your check-cashing name in the corner of the manuscript. Then, under the title of the story, type whatever byline you want, and the editor will know what you mean. Repeat a key word of the story title, and the last name of your byline, and a page number, at the *top* of each succeeding page.

A few additional general rules about the mechanics of submitting a story:

It doesn't matter whether you use a typewriter or a word processor, but if you use a word processor don't set your printer to create a straight *right*-hand margin. (No editors insist on justification, as it's called, and some editors actively hate it. Typesetters are infuriated by it.)

Don't use a dot-matrix printer unless it's a very good one. There's no harm in using tractor-feed paper, but use paper that looks as much like letterhead bond as possible, with a minimum of perforations along the edges.

If your printer (or typewriter) lets you do fancy things, don't do them. Don't italicize; underline instead. Otherwise the copy editor has to do the underlining for you, because typesetters require it.

Don't use odd typefaces—small caps, semi-script, sans-serif—they're sometimes hard to read, and often annoying. Besides which, typesetters don't like them, and sometimes charge extra for setting "difficult copy." Editors don't like extra charges—their publishers speak to them about it.

Finally, don't try to cram a 40-page manuscript into a letter-sized envelope. For a short manuscript of five or maybe ten pages you *can* fold it in half, although a fold makes copy-editing more difficult; anything longer should be mailed flat.

Remember, these mechanical things are the first thing the editor sees. They are, God knows, not important to the merits of the story—but blunders with the manuscript can keep your *story* from ever being read.

Sloppy manuscripting will not, in the long run, keep a real masterpiece from being published. But the facts of life are that most stories aren't masterpieces. There is no clear-cut line between the story that gets bought—reluctantly—and the story that gets bounced—regretfully. Many stories are right on the cusp. They can go either way. How well or badly you do the mechanical things can push your story one way or the other.

If you've done all the mechanical stuff more or less correctly, then you've passed the first test. At least now somebody will evaluate your story. The person who reads it probably is not the person who will make the final decision about buying it, because nearly all editors use first readers to eliminate the worst of the "slush." And you are by no means guaranteed that he will read it all the way through. But at least you've got the story in the hands of someone who has the authority to move it one step closer to print, and what happens now is up to your story. There are many ingredients that can sway the decision for you or against. Here are some of them:

Title. A catchy title encourages the reader to read on—whether he is an editor who gets paid to read or is your cash customer in the store. What makes a good title? Some answers to that question would be "relevance to your story," "tickling curiosity," "graceful use of language," maybe even "humor"—but it would be more truthful to say, "I don't know." I do know a good title when I see one, and so does everyone else, but there isn't any formula for generating them. Probably you'll know a good title when you think of it . . . so always try a few different ones.

One other way to come up with a decent title is to make a list of as many possible titles as you would be *willing* to have on your story, then ask friends which one would make them want to read the piece. If you agree with one, use it. But don't get hung up on this. If you have a good title, that's a *plus*. If you don't, it's not fatal. Editors are willing to improve titles; some of them, in fact, actually feel left out if they can't.

Opening. Once past the title, your editor naturally starts reading on Page One. If at all possible, have something there to interest him, for if you don't he may never get to Page Two.

The technical name for the kind of opening you want is a "narrative hook," meaning something which so piques the curiosity, arouses the sympathy or otherwise engages the attention of the reader that he is hooked and wants to get on with the narrative. There aren't any good rules for constructing a narrative hook, either, but a good way to *find* one is to start your story at the point where something interesting is happening. The art of writing, to some degree, is the art of leaving out the dull parts. If you can't quite leave out all the dull parts, at least try not to start with one. It is a useful exercise to look over some of your unsuccessful stories as though the author were someone you didn't know and didn't particularly want to know, and ask yourself, at every page and even every sentence, "Why is he telling me all this?" If you can't think of a reason, cut that part out.

Page-Turning. The above applies not only to the opening of your story, but all the way through it. Students of playwriting at the University of Texas (so one of them told me long ago, leaving an indelible impression on my mind) used to be told that there were only three reasons for including any given line in a play: To show character; to advance the action; or to get a laugh. If you make the last stricture "to give the reader pleasure of some kind," I would think those rules apply just as well to prose fiction.

However, you can't make a rotten story good just by cutting it to the bone. The bone may be rotten. To make a reader turn the pages it is not enough to get to what you have to say quickly; you must also have something to say.

You also need someone to say it about, and that

element is called *characterization*. It is characters who make a story move. If you read in a newspaper that 1800 Bolivians have died in an earthquake you may not be greatly moved; but if your bridge partner is run over by a truck you *care*. The difference is that you know your bridge partner, and you didn't know all those other people; events are more interesting when you know who they are happening to.

Characterization is making the reader know the characters, so that he will care what happens to them. You can do that in a quick-and-dirty way—that is, by what is called "funny hat" characterization, meaning that you tag one of your people by giving him an odd and picturesque trait. Perhaps you have him wear a funny hat, or give him a wooden leg or the habit of saying "Bless my watchfob!" Or you can do it by letting the reader understand what the character is like through showing what he does and what he feels. Understand better, if it is done right, than the character himself understands. Mark Twain did both: You remember the heroine of *A Connecticut Yankee in King Arthur's Court* because of her "funny hat"—actually, her habit of telling interminably dull stories—you remember Huckleberry Finn because Twain made you see right into his stubborn, cynical, quirky but decent and generous soul. The second way is harder, and better. But both work, and if you can't manage the hard way then at least do it the easy. If you can't tell us anything else about your characters, at least let us know something about what they want, what they fear—what their problems are; because these should enter into the action of the story.

Which brings us to *story*. A story involves change. Something has to happen. What happens does not have to be on a physical level; it can be the inside of the characters that changes, and maybe the only thing that changes is that the characters positively make up their minds that change just isn't going to happen. (That's an approximate outline of William Saroyan's most famous story, *The Daring Young Man on the Flying Trapeze*). It should not happen in a straight line, of course. If your character's problem is that he wants to marry The Girl, and he asks her, and she says yes, then that's a kind of story but, oh, what a dull one!

Some pulp writers of a generation ago used to follow a "Plot Skeleton." It was articulated by the literary agent, Scott Meredith, in a book on writing, and it says, basically, that the structure of any story has three parts. In the first part, the lead character is in a hellish bad fix. In the second part he almost gets out of it but, through no fault of his own, fails. In the last part he successfully solves the problem.

According to Meredith, this plot skeleton is actually present in every novel and short story ever written, from *The Satyricon of Petronius Arbiter* right up to the novelization of the latest *Star Trek* film. I wouldn't go that far, but the ingredients are all useful: An opening problem, the more urgent the better; a complication that keeps the hero on the hook and the reader turning pages; a satisfying resolution so the reader knows when the story's over.

Then there is *pace*. There are, it is true, some kinds of stories that require a good deal of elapsed story time for the events to unfold. Most stories don't. Particularly in a short story, avoid like poison the sentence, "Several months went by without anything happening," or anything much like it. The attention wanders. Once again, it is a matter of leaving out the dull parts—not only in the parts you describe but in those you don't.

Last of all, *accuracy*. In writing science fiction in particular, get at least your basic science right. You can't have helicopters flying around the Moon (there's no air), or take a rocket ship to Alpha Centauri in a week (a rocket can't go that fast). It is a matter of trust. If your reader doesn't have trust in you, he won't enjoy your story, and one sure way to forfeit that trust is to be caught in a fat-headed blunder. You don't need to know much about science to write some kinds of science fiction, but don't pretend to know more than you do.

What I have described is a sort of catalogue of the elements of an acceptable manuscript, as an editor might see them. The manuscript should be mechanically adequate. The story shouldn't sprawl, either in wordage or in draggy action. The characters should be solid enough to make the editor (and the ultimate reader) care what happens to them. And something should *happen* in the story.

If you've performed the thought experiment of looking at your manuscript through an editor's eyes, you now should be able to see some reasons why you've been rejected—if that has been the case—and in fact you can analyze your story, or anyone else's, quite expertly. For that's all there is to it . . . except for one thing, one element, one quality that I haven't touched on at all, and that was quite unfair, since it happens to be the most important thing of all. I've talked about everything that goes into your story, except *you*.

The only thing any writer has to sell is his own personal, idiosyncratic view of the world. What is it that you have to say? What have you seen that nobody else has seen, that you can set down for others?

When the editor reads your story he does not compare it against the checklist above. But all of these things will be in the back of his mind, along with a hundred other things that have to do with his own personal needs and preferences. However, if all he is doing is no more than to count off the ways in which your story matches a standard recipe, you may sell, but you're in trouble. That means your story is at best marginal, one of the dozen or so that he can probably print without stinking up the magazine (or the line of books) too badly, but which no one will miss if it doesn't get published. And there really is no point in being a writer if you don't intend to set your sights higher than that.

So . . . do all the things that are said or implied above, but don't stop there. Do more. Do your best to write stories that no one but you could have written, and write them as well as you can.

And good luck to you in the attempt!

The Very Last Party at #13 Mallory Way
by
L. E. Carroll

About the Author

L. E. Carroll is the first W.O.T.F. writer to appear in these anthologies twice. As a finalist, she contributed the delightful fantasy, "Without Wings," to Writers of the Future, Vol. I. Finalists can re-enter the Contest until they've had three short stories professionally published. So she continued to submit stories; won Second Prize in the first Quarter of this year, and the result awaits your pleasure on the following pages.

Doctor Carroll has recently also been writing extensively on music and music history, her career specialties. She has been asked to write a reference book on those topics. An additional series of activities centers on producing musicals at a variety of central East Coast theaters. A fascinating outgrowth of this pursuit has been her reconstruction and production, for the Kelpius Society in Philadelphia, of the very first music drama written in Colonial America.

How are you going to top a credential like that? Turn the page. . . .

Her gaudy jewelry caught my head-lights and reflected a flash of light into my eyes. It was just enough to keep me from hitting the woman sprawled in front of my driveway. Without that, I'd probably have ridden right over her, and this story would have had a very different ending. As it was, I hit the brakes and the car skidded, back end to the right, front end to the left, paralleling the body. There was no one else about, just a lot of noise from the house across the way. As the car skidded and stopped, as my heart thudded its way toward my mouth, I opened the car door and went out into the moist Fall night air toward the figure in the roadway.

Despite the seasonal chill, the woman wore only a thin cotton tee reaching to her knees. We found out later that she was sixteen, but in the twilight, with only the car lights, with all that jewelry and makeup, she looked much older. I was relieved to see that she was breathing. I dragged her body over to the sidewalk—our side, since it was the closest—pulled the car into the driveway, and went to find Howard, my husband.

Now, Howie is not a violent man. But enough, as he likes to say, is too much. While I tried to get him to keep his voice and blood pressure down, he ranted about the incessant problem at #13 and the inability of the common man to seek redress. Those are Howie's words. When Howie rants, it's with class.

I went with him to the liquor-scented body. Howie continued ranting as he went back into the house to call the police. I stood at the door, keeping an eye on the body, making sure it didn't, in fact, walk away before the police arrived, as the last one had.

On a diagonal from our house was the source of the problem, #13 Mallory Way. The neighborhood called it the "party house," but parties were the least of it. (Some "parties," anyway, with admission charged!) The house looked like any other in the development, a nice split-level with fake shutters. The difference was that light streamed out of the windows 'way into the morning on most nights, and the blaring discords that some called music fought the silence across the streets to complaining neighbors. The sound level was particularly high that night, and Howie's voice added to the din as he shouted into the telephone receiver.

"Damn it, enough is too much!" he yelled. "Hello, hello? Don't you *dare* put me on hold. Give me the Chief of Police right now. What? My name is Rodgers. With a D.... What do you mean, again? Of course again, until you do something about it. Yes, I'll hold, but not for long. Sharon," he called to me without bothering to cover the receiver, "... get away from that door. We don't want anybody else wandering in here like last week.... Hello?" he turned his attention back to the phone. "Elroy? Is that you? Listen, this is Howie Rodgers. Listen, I ... of *course* it's about #13 Mallory ... I ... no, I ... listen to me, damn it! This time there's another body, and it's on our lawn. Sharon damn near ran over it. Hauled it over to the sidewalk."

" 'Her,' Howie," I corrected, "not 'it'."

He ignored me. "It's still there," he said, glowering at me. "Get your men over here or we'll put it back in the road. NO, it's alive. Drunk. Probably drugged, too. Get it out of here. And if it's all you can do, slap another disturbance citation on #13. It's louder than. . . ."

He was interrupted by the sound of shattered glass from the house in question as some small object went hurtling through a front window and into the street.

"Damn it, Elroy, it's out of hand. Do something, and now. They're breaking windows." In kind, he slammed down the receiver, the phone objecting with an extra "ding."

During Howie's tirade, and before the window shattered, Betty had come to our porch and motioned for me to join her. While Howie fumed, I did, and we stood staring at the house at #13 Mallory Way, the Kohn house. It had a large back yard that faced the parking lot of the community high school. From there, the road ran upward and around in a sort of half-a-Valentine-heart. At that point, Mallory met Clearview Road. We're on that corner, directly catty-corner from the Kohn house.

Because #13 jutted onto the school lot, there was a steady stream of kids coming to the door all day. Two minutes was all they ever stayed. We saw the money and the little white bags change hands. We've called the police, as we do with the parties. We've complained about abandoned cars; about abandoned, drunken, drugged bodies. Elroy Watson's answer is always the same: "We have the place under surveillance."

The neighbors on either side of the Kohn house moved out in aggravation. That made it worse. The empty, unsold houses became fair game for transients, for kids sleeping off drink and drugs, and Lord-knows-what-else.

If you stood in our master bedroom and looked out the window, you could see it all, in embarrassingly clear detail. I'd offered the view to Elroy and the police, but they always turned me down. "It's already under surveillance" was all they ever said. But from where were they surveilling?

None of us wanted to believe Elroy was on the take, as they say. We just figured it was too much for our pitifully understaffed police force.

This used to be such a nice, quiet neighborhood. Well, it was another hour that night before the squad car came and took the poor girl to Fairfield General Hospital. I understand she threw up all over the patrolman who tried to wake her. At least this time it didn't happen on my new shag rugs, the way it had the week before.

It was only the girl's fourth offense for underage drinking, they said, so she got probation—again. There was no evidence she got the alcohol at #13, so the house got away with it—again. The party was just as loud after the citation was delivered as before—again.

Betty stayed on the porch with us through all the sirens, the flashing lights, the ambulance. She was unusually quiet, and her face held an odd look of determination.

Her son Mark and my daughter Lori are both in their high school play, and they arrived home from rehearsal right as the ambulance workers were putting the girl's body on the gurney.

"Looks like Cindy's caught again, huh, Mom?" was Lori's greeting to me.

"*Cindy*? Lori, do you know that girl?" I asked in horror, surprised that anything could still shock me after four years of living across from #13 Mallory Way.

"Sure. She's in my English class," Lori explained.

"Borrows my notes sometimes. Comes to class spaced more than not. She'll probably get grounded for a whole weekend for this."

"A whole weekend?" I feigned dismay at the supposed harshness of the sentence.

"Yeah. And too bad. She'll miss the Death concert. She really likes the Death. Maybe I can buy her tickets from her."

"Now wait a minute. I—" She didn't let me finish.

"Well, g'night, mom. I've gotta do my calc' homework. Rehearsal ran late tonight." With that, she ran up to her room, humming.

When Howie came back in the house and Betty had gone home, I was on the sofa, wringing my hands in imitation of a certain Mrs. Macbeth.

"Well, Lori saw it," Howie said. "Again. Should teach her a lesson, at any rate. We shouldn't have to worry about her getting involved in all that."

I didn't tell him that Lori was basically untouched by it all, that she was, in fact, quietly pleased that she had a chance at the Death tickets. (What a name, I shuddered. Death. Yecch.)

That night, despite the ear plugs, mask, and sleeping pills that were *de rigeur* for me on party nights at #13, I lay awake, thinking of the girl. I kept seeing her body in the road, but when I turned her over, she had Lori's face. Could it be? Could that happen to my baby? With drugs and booze and whatnot available right across the street, and so close to school for lunch breaks and study halls, was Lori really immune?

The next morning I called Betty over for coffee. I had

forgotten she taught Friday classes. I left a message on her machine. Betty would come up with a solution, I was certain. She teaches at a large university in the city. She also writes. The money from her books pulled her through when her husband died after a lengthy battle with lung disease.

Now me, I work for one of those companies that still sells things door-to-door. In this age of catalogs and malls, Willy Loman's descendants are pretty sparse, but out here in the wilds of suburbia it's a convenience some people still want. I work at home, my own time, my own schedule. Betty and I met when she was home one day and I was out on a sales campaign. We discovered that our kids went to the same school, same grade. We've been close friends ever since.

I digress.

That afternoon, before Howie came home, Betty Martin came over in answer to my phone message. I told her about my dream, about my very real fear that my daughter could get mixed up in that hell-hole of a house. Told her how that poor girl, that Cindy, was in the same English class as my Lori. The same class.

She listened quietly, nodding occasionally.

"And I'm not worried about my son Mark?" she asked finally, softness and a wan smile on her face.

"Of course you are. It's just that a girl is so much more. . . ."

"Stop!" she interrupted. "Don't even say it. They're *both* just as vulnerable, Sharon. And you're right. We have to do something. In fact, I've been trying to work out the details since last week when that awful man wandered into your house from a party at #13 and puked all over your new shag rugs."

She was silent then, a distant look in her eyes.

I tried to draw her back. "Betty?" I asked timidly. She turned to me, took my hands together, surrounding them with her own. "I have a plan," she said at last. "It's pretty bizarre, but I have every reason to believe it can work. It may cost us some money."

"A plan? What? Oh, I know. We're going to hire an investigator, right? Like Magnum? Or Spenser?"

"Oh, Sharon," she snarled. "Be real! What could an investigator do, report it all to the police? No. We have to go about this in a discreet and . . . um . . . unorthodox manner. Now, will you join me?"

"What is it you want to do?"

"First you must promise that, no matter what happens, whether you join me or not, you'll never tell what I'm about to tell you. Not even to Howie. Swear it."

"Sharon? Is this something illegal? Two illegals don't make a legal. I don't want to do anything illegal. . . ."

"It's not illegal, at least, not anymore. I don't think it is, in Pennsylvania. It's just . . . just a little unorthodox. Swear it, Sharon, or I'll do it myself, and you'll never know."

It wasn't fair, appealing to my curiosity like that. I'd always been a little in awe of Betty, professor and writer that she was. And some big Mahoff in a folklore society. Oh what the hell, I thought to myself, we had to try something. Elroy'd been "surveilling" the house for four years. It was time for a new approach.

"Okay," I said, then, "Ouch! Hey, what are you doing?" The little knife was in and out of her purse in seconds and the little droplet of blood on my finger matched hers.

"Swear," she repeated as she touched her bloodied

finger to mine. I wonder now, if I hadn't joined her, would she have gone ahead anyway. And after all, didn't we accomplish what we set out to do?

Betty set to work in my study. I have a small room off the basement for my computer, product samples, and all my files. I keep the bottles, lotions, and other items untidily on shelves. No one invades that sanctum but me. It was the perfect place. Betty brought her own floppy disks and a nice little file box to keep all the printouts, bills, whatever.

She was right: it *was* expensive. Oh, not at first. At first it was just all the on-line time with the modem. She had a lot of research, she said, before we could do our work. I helped by organizing the notes, keeping her plied with coffee and muffins, and reading through the material when I could. She certainly did pile up the access time. She tapped into every library reference that was available, and a lot more that weren't.

She kept turning up false leads, descriptive verbiage, false promises.

One morning she declared, "I think I'm getting somewhere. The trail leads to Snagov. Name ring a bell?"

"Hmmm," I thought aloud. "Snag-off. Is he a P.I.?"

"Oh, Sharon, be real!" she snapped. "No. Snagov is a town, in Transylvania."

"Transylv—" The name suddenly clicked. "Transylvania? Vampires! Vampires!" I spoke warily, pronouncing the word more in breathiness than voice, lest the dreaded objects materialize somehow.

"Well, sort of. That's the town where the church is where Vlad Dracul is buried. He *was* the model for the Dracula stories."

"A vampire!" I repeated. "We're getting a vampire? Oh, no, Betts, we can't. What if he keeps on biting? What if he. . . ."

"No, no, Sharon, *please* be real! Vlad Tepes, called Dracul or Dragon, wasn't a vampire. He was just a bloodthirsty, excessively cruel warlord. He was said to dabble in demons, not bats. And for power and gain, not for a bizarre appetite."

I shuddered. "So who *do* we want in Snagov?"

"Not 'who,' Sharon, but 'what.' In the old monastery archives at Snagov are the documents I need. Vlad Tepes used them."

I waited for further clarification, but she just kept tapping at the console.

"Uh, Betts, I really do need some time on my computer tonight," I stammered. "My accounts are behind and. . . ."

She ignored me, as she often did those days. She mumbled something about the Patriarch and special orders, and not-really-illegal, and then incredible-that-there-are-copies-in-the-data-bank at such-and-such a university.

It was fully another hour before she spoke to me. She tapped out the command for the printer. Then, as the high little whine indicated the machine was at work, she left the computer table and stretched out in a more comfortable chair.

"We're getting there, Sharon. God, it's incredible the research you can do seated in one place! Anyway, what I've got now is a repeat of the trappings of the Ritual, with a few refinements. It'll take a little longer to get the Calls. I'll need some translation, too, because all they have is microfilm or fiche of the originals, but we're well under way." She stood up suddenly. "Now I have to go.

When the printer's done, just put the sheets under "S," will you? I've already programmed it to store in memory. Please don't touch the computer until I have a chance to go through it all tomorrow. I don't want you erasing anything." With that, she left.

I shook my head and went to the printer, picking up the first finished sheets. Partly in Latin, partly in a language I didn't recognize. What did they speak in Snagov? Transylvanian? I put the sheets down and went upstairs to prepare supper for my family.

I didn't think about it again until the next day, when I went downstairs to do my accounts. When I turned the console on, the material Betty had been researching danced across the screen.

This time I took the time to read it. It was just as she said. She was going to call on the Powers of Evil to get rid of the lesser demons at #13. My God! She meant it!

Some of the material was the same folklore I'd been cross-referencing for her. This stuff, however, was in deadly earnest. I read through some Latin, after I hunted my old, thumbed-through Cassell's, and my notes from Catholic high school.

This stuff talked about the "minor Powers" and "Disciples" and how they could be "eradicated" by calling the "Higher Power." To do this, one needed the "Calls" to bring the proper Higher Power.

I left the computer, my accounts forgotten, and called Betty. She promised to come right over. She gave her afternoon classes to a grad assistant so she could finish researching the Calls.

She came over, breathless. "Good news! Ted is going to help us!"

I looked at her in disbelief. "He knows what we're doing and he's going to help?"

"Well, not really. I couldn't tell him. Our oath, remember." She looked befuddled. "He'll help, but he doesn't know what we're doing. Sharon, he'll think I'm dotty. He's the first man I cared about since . . . since Richard's death. I don't want to lose him." She sniffed ungracefully. "Anyway, I just told him I needed the information for a new novel I'm writing, and I need to know how to prepare the computers to—to . . . do what needs to be done. He told me everything. It's really easy. Bless these computers. I just have to get the right software into #13, and be sure they have a modem. . . ."

I stared at her. She *had* gone wifty on me, after all. "Computer? for magic? Isn't that a bit contradict—wait a minute!" Lights flashed in my poor head. "you're not taking *my* computer over there. . . ."

"Not yours. Theirs."

"They have a computer?"

"I don't know. Do they? I thought you could see everything in that house from your bedroom window."

"Not everything. Wait. Why do they need a computer? What's all this stuff from Snag-off?"

"Snagov," she corrected placidly, waving my questions aside. She threw back her mane of unevenly-frosted hair and said, grandly, "It's time for you to do your part, Sharon. You have to be convincing. Now, here's what you have to do. . . ."

And so it was that the next day I found myself knocking at the door of #13, sample case in hand. My heart was as skittery as a squirrel in an ice rink. The door was opened by a woman of indeterminate age, the sides of her hair shaved into ripply rows, a thick shock of

tri-colored hair sticking off the top of her head and to
the right in defiance of gravity and other laws of hair.

"Yeah? What is it, Scout brownie time?"

I swallowed my fear and forged right ahead. "Good
morning, ma'am! I have really good news for you. You
have been selected by computer to participate in our
survey on contemporary mores."

"Maw-rays? What's that? Say, you a cop?" she started
to shove the door closed in my face. I put on my cheeriest
smile and wedged my foot, with some little discomfort,
in the doorway.

"All I ask are a few minutes of your time to answer
some questions for our computer survey. You'll receive a
nice free gift, and some free chances in our big sweepstakes."

"Well, I dunno," she said, scratching where her bra
should have been but wasn't. "You sure you're no cop?"

"Just a saleswoman, ma'am. If you don't want me to
come in, you can answer the questions out here."

She considered that. "Well, it won't hurt none. Sid's
asleep. Free gift, you say?"

I gulped and nodded, aware of the tremor in my right
knee.

"Shoot," she said, leaning on the door. I noticed the
floor behind her, littered with beer cans and the smoky
haze that permeated the house. I held up the clipboard
and began to read.

"First, do you own any of the following. . . ."

She nodded or grunted for things like a VCR, stereo,
corn poppers and such, but shook her head when I
mentioned a home computer.

"Nah. What do I want with that?"

"Oh," I said, smiling brightly, "Computers are wonderful. I use mine to keep my accounts, lists, everything

in perfect order and complete privacy."

"Privacy?" she snorted. "I seen that movie about a kid that broke into the Pentagon stuff. Don't tell *me* they're privacy."

"No, no," I soothed, ignoring her word misusage. "That's just a story. . . ."

"You selling computers?" She started to shut the door again.

"No, no. As a matter of fact, I deal in other things. I do have a computer, though. I can code anything so no one else can get at it and I can erase things at the touch of a button." Sometimes, I added silently, even when I don't want to.

She considered that. "Yeah, I guess it could be a help with the . . . accounts. I gotta keep 'em all straight, Sid don't help. All them little slips. . . ." She caught herself mid-scratch, peered at me through her bloodshot eyes. "You *sure* you ain't a cop? Maybe I should call Sid, huh?"

"If you think he'd be interested, certainly, ma'am, call him," I bluffed. She looked at me, her head tilted.

"Nah. You can't be a cop. Besides, there'd be hell to pay if I woke him up this early." Early? By my watch, it was half-past eleven. "What's in the case?" she continued.

Before long I was in her house, and had sold her a facial cream guaranteed to remove morning puffiness, an under-eye concealer, and several gaudy colors of eye makeup. I had also gotten her attention back to the 'Survey.'

She was unembarrassed. If anyone had asked *me* those questions, I'd have fainted dead away. How *could* Betty have written all that? The woman gave lengthy answers to the most intimate of queries. She was interested in 'exotic sexual practices' as she and the Survey called it. I tried to keep my voice steady.

I was not surprised when she answered the question about a favorite television program with "That lady doctor, you know, the therapist. I called her a coupla times. She's got good ideas. We like to experiment, Sid and me. Say, did I tell you how. . . ."

I hoped my blushes didn't show. Betty hadn't told me *why* we needed to know all this, so I just kept going until the 'Survey' was mercifully over.

For her 'free gift' I gave her a nice recipe card file and a bottle of a new perfume called *Outrage*. She grunted an approval.

"Oh, I almost forgot," I said as I stood to leave. "Your raffle tickets." I handed her a batch of tickets, and told her to pick five. She did, and filled them out with her name and phone number.

"Hey, maybe I'll get a computer, huh?"

"If so, I hope you get a modem."

"A what?"

I explained about access, on-line time, networks. I told her she could even find information on some of the 'exotic' things she had checked off in the survey. She seemed interested.

"Well, good luck with the raffle." I resisted the impulse to leave her my card in case she wanted more face cream. I hoped she'd be gone before the jar was empty.

"You were gone long enough." Betty greeted me at my back door. "Did you get all the information?"

I was shaking so hard, all I could do was nod my head.

"Good job, Sharon. We're on our way."

"Wait!" I managed to call as she turned to leave. "Aren't you going to explain?"

"All in good time," she said.

That night after dinner I gave myself a facial to try to get rid of the worry lines. It didn't work. I wandered to my study to work on my long-overdue accounts. Lori was at my computer, studying the screen.

"What *is* this stuff, Ma?" she asked without looking up.

I ran to the screen to see, in horror, that the Romanian-Latin manuscripts were glittering in front of my daughter's wide eyes.

"Uh, um . . . it's . . . that is, Betty . . . you see . . . I—" I said.

"Oh, I get it," she interrupted mercifully, "Stuff for Mrs. Martin's next novel, huh? Research? Neat." Then, "Uh-oh."

I didn't care for the "uh-oh" or the silence that followed. I didn't like the suddenly-blank screen, either.

"Lori," I shrieked, pointing to a switch which should have been flicked up but wasn't. "The fan! Oh no. It's overheated. It's all gone."

"Don't worry, ma. I'll just turn the computer off and on again. See, it's . . . uh-oh."

"Again with the uh-oh. Lori!"

I sent her upstairs after eliciting a promise that she would never touch my computer, even when her father *was* playing Star Trek on hers and refused to surrender it to homework time.

I tapped at the keyboard, but the Snagov material was lost.

Betty came over when I called.

"Not to worry." she consoled me. "The Calls are on printout. We've lost some of Radu's translation, but I remember most of the important parts, especially the conditions of the Call. No problem."

"No?" I asked. "Who's Radu?"

"I found him on the network. He can translate Romanian. Ancient Romanian. I told him it was for a novel—you know, I may get a book out of this yet, since Ted and Radu both. . . ."

"Betts!" I screamed.

"Oh, yes. I gave him unconnected segments. If he ever wondered, he never said. Sharon, it's all right," she repeated. "Just be sure it doesn't happen again."

That night two kids from Lori's class drove their cars into a telephone pole. They'd just left a party at #13 Mallory Way. Three seniors were found wandering around the school parking lot, spaced. Where were their parents? I wondered. Had they given up the way Cindy's had? And could *we* really do anything about this?

When Howie heard the news he reacted with his usual verbosity, but then took me upstairs to show me something he'd bought just that afternoon. A gun.

"Howie, what are you thinking? You can't use that!" I shrieked.

"So help me, Sharon, I'd kill them before I let them get Lori involved. One of those monsters comes anywhere near her and I'll. . . ."

I took his hand. I knew just how he felt. This was his answer. I had Betty's, whatever it was. I prayed for Betty's plan, what*ever* it was, to be successful and soon over, before Howie would feel the need to test the gun. Oh God, I prayed silently, let this all end soon.

The next day was quiet, and the next. The Kohns didn't get a computer. Betty and I went to a large factory outlet and we bought a complete computer outfit, with modem and other features. Magazines, too. Even at a cut rate, my half came to more than I wanted to spend on a computer for someone else, especially for the Kohns. Well, at least it was my money, from sales. Howie wouldn't know. We'd been spending a fortune on access time lately, Betty and I. She never batted a lash, just kept writing checks for her half. "Soon you'll be telling me it was worth every penny," she cooed.

We brought the computer outfit home. Betty worked at it a while. There was one attachment I didn't have, but she just mumbled when I asked. I was getting a headache from all the secrecy.

We wrapped everything up, with a nicely-typed letter telling Mrs. Kohn she had won third prize in the "Survey Sweepstakes" and may she enjoy her new computer. Betty also included detailed installation instructions that even (she said) a freshman with the mentality of a waterlogged clam could decipher. There were lots of floppy disks she had programmed herself and labeled to look like commercial programs. I guessed it was Ted's expertise unknowingly at work.

The next day when the UPS van delivered the package to #13 Mallory Way, I watched through Howie's binoculars. Damn if that face cream wasn't helping the woman! I made a note to try the product myself; I'd been looking a little peaked lately.

She never questioned the delivery, just took everything into the house. I watched through the window as she opened it all and began to put it to use. Betty came over after classes, and we went downstairs to my study. She turned on the computer, and we could see everything on our screen that Mrs. Kohn was tapping into hers. She called up a menu and tapped in for "adult recreation." Then she tapped for "procedures."

"It's working," Betty crowed. "We're in."

"Wow!" I said in real admiration. "How did you do that? No, no, scratch that. Don't explain. Look, why are we doing this, will this get rid of them? And is there any way she can trace it to my place?"

"Trace it here? Oh, probably." Betty laughed.

"*Probably*?" I wailed.

"Never mind. It won't be long now. Within a week. Just a few days. We can hold out for the full moon. Relax."

"Computers are affected by the moon?" I asked.

"Not computers, silly, The Ritual, The Call."

The Rituals that Betty had been storing in my computer were all unified by the common expected ingredients of candles, incense, and such, but some, thank heaven, she had dismissed as "impractical."

"Impractical?" I had asked on first reading. "Sacrificing goats? Sprinkling powdered unicorn horn over aged bat liver, and all you can say is 'impractical'?"

Betty only shrugged.

It all seemed so bizarre. The rituals, the computer outfit. I still didn't understand. The rituals all called for the Reader of the Call to be present. And why was Betty giving sex therapy over the computer? It made no sense.

I finally decided that she was just gathering material for a novel, as she had told Ted and Radu. When I tried to accuse her of that, she shushed me and pointed to the computer screen.

"Look, Sharon, she's using the bookkeeping program."

Sure enough, our screen mirrored that at #13. There

it all was, who, when, how much, even the suppliers. Her code was surprisingly transparent.

"Bless your Ted," I said. "We can see everything they've done." Suddenly lights flashed in my mind. We could see everything they've done. I repeated to myself. "Betty! So this is what it's all about, after all. Evidence! Look at the evidence! Wow! We've got them!" Then I turned to her, annoyed. "Why did you give me all that mumbo-jumbo about magic and rituals and calls? And vampires? We've got real evidence."

"Inadmissable," she pronounced. She looked up at me with sad eyes. "Wiretapping is illegal. We can't show this to anyone."

"Then what . . . ?"

"Sharon, it's almost over . . . a few days." Her eyes slit, her voice somber, she intoned, "Those people, Sharon, are evil. Just remember that. Whatever happens, remember that. No guilt trips later, okay?"

I nodded, confused.

"Okay. Thursday, then. From the neighborhood grapevine, no party is scheduled at #13, because there's a big bash for Friday. I don't want any of those kids there. They deserve a second chance. I don't want them taken, too."

"Taken?" Somehow, I didn't think she meant by the police.

"The Prince Himself. Evil for Evil. Remember that."

Wednesday morning I found a note taped to my study door. Lori's handwriting. Long by her standards.

MOM. HAD TO USE JUNIOR. DAD WOULDN'T GIVE UP MINE IN THE MIDDLE OF A KLINGON INVASION. YOU REALLY SHOULD GET A NEW

ONE WITH BUILT-IN FAN. SORRY. TALK TO YOU
LATER. DRESS REHEARSALS ALL WEEK. LORI.

I didn't think much of it at the time, just filed it away
until I could check with Betty.

Thursday night our house was mercifully clear. My
Howie was at a club or civic meeting and Lori was at a
dress rehearsal. Betty came over, clutching two garment
bags and an overnighter.

"Staying?" I asked.

She waved this aside, and went to the computer. Right
on schedule, Mrs. Kohn had tapped in for her "adult
recreation" program. I watched as Betty answered, giving a new choice for a special "Ultimate Party for Two."
Mrs. Kohn, true to expectations, selected it. It didn't
matter, actually, what she selected. Betty had the program ready under any name. She tapped in that the
program would be ready at 9:30 p.m.

"Darker then," she explained. "The Ritual needs
darkness. We can't use drugs or drink, poetic as that
might be," she mused, "because that would interfere
with the vibrations. The Ritual was very specific about
certain things, if Radu's translation is to be trusted. He
had some difficulty with the archaic text. . . ."

I interrupted her reverie, because the computer lights
indicated that a message had been held on line for her. I
pointed this out to Betty. She ignored it.

"I think we should at least look at it." I tried.

"No time. We've got to take advantage of the situation, the darkness, and the full Moon, now."

"Well, it should only take a minute. We've a little time
before nine-thirty, anyway." I tapped in for the message.

"It's from Radu. Uh-oh. Betty . . . look at this."

The letters danced on the screen.

IGNORE EARLIER TRANSLATION. WEDNESDAY'S REVISIONS CORRECT. USE SECOND ALTERNATE USAGE. SEGMENT 34:5 NOT DARKNESS, BUT POSSIBLY MIDNIGHT. PERHAPS PRE-DAWN: VAGUE. SEGMENT 41:14-ON IS *UNBROKEN*, ONE MAY BE "NOT UNBROKEN." AGAIN, VAGUE. NEED ANTECEDENTS. YOU HAVE ANCIENT CALLS HERE. DO YOU KNOW THE CONSEQUENCES IF NOT FOLLOWED EXACTLY?

I looked at Betty who was scowling now in earnest. "Wednesday's revisions? We didn't get any revisions yesterday, did we?"

I paled. Lori's note. I had forgotten all about it. The revisions had met the fate of the fan-less computer. I explained to Betty.

"But which?" she mumbled. "Which is unbroken? And is it "must be at midnight" or "must not be at midnight?"

"You are asking me? Okay. Game's over. Let's pack up."

"Pack up?" she moaned. Her eyes were wild. "NO, no. We've got to do this—"

"No. Pack up. The game is over, at least for now. The rules have changed, and we don't know them."

She tapped at the computer, calling up material and mumbling in a frenzy. "Ready . . . program engaged . . . can't wait for another full Moon . . . Can't keep this up four weeks . . . got to do this now. . . ."

"Look," I tried to reason with her. "At least call Radu."

She tried to tap into his line, but was unsuccessful.

"Betty," I reasoned, "While I don't really believe all this magic stuff, I will NOT let you do anything while you're in such a state. Phone Radu. You have his number, don't you?"

She tried, but the operator said the number had been disconnected that afternoon.

Betty was really wild-eyed now. "They've got him!" she wailed. "They'll get us, too, unless we get them first."

"Betty? Who's 'them'? You've been reading too much of your own folklore and fiction. Come on, let's pack up."

"NO!" she was adamant. "We do it NOW, Sharon. Don't you see? HE knows we know. HE got Radu. Maybe HE sent the message. The translations must be right. There were no revisions. He—"

"Betty, do you hear yourself? For God's sake. . . ."

"Yes, yes, for God's sake. Not for HIS! But we KNOW, Sharon. We can tap HIS power, and for God's sake! But we have to do it now. We can't wait for another full Moon!"

I was really afraid then. Oh, not of "Him" whoever that was. Not of demons or darkness. I was afraid for Betty's sanity. Why didn't I see this coming? Before I could say or do anything, the phone rang, jangling the awkward silence and my ragged nerves.

"Mrs. Rodgers?" the voice asked. "Mrs. Rodgers, this is Byron Cantwell, Drama instructor at Fairfield High. Lori's not feeling well. She's passed out. She's quite hot. Fever, I guess. Really severe. She seems to be hallucinating. Shall I call an ambulance?"

Betty, who had been listening over my shoulder, grabbed the phone and screamed into it. "Don't let anyone touch her. We'll be right there!" then hung up before I could say anything.

We got Lori home. She was raving. And Lord, she was hot. Of course, Howie came home from the meeting just as we were carrying Lori upstairs.

"Good God!" he screamed. "They got her! She's drugged! I'm gonna kill those bastards!"

"Howie, no, I—"

He had the gun out and was across the street before I could stop him. I watched in a daze as he ran across the street, and directly into Elroy's police car. Elroy took the gun, cuffed Howie, and started lecturing about jaywalking. I couldn't believe it. My head hurt.

From that point on, things were really blurry. Howie went off in Elroy's car. Betty carried Lori to our guest room, placed three rosaries around her neck, and sprinkled her with enough herbs to season meals for both our families for a month.

"All right," Betty pronounced. "We have to get busy. It's almost nine-thirty."

My head pounding, I followed Betty down to my workroom. She tapped into the computer, giving a list of procedures for the "Ultimate Party for Two." Incredibly, the woman followed along. Betts tapped instructions about drinking ginseng tea, (a sample of which had been delivered quite coincidentally that morning by me), about bathing in lemon oil. Most importantly, she instructed them to wear white robes and brush their hair so there were no knots.

"Betty. This is really crazy. Howie's in jail, or at least at the station, Lori's feverish, and how do you know Mrs. Kohn will do what you say?"

"She's been doing it all week."

I pouted.

"Here," Betty said as she threw a garment bag at me. "Put this on, and hurry."

"Me? Now, wait just a minute, here. . . ."

"Don't argue. Everything's ready. Before Howie gets

back. And wipe off your makeup and brush down your
hair."

"I am not going over there."

"You don't have to. The computer is there."

On that cryptic remark, she donned a robe herself
and brushed her hair down. Soon the two of us were
looking like escapee Druids or leftover Trick-or-Treaters.

Betty ran to the master bedroom and looked through
the binocs. I took them in turn. Sure enough, the Kohns
were dressed pretty much as we were, in toga-like white
sheets. Who'd believe it? Betty ran back down to the
computer. I spent half the time watching, the other
running downstairs to report to Betty.

They were following the computer instructions, all
right, as fast as Betty tapped them in. Soon all the house
lights were extinguished and all the appliances pulled. I
had a tough time seeing after that. Mrs. Kohn took a
box of white powder and poured a thin line in the form
of a large circle. She placed five little candles along the
perimeter, then lit some incense. (I'd brought that over
too. Samples.)

Betty called me downstairs. She was still tapping out
instructions about not leaving the circle, then left and
pulled me aside. She had drawn a chalk circle on my nice
clean linoleum floor. A part of me fretted that it had just
been waxed, but another part noticed the five-pointed
star outlined inside the circle. Now Betty lit five candles,
one at each point of the pentagram. The computer was
within the diagram. There was incense burning, too, but
not the scent I had delivered across the street. Betty
tapped some things into the console, dimmed the room
lights, then pulled me close to her, in the center, near the
computer. Her eyes were closed, her brows drawn tightly
together. She called out something in a language I

now recognized as Romanian. Then she instructed me, "Quick, take off the robe!"

"Now, wait just a minute, here . . . !" I started to protest, but she repeated the orders.

"Take it off, and hurry."

Hers had already been thrown clear of the pentagram. I watched in horror as it began to smoke. I pulled at my own, the fabric strangely warm to my touch, and threw it outside the circle.

Her eyes closed, her arms raised, Betty called out in a loud voice a memorized speech partly in Latin, partly in Romanian. It was the Call. About then, I really got nervous. Here I was, stark naked, with my neighbor starkers beside me, babbling in ancient languages. Candles, incense, rigged computers. My daughter in heaven-knew *what* condition upstairs, my husband probably behind bars. I could see the headlines in the local paper: witch hunt in Fairfield. Suddenly my thoughts were pierced by a very loud roar. The ground around us rumbled, the room blurred. Then the screams started. Horrid, hellish screams. Life, death, pain screams. I wondered how many neighbors could hear the screams. After a few minutes, the room grew quiet. I noticed smoke and dancing shadows. The robes outside the circle had quietly burst into flame while I was distracted. Had candle sparks done that?

Betty opened her eyes. I couldn't budge. She extinguished the candles, scooped up the ashes of the robes, and started putting on her clothes.

"Come on," she called. "It's over. Get dressed."

I stood still, watching her. "Just . . . like that? Over?"

"Yes, didn't you hear them?"

"Them?"

"The Kohns. They're gone."

I watched as she calmly buttoned her blouse.

"Just what did you put in their computer? A bomb?"

"Sharon, be real," she snapped. "And get dressed, will you? Don't you want to see what we did?"

"Not until you tell me what's going on!" I cried with only a touch of the hysteria I really felt.

"In good time. Get dressed, for Chrissakes."

"Did we kill them? Are we murderers? As bad as they?"

"We didn't kill anybody. Get dressed."

She tidied up as she explained. "It was the Call. IT had to be spoken during the Ritual, in the presence of . . . of the Evil. Neither one of us could do it, because the Caller endangers himself. I sent the call over the network, and the voice synthesizer we gave the Kohns with the computer actually said the words. The Call was *spoken* aloud, if electronically. We were safely within an unbroken pentagram, so we were safe. Otherwise, we might have been claimed."

"Claimed? By what? Whom?"

"Do you really want to know?"

"No," I recanted. "Don't tell me."

"Amazing," Betty mused, "the Call. The supreme Evil came and recalled his own. Now," she turned to me, "will you PLEASE put some clothes on!"

We hurried across the street, drawn by curiosity and the fire sirens. The Kohn house oozed black smoke, and the trucks were just arriving. Fred Saunders, a neighbor, met us at the driveway to #13. "Did you hear those screams?" he asked. "Wonder how many kids are caught in there?"

We didn't answer, just watched as breathing-masked

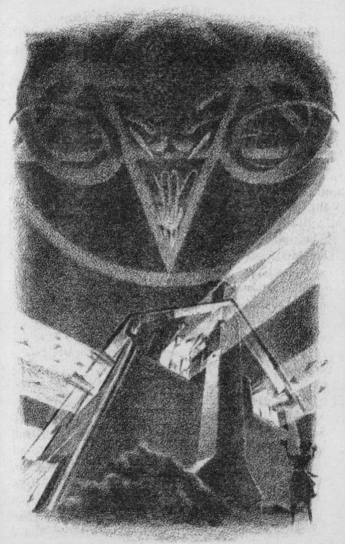

Illustrated by J. Kenton Manning

firemen hurried in and out. They were apparently trying
to extinguish a blaze inside that swirled and grew no
matter how much water was poured on it or what
chemicals they tried.

Then in minutes there was nothing. The flames
seemed to have simply stopped. Elroy drew up in his
police car, Howie beside him. I ran to the car.

"Elroy, listen, he didn't mean anything. The gun—"

"Gun?" Elroy asked.

"Sharon, you been dipping into the cooking sherry?
What are you babbling about?"

I looked at them both. "Why'd you haul Howie in,
then?"

"The smoke make her crazy, Howard?" Elroy asked.
To me he said, "You know we've been at a zoning meeting, Mrs. Rodgers." Betty poked me hard in the ribs and I
stopped asking.

My headache was worse, no question. The whole
world seemed to throb with the pain in my head.

The firemen came out, shaking their heads, heading
toward Elroy. "Damnedest thing I ever saw," one said.
"Just a big burned circle. Nothing outside the circle was
even touched."

Later, at the official inquiry, the cause of the fire was
listed as accidental, probably caused by candles in the
living room. Amazingly, the candles had still been burning in place when the firemen investigated the house.

People talked about it for weeks, about how good it
was there was no party that night, but wasn't it a shame
about the fire?

Lori is fine. She has no recollection of that night, but
we have a letter from the drama director explaining how a
stage crew member spiked her on-stage drinking water,

making her sick. The guest room still smells of parsley and thyme.

The Kohns were declared dead, even though no trace of them was found. Their belongings were sold. The school, Lori's school, got the computer setup, so it didn't seem a total loss.

The local drug and drink source is gone, although I'm sure the kids who want it will find another. There haven't been any parties at #13 or anywhere else in this neighborhood.

Betty asked me about love potions. I told her I thought they were dishonest. She just shrugged.

I hope the people who move in to the houses on either side of #13 make their money honestly. I don't want to go halves on another computer outfit.

And that, I thought, was that. But just this afternoon Betty was in my work room, shaking and pointing at the computer. She wasn't making any sense, so I just looked.

Mrs. Kohn was asking about further instructions on the Ultimate Party. Now, where is she? Is she in the computer at the school? Or somewhere else? Or is someone playing a joke on us? I'll have to wait until Betty comes to, to find out.

Monsters
by
Jean Reitz

About the Author

As well as being a writer, Jean Reitz is an artist in Kansas. She majored in English at Kansas State Teachers' College and minored in art. She attends several writing workshops in her city. The key scene in her story came to her in a dream.

None of this information, of course, explains much about her. Writers are not in who they are or how they work; writers are in the writing. The writing, of course, is in who the writers are and how they got that way . . . the hard knocks, the patient building of skills. Does that make sense to you? Then you probably stand a good chance of being a writer yourself, now or some day.

Jean's preference for SF stems, she says, from the fact that this form of fiction is not confined; the writer can do whatever the imagination allows. In the next breath, she says—as a writer will—that it enables her to "look underneath the real, and see what's really there." Does that seem logical? For our money, it's exactly right. It's the nurture of the inherent talent, the application of the writer's "eye." And here in this vivid, realistic portrayal of the fantastic and its terrible beauty, she shows what she has seen. . . .

Once upon a time, Wayne knows where he is going. He isn't happy about it.

Four jobs in fifteen years; I've put my ass on the line every time and I'm tired of it, says Wayne to himself.

Road and fences and telephone poles weave with subtle regularity through rusty hills that lean on the winter sky. Wayne doesn't see the prairie things, quail and coyotes and deer in the cottonwood trees that outline the creeks; they hide out in the open and watch his cloud of dust go by. Wayne thinks he is alone in the tarnished landscape.

Alone and bitter bored. He likes mountains, big purple mountains with ice cream snow and green bright pine trees and a blue lake at the bottom reflecting the whole thing back. They have a picture like that over the sofa at home. Janis picked it out.

I need something, a new challenge, or a new car, or maybe a vacation, says Wayne to himself. Something, something, hum the tires. There are mysteries in the grass and marvels in the weeds, but Wayne would have to stop and wait if he wanted to see them. "Baby, baby," sings the radio and the song is lost in static. Wayne swears and turns the static off; then all he can hear is the cold wind whistling by the car windows.

Wayne can't see the red-tailed hawk gliding above,

watching the car's exhaust fumes climb to the sky, but he does spot the wind-hurried tumbleweeds caught against the fences and he thinks they look like desperate brown spikey animals trying to escape from the hills. He wouldn't notice the hills if the road didn't have to go up and down to get over them.

The car begins a small, persistent rattle somewhere in the right front dash. Damn it, I need a new car, says Wayne to himself. How in the hell can a man work year after year and never have any money? Where does it all go? Money, money, money hum the tires.

The road lifts him over one last hill; there in the midst of the pasture grass and the wild weeds, fences turn into buildings; he has found it at last, the little town, lingering in the same run-together, dead-grass colors as the hills. The town is dying, going broke along with the farmers.

What a dump, says Wayne to himself.

The main street buildings press together and watch through dark-eyed windows as he parks in front of Harter's Farm and Home, where he takes a few minutes to chew a breath mint and think positive. If sales don't pick up soon he will be out of a job again, and Janis will be hell to live with.

I've made more money in the last five years than her old man did in his whole lifetime, says Wayne to himself. She's got nothing to complain about.

When he gets out of the car his legs are stiff from too many years of sitting bent-kneed behind the wheel of an automobile. In the store, he finds a lady dancing her bright red fingernails over typewriter keys, telling tales of inventories and accounts past due. Wayne learns that her name is Mavis. Wayne discovers that Mavis can sell batteries and bolts, but she can't place orders because

Mr. Harter places the orders, and Mr. Harter has gone
to take his kid to the nearest clinic at Collins, and that is
over thirty miles away.

It always pays to butter up the women; Wayne stays
and teases Mavis for a while, always in good taste, and
he is careful to notice when his welcome is gone.

I'll be damned if I'll sit in that cold car for an hour
and a half, says Wayne to himself, looking around for
something else to do. The only other person in the store
is an old guy shuffling a dust mop over the linoleum.
His back pockets are barely hanging on to his powder
blue, polyester, bell-bottom pants that drag the floor,
picking up the dust that his mop misses.

"Say, friend," says Wayne, "Is there a spot in this
town where a man could get a cup of coffee and a chair
to sit in?"

Something secret brightens at the bottom of the old
man's stupid eyes and a lazy smile spreads the gray
stubble on his face. "Go on down the street a block to
Harry's Cafe. You can get a cup of coffee and if you got
the money, he'll take you upstairs. He took me upstairs,
once."

"What's upstairs, friend?"

The old man has said all that he wants to say and
shuts off his smile. He turns his back on Wayne and
resumes shuffling dust across the floor. Wayne opens
the door, stepping into the dusty cold. The wind shoves
dirt and tumbleweeds and Wayne down the street.
Wayne blows by a building with boarded-up windows
and a sign on the door that says FOR RENT. The sign
and the boards on the windows are old. Wayne's teeth
feel gritty; as he stops in front of Harry's Hurry Back
Cafe, he hopes for at least a decent cup of coffee.

A woman is approaching him from the south, the

only other person he has seen on the street. She wears a long green coat trimmed with dirty fake fur and a farmer's hat jammed down on her ears. The wind blows her coat apart, shows her skirt, shows her legs are built without curves, one thickness from ankle to knees. She reaches Wayne and stops in front of him. "Bloodsucker," she says to the cafe.

Crazy old lady, says Wayne to himself.

Harry's Hurry Back Cafe has stools for sitters at the counter and booths for sitters by the window. The booths, at the back, in the shadows are filled with men who wear the same bitter face repeated. They appear to be making a career out of the hard work of waiting.

Thank God, I don't have to live here, says Wayne to himself.

Being a transient waiter, not one of the regulars, Wayne sits down on a bar stool and takes some time to look around. Nothing has been added here for thirty years, except the newspaper on the dusty counter which has today's date. CAPITAL ALLEGED TO BE CENTER OF PROSTITUTION RING say the headlines. A yellow sign over the coffee maker gives directions in case of an enemy air raid. A bigger and newer sign hangs over the doorway behind the counter. It is hand-lettered in magic marker: SEE THE STAR MONSTER RAVISH THE WILD MYSTERY WOMAN.

"Coffee, black, please," says Wayne to the man behind the counter who looks rosy and prosperous with rings that sparkle on his white fat fingers as he pours a cup of coffee, black, for Wayne.

"Tell me, friend," says Wayne, "Are things around here as bad as they look?"

"Well, they are and then they aren't. An entrepreneur with a good idea and a feel for the market, he can always

profit from any situation, and some of us are doing fine,
just fine. What might your business be?"

"I'm calling on Harter's Farm and Home for my
company; let me give you one of my cards."

The fat man examines Wayne's card. "You take a
look at these poor losers at the back of my place, Wayne.
Why, they can't afford more than one cup of coffee with
free refills all morning long. Harry has a heart as big as
the rest of him," he says, pointing a fat finger at his own
chest. "I let them sit here where it's warm, and they can
be miserable together instead of having to sit at home in
the kitchen and listen to the old lady nag about money."
He pushes his voice into the dim silence at the back of
the room, "Ain't that right, boys? You don't like me, do
you boys, but you keep coming back. How come is
that?"

His jeering tone makes Wayne uneasy. "Do you really
have a monster upstairs?"

"A Star Monster and a Wild Mystery Woman, quite a
thing to see, and well worth the money, Wayne. Gentlemen only, it just upsets the ladies, right, boys? These
boys in the back have spent all their cash and can't
afford any fun for a while. Tell you what, Wayne. It's
been a slow week and looks to stay slow for a while. I'll
take you upstairs and let you see the show, by yourself,
for an all time bargain price of twenty-five dollars, cash;
understand now, that is my regular crowd rate. It will
change your life, or my name ain't Harry."

What the hell, I can fiddle twenty-five dollars on my
expense report, says Wayne to himself, watching an oil
skin forming on the surface of his coffee, black. "Hell,
Harry, why not. I work hard enough to deserve a little
fun once in a while."

"That's the spirit, Wayne. Best money you ever spent.

Make a man out of you. Right over here behind the counter with me; we have to climb these stairs to get there."

The waiting men watch Wayne as he moves to join Harry behind the counter. Wayne can feel them glare; he wonders if their eyes are covered with dust, too.

"Too bad, boys, no pay, no play," chuckles Harry, "Follow me, Wayne."

The way up is narrow and the stairs are steep, the air filled with memories of onions. Wayne follows the gleams of the silver threads on the yoke of Harry's fancy western shirt. A small square of daylight waits at the top, somewhere up there in front of Harry's body which nearly fills the narrow stairway.

"Men come clear from Wideford to see this, Wayne. They come regular, just as often as they got the cash. It affords me a good living, not like some of these losers around here. I drive a new car, and I can dress right to go anywhere, Denver, Kansas City, anywhere at all, but never forget, Wayne, I work for it.

"Nobody else wants to sit up, waiting all night at the right places, nobody else is going to fix up a good strong safe place with iron and straw so these creatures can educate the public. Now why ain't I a more popular man? I provide all this entertainment and people won't speak to me on the street."

Harry stops at the top of the stairs, looks down at Wayne, showing the white rolls of flesh under his chin. "It's just up here to the right. I need the cash before you come any farther."

Wayne hands over a twenty and a five, and moves past Harry's bulky body. On one side is a row of dirty windows and he can see that they are high in the air above the other roofs, looking over the town to the

Illustrated by J. Kenton Manning

prairie. On the right side of the hall are two cages with iron bars that reach to the ceiling. Wayne scuffs the toe of his shoe at some granular white stuff, sprinkled where the bars meet the floor.

"Don't mess with that Wayne, that's salt, that's one of the few things that will hold these creatures, that and the iron bars. Don't stick your fingers between the bars, neither. I only guarantee your safety on this side of the cage."

The air has a muddy smell. Wayne is sure that the straw on the floor of the cage needs to be changed. An old pile of fur rugs lying at the back begins to move in a slow, slouchy way. Wayne has never seen anything like it. It is as scary as hell with long sharp teeth and claws, and hooves and horns, and eyes that sort of radiate red hate. Suddenly, its long narrow face is about two inches from Wayne's; its ugly snarling mouth right against the bars. Wayne steps back in a hurry.

"Just between you and me, Wayne, it ain't really from the stars. I catch them right around here. I made up the star monster thing to get some interest up among the locals. I think it's something magic. I suppose the Indians knew what they were but there ain't any Indians left around here to tell me."

"Are there a lot of them around?"

"Not like there used to be. You've got to want to find them awful bad and you have to know where to get them, mostly at edges and borders of things, and then you have to be very careful. If it weren't for those iron bars, he would have had you right here and now, and you wouldn't have walked away, neither. Come on over here and take a look at my Wild Mystery Woman."

A barred gate separates the two cages. Flattened against the far wall of the second cage is a glowing,

golden woman. By God, says Wayne to himself, that
SOB is part of the Oriental prostitution ring, but when
she moves closer to the bars, he can see that she isn't
Oriental or anything else that he can identify. Her eyes
and skin and hair are variations of the same golden
color. A glow comes from the color and from within her,
shining out topaz into the dim, dusty cage.

As she moves, Wayne thinks of water flowing. She
looks at him with amber eyes and begins to speak in
words that shimmer like cottonwood leaves in the wind.
Wayne doesn't understand but as she speaks, strange
ideas come glimmering into his head.

Sweet with wild, unknowing, I hear a fairy song, says
Wayne to himself and asks himself where the thoughts
came from.

She holds all the light that is in the room and reflects
it back to him. She shines for him and sings for him.
Wayne is lost in her brightness. He wants to understand.
He wants to ask her questions: How are you different
from me? How are you the same? He wants to touch her
hand.

"Don't do that, Wayne. She is just as dangerous as
the other one. She could change into any damn thing she
wanted if I didn't have all this iron and salt around. She
is a beauty, though I do think she's losing some of her
glow. They don't keep at all well indoors away from the
sun and the open air. I could put in some kind of
skylight, but I have to watch my cash-flow until I get my
last car payments made over to Wideford."

Wayne stands enchanted, not even hearing.

"Think you got your money's worth already, don't
you. You ain't seen nothin' yet," Harry chuckles. "You
just wait until I get the chain on this one in here."

Wayne puts his fingers through the bars, and she

touches them with her slender glowing hands, soft, strange and warm. He looks into her ancient amber eyes and feels the golden fall of her hair. "You are so beautiful. What are you?" asks Wayne and doesn't know that he has spoken, until he hears the sound of his voice. "You are starlight and moonlight. You are the dancing grass," says Wayne and wonders where he learned the words.

"My God, but he is ready. You want a taste of that, don't you, big fellow. All right, there she is. Go get her." Harry pulls on a rope that raises the gate between the two cages, and the monster comes snarling through. She hesitates, giving Wayne a sad, golden look, and then she vanishes in a flashbulb pop of light, reappearing at the back of the cage.

"Look at that, Wayne, look at her go! By God. You know he'd never touch her out on the prairie. She is fast and she hates him, too. They are natural enemies."

Wayne freezes in icy amazement. He has never seen anything like this before. In a crouching shamble, the monster menaces her; she watches him intently, and just before he reaches her, light dazzles and she is gone, only to appear behind him, shining defiance. She darts about the cage, flashing, but in a little time she begins to tire, and all at once, he has her.

"She has the speed, but he has the endurance. Look at him go. Makes a man stop and think, don't it, Wayne."

That monster and that beautiful shining woman. . . . It is awful. Wayne's heart wants to shake his whole body; he can't stop watching.

"If I could get this on video tape, I could make a fortune but my outfit never picks up anything but shadows. I need a book on photography or something."

A steady shriek stabs into their ears from somewhere downstairs. "Damn, that is the smoke alarm. Something's burning." Harry pushes the chain into Wayne's hands. "Hang onto this sucker for all you're worth, Wayne; he always turns mean afterwards. I'll be right back."

Wayne is not sure why he is still standing. He feels the hard chain links; in a daze, he watches Harry leave. There is a strong pull; he remembers that there is a monster on the other end. Wayne holds tight but he is slammed against the bars and the metal tears through his hands, punishing his fingers.

Wayne is stunned by the shock of the blow; his hand hurts, and then he looks. The monster has her; he is sort of tearing at her there in the cage; there is a wispy little sigh, no more noise than a soft breeze in the treetops on a spring day, and she is gone, poof, in a little circle of golden sparkles; her brightness vanished away; the fairy voice, still.

"No big deal, Wayne, just a pan full of grease that fool of a cook left on the stove. What in the hell happened here? Oh, fine! Do you know how hard I have to work to get these creatures? It took me two weeks out on the prairie in all kinds of weather to catch her. They ain't nearly so frequent as they used to be. Well, it is going to cost you twice the price to see a kill, another twenty-five smackeroos, kiddo."

Wayne gives Harry the money; he walks down the stairs past the waiting group of dusty men, out of the door, away from the Hurry Back Cafe. Wayne sits in his car until he can conclude his business with Mr. Harter of Harter's Home and Farm Supply, and Wayne drives away in his car as fast as he can, away over the road that goes up and down over the hills, through the wide,

wild, secret places, knowing that he is not alone in the
tarnished landscape. Wayne tries hard to keep his mind
on Janis and the ordinary things that he will find at
home. Starlight, moonlight, beauty, beauty, monster,
hum the tires.

It is all right for a week or so, until one day the phone
rings; something about the way it rings sets Wayne's
teeth ajar. He answers and Harry's voice pulls him to
the Hurry Back Cafe, the row of waiting men, the wet
dirt smell, the monster, the sunlight beauty. The remembering has been waiting all week, lurking, waiting to
take him like the monster took her.

"I called to give you the news, Wayne; I managed to
get some more of that prairie wildlife, really prime stuff.
I'm holding group shows at 4:00, every day but Sunday."

"How did you get my number?" Wayne is shaking.

"You gave me your card, bud. Last time you got the
special introductory rates. It's going to cost you more
this time. Fifty dollars for a group show, that's fifty a
head, Wayne, and you are kind of a little guy. You might
not get to see much in a crowd. Private shows are five
hundred, cash. You let me know."

Wayne hangs up the phone.

I don't have any reason to go back there, says Wayne
to himself.

Hell, I can think of something.

Once upon a time, Wayne knew where he was going.

Long Knives
by
J. R. Dunn

About the Author

At the age of thirty-three, J.R. Dunn has no intention of returning to the successful real-estate career he abandoned a year since. He had always wanted to write, and that year has been spent in practicing those skills. As a Second Place winner in the Fourth Quarter, he practiced them well.

Born in Utica, New York, after high school he moved to the New York City metropolitan area, where he is now working as a political technician. He is co-founder of the Llewellyn Group, a political research organization. As you will see from his story, he takes a serious view of human social interactions.

There is some mysterious affinity between SF writers and the world of foreign-intrigue adventure. Overtones of it can frequently be seen in science fiction. In particular, there are the parallel-world stories on such themes as the Nazis having won World War II. But suppose, now, that World War II had been prevented, and Hitler were alive and . . . safe? . . . .

A lthough he knew that nothing would happen that day, Keegan still kept an eye open while reading the *Zeitung;* it had become a habit over the last few months. He finished the article, a barely comprehensible tirade against the "invaders from the future," and tossed the paper onto the other seat. The Uzi, jammed between seat and handbrake, was sticking into his hip so he picked that up and threw it over, too. He leaned against the steering wheel and pulled at his shirt where it had pasted itself to his back: it was a warm April in Vienna.

He glanced over at the shabby brick building across the street. The old bastard was nowhere in sight, but the two Brownshirts stood flanking the door as always: Sam Brownes, heavy boots, and armbands that matched the red banners waving languidly in the breeze over their heads. One of them, the new boy, caught his eye, stiffened, and took a step forward. He spat deliberately in the direction of the car, as if he had been planning it for a month, and began cursing in a low, guttural monotone. An order barked by the older man brought him back to his place, though he still glared at Keegan.

The door opened and a group of men walked out, answering the salutes that the guards gave them. Keegan leaned over to the radio, but no, it was just Rosenberg.

He relaxed as they crossed the street and walked

Illustrated by Rich Lynes

toward the touring car a half block up, studiously ignoring the compact. Adolf himself had rather liked it, the last time he had been out. He had stepped from the building, surrounded, as always, by his four guards, dressed in the double-breasted mock military jacket he had worn as Chancellor. He had been ashen-faced, with bags under those weird, piercing eyes, and Keegan had thought that he had looked much as he would on the main line, eight years on as the Red Army closed in on the bunker.

He had stopped and inspected the car as he pulled on his gloves—gloves, in this kind of weather—then mumbled something to the others of which Keegan had only caught the word "Volkswagen." Keegan had leaned out the window and said, "It's a Subaru, Mein Herr." Hitler had stared at him for a moment, eyes narrowing, then had turned abruptly and stalked to his own Mercedes farther up the street.

That had been five days ago, and Keegan hadn't seen him since, which suited him fine. If there was one thing he hated more than sitting here in front of NSDAP headquarters it was following the son of a bitch around town, watching while he waved to the crowds, patted kids on the head, and generally behaved like a small town councilman up for reelection.

Rosenberg's touring car, one of the last the Party had, disappeared around the corner, and Hendricks sauntered out to watch it pass. Keegan thought for a moment that he'd give the car a salute. Hendricks was a strange bird, the only one of the unit who seemed to enjoy the assignment. More than enjoy it, he loved it: treating the guards and party members with respect, speaking of the Fuehrer in hushed tones. The Service had been careful not to send back anyone who had a personal reason for hating Hitler, nobody of Jewish or Slavic background, nobody who had a relative killed in the war. With Hendricks they had erred in the opposite direction.

Keegan sighed and leaned back against the headrest with his eyes closed. It had seemed exciting when they had offered it to him—Vienna, 1937, remaking history, righting old wrongs, but it had come down to this, getting spat at by Nazis, working with people who were no better, and being treated by the Vienners like some kind of Turk. Oh, they were polite about it, no one on Earth was more polite than they were, but it still came through. Throw the Israelis in on top of that, and it all came damn near to being intolerable. But it could be worse. He could be in Japan or Russia, where it was a running battle with the old regimes. And the city was beautiful, the people, at worst, civil, and he would never have met Yetta otherwise. . . .

He started as a car horn blared next to him, and looked up to see Fusco's big Daimler, Marshall's Service shield painted on the door, and Fusco himself glaring out the window at him, face ablaze. Aytrigg, the intelligence liaison, was at the wheel, a smile on his round face and his sunglasses resting on the tip of his nose. Keegan pulled himself up in the seat and leaned out the window.

"Hey, Chief, what's the good word?"

"Don't you good word me, Keegan. What were you, sleeping?"

Keegan frowned and shook his head.

"Well, how the hell did I get up this street without anybody but the end man seeing me? Your pal Petricci is just as bad as you are. Sitting there filing his nails."

Keegan glanced back down the street. Petricci was sitting in the other car with a disgusted look on his face.

Keegan turned back to Fusco. "Anything up?"

Aytrigg pushed his sunglasses up. "Little bad luck in Tbilisi."

"Damn straight bad luck," said Fusco. "They got Uncle Joe."

Keegan's eyebrows went up. "No kidding?"

"No, no kidding, and they got two of our people while they were at it and I'm not kidding about that, either." Fusco sat back, his face returning to its normal color. "Look, Keegan, I know you don't like guarding the Fuehrer any more than I do, but you'll keep your eyes open or you'll end up the same way they did." He looked over at the building, where the two Brownshirts gazed back with interest, then turned back to Keegan. "One more thing," he said. "There's a meeting tonight at six. No exceptions." He leaned farther out the window. "I'm not taking any excuses this time, Mister. Be there."

Keegan nodded. "Duly noted."

Satisfied, Fusco gestured to Aytrigg and the car started moving. It stopped when they reached the corner, and Fusco gestured Hendricks over, pointing back down the street as he spoke to him. Hendricks looked back and nodded, then waved the car off as it started around the corner.

Keegan reached up to adjust the mirror and saw Petricci approaching the car. He opened the door and got out to meet him.

"Jesus," said Petricci. "I thought he was gonna crawl out the window at me."

"Yeah, same here. This Stalin deal has got him going."

"Well, it is pretty bad. Two of our boys."

Keegan kicked at a loose stone in the street. "No, not

Marshall's. The NKVD was giving them too hard a
time. They put Aytrigg's people in there."

Petricci shook his head. "Same thing, Danny, same
damn thing." He looked at the building, where the two
Nazis were muttering to each other. "Makes you wonder
when it'll happen here."

Keegan looked away, unwilling to meet Petricci's eyes.
"Yeah." Up the street he could still see Hendricks still
standing on the corner. "The übermensch is checking us
out."

Petricci nodded. "Asshole." He turned to walk back
to his car. "Better get back in case Baldy makes another
sweep. I'll see you later."

"Right," Keegan said and got back in his car. He
picked up the paper and shoved it in the glove compartment, then took the Uzi and put it on his lap. No telling
what the Israelis would do when they heard about Stalin. In front of the building the Brownshirts were back at
their posts, booted feet set wide, hands clasped behind
their backs. Up the street, Hendricks walked out of
sight. Keegan settled back in the seat. So the man of
steel was dead on this line. Hero of the Revolution, light
of the proletariat, Sun and Moon of the Soviet people.
Too bad.

He was relieved at five and drove back into the city
proper, toward the tower of St. Stephen's that loomed
over all. He had an hour before the meeting, just enough
time to meet Yetta and explain things. The Nazis had
ended up in a pretty bad part of town, what the Vienners
considered to be a slum, though Keegan, used to Bed-
Stuy, Newark and Harlem, didn't see it that way. It was
inhabited by small shopkeepers and down-at-heel clerks
and professionals, and if it didn't have the grace of the

rest of the city, it shared the solidity of a place that
had been a seat of empire before most nations had
existed. Keegan loved the town itself: the monuments,
the parks, the buildings, the air of civility that pervaded
it. The people were genial, easygoing, as sybaritic as
it was possible to be without going over the line into
decadence. They were not pleased to have the InTemp
Bureau around—nobody in this era was—but they treated it with an aloof correctness; there were none of the
incidents that occurred elsewhere. They had no idea
what would have befallen them had the Bureau not
intervened. Policy was to keep quiet about the mainline
events that would now never occur. To the Austrians,
the Anschluss, the war, and the Occupation, were un-
born ghosts.

He drove onto the Ring and after two blocks turned
toward the inner city. The traffic began to get heavier,
but nothing comparable to back home. He was low on
gas, which was a pain. Using compacts had been the
brainstorm of some genius at OMB who had figured
that they'd save on mileage. The cars had already been
shipped out to the field before anyone had realized that
unleaded gas was unknown here and would remain so
until the refineries were modernized. In the meantime it
was necessary to go to a rented garage for gas, not an
easy business since they kept bureaucrat's hours and as a
rule everybody picked the same time to fill up.

He parked the car on a dark, cobblestoned side street
filled with staid brick buildings near the cafe where he
had told Yetta to meet him. An older man dressed in a
baggy business suit and homburg stopped to inspect the
car, pursing his lips as he peered at the interior. Keegan
got out and the man stood up and tipped his hat to him.

Surprised, Keegan nodded back, then turned and walked to the end of the street.

He stopped at the corner and looked across at the cafe. Yetta was seated at a small table near the sidewalk. She saw him and waved a white-gloved hand. He waved back and crossed the street.

"How's my little Polish rose," he said, leaning over to kiss her. They had met two months before, when he had been new to the city, a man from another time in a place that didn't want him. She was a student, taking classes at the Academy of Arts while working as a clerk. She had learned some English from her father, a teacher, and had picked up more from Keegan in the time that he had known her. She was from the part of Poland that had once been Russian, and would have been again. She was a woman of her time, different from any other that he had known, and he believed that he loved her.

He pulled a chair over to her side of the table and sat down. A waiter approached and Keegan ordered a schnapps and a coffee for himself and another for Yetta. She touched his hand as the waiter left. "How was your day, Danny?"

He shook his head. "Trouble."

Yetta stiffened and withdrew her hand. "What did he do now?"

"Who?"

"That beast that you are guarding."

"No, it wasn't him, it was Stalin."

She drank the last of her coffee. "So? They bring him here to keep company?"

"No, they bring him to the devil. Somebody killed him last night."

She held her cup before her for a moment before

placing it on the table. "A good thing," she said. "Terrible for me to say like that, but it is true. They will do to Hitler the same, as well as those who guard him.

Keegan looked down at the table. "Probably. They got two of us last night."

Yetta softened and reached out again for his hand. "Oh, Danny, I'm sorry. It's that horrible man. . . . You should ask to do something else."

"Yetta, I told you. If I do, I'll be sent away. You want that to happen?"

She shook her head miserably. The waiter returned and placed the order on the table, the coffee smothered in whipped cream the way they liked it here. He glanced at Keegan's mainline clothing as he did so but said nothing.

Keegan threw back the schnapps, then spooned up a bit of the cream, not looking at Yetta. It was an old story, something that seemed to come up now every time he saw her. Her father had been aware of the Nazis, much more so than most, had read *Mein Kampf* and kept an eye on events in Germany. He had told her about them, as he had told her, his only child, everything else, and she had remembered. "He wanted a new Reich, to conquer Poland, to deport the Slavs and Jews," she had said. "He did all that," Keegan had told her. "He did worse." It had gone on from there, arguments, recriminations, appeals, that he could only answer by saying, "It's my job."

Keegan finished his coffee and looked at her, his chin on his folded hands. "I've got a meeting tonight," he said. She grimaced but did not look up from her coffee. "It's Fusco. You know him—the bald guy. He's in an uproar about this Stalin thing. It'll only take an hour." He reached for her hand. "Will you wait for me?"

She looked up and smiled, and entwined her fingers with his. "My little wagon is tied to yours, Herr Keegan."

He lifted her hand to his lips, then got up and stepped away from the table. "Danny," she said quietly. He turned back to her. "I'm sorry I am this way." He smiled down at her. "It's all right," he said. "I do understand." He stood looking at her for a few seconds, then turned and walked across the street.

The InTemp offices were a few blocks away, in an old Hohenzollern-era building near the Bourse. They took up an entire floor and were open to anyone who cared to walk in, though few did. The Bureau wasn't afraid of any kind of terrorism here, or the kind of attacks that were common in Japan and Russia. The Austrians, like everybody else, had seen newsreels of the destruction of the Rhineland occupation force, the Marines liberating the Gulag, and the demonstration bomb set off over the Libyan desert. Showing more sense than most, they had declined to interfere with the Amerikanner. The building had had a lot of work done to upgrade it for modern equipment, but the old cagework elevator had been left unchanged and made him later than he thought.

Fusco was standing in the middle of the main office when he walked in, his tie loosened, shirt-sleeves rolled up and what little hair he had left sticking out from the sides of his head. He turned as Keegan entered and put his hands on his hips. "You're late," he snapped.

"I had to arrange something," Keegan said.

"Well, get in here and sit down." Fusco picked a folder from the desk behind him and tossed it to Keegan as he passed. "We've been going over this, but you'll have to pick it up as we go along."

He walked over and sat on a desk next to Petricci.

The rest of the day team was scattered around the office, some in period clothes but the majority in mainline dress. Aytrigg was sitting behind Fusco, polishing his sunglasses with the end of his tie.

Fusco waited until Keegan was seated, then turned a chair around and put his foot on it.

"All right," he said. "You've all heard about Stalin. They got him last night in the wee hours at that dacha of his outside Tbilisi, along with Yagoda and some of his other pals. Yeah, Petricci?"

"They get Krushchev?"

"No, Nikita dropped out of sight a year back, and nobody knows where he is."

"That's good," said Petricci. "I always kinda liked him."

Fusco glared at him before going on. "In any case, this was one of the five safe houses he had scattered around Georgia. He used them pretty randomly, more out of fear of the Socialists than anybody else. Seems that somebody had inside information."

Keegan raised his hand. "Maybe it was them."

"Nope. They used modern weapons. Mostly our stuff. LAAWs, M-40 grenade launchers. They shot the place up with Kalashnikovs after they blew the walls in, which was kinda cute, but you can get them anywhere." He walked away from the chair, his hands in his pockets, and began to pace back and forth in front of them.

"Now, what does this mean to us. We always thought that Hitler would get it first. Well, we were wrong. We also thought it would come from somebody on this end. Wrong again." He stopped pacing and faced them. "The main point is that somebody—doesn't matter who— took out a leader under our protection. It'll be tried again, and dollars to doughnuts Adolf is next on the list." He leaned back against a desk. "Now, I've talked to Washington, and they're sending us reinforcements. By the end of the week, that block will be crawling with our people, and Hitler won't go anywhere except in a convoy. Until then we've all gotta straighten up. We can't afford another mistake. There were two of our people killed in Tbilisi." He glanced at Aytrigg, who ignored him. "It was sheer sloppiness, and it's not going to happen here. You got something to say, Mitshele?"

Annie Mitshele was sitting on the edge of a desk with an angry look on her face. "Yes, I do," she said. "You're telling me that we're going to waste more money on that son of a bitch?"

"That's what I'm telling you."

"Well, it's hypocrisy. Thousands of kids killed in the Rhineland, and because we made a deal with him we're protecting the guy who sent them there. I think it sucks."

Fusco shambled over to her, bent over, his arms dangling. "Mitshele," he said, "You are relieved." He stood up and put his hands in his pockets. "You work in the office until we send you home." Annie reddened and opened her mouth. Fusco turned, waving his hand at her. "I don't want to hear it."

He walked back to the chair and straddled it. "Anybody else want to cry to me about how bad we are?" He sat down and waited a few seconds before going on. "Well, I've told you a thousand times but I guess I've got to tell you again. This project is going very well so far. We've stopped the wars, broken up the worst governments, started transferring technology. We're doing better for them than we are for ourselves. In a few years we'll be able to start sending back some of the population of the Sahel and Bengladesh back to the areas they're not using, bring up some of the great minds to work with us, big plans." He leaned forward, clutching the back of the chair. "But it won't work without the cooperation of the governments. They're helping us now out of fear, but that won't last. They've got to trust us. If the leaders we've deposed start dying off, it all goes out the window. Remember, they don't know their future history. Mussolini, Hitler and the rest of them aren't thought of as being the bad guys we know they are. A lot of the best people here and over in England and the U.S. think we were way out of line for dumping them in the first place. They think that Roosevelt, Baldwin, whoever, will be next." He stood up and turned to Annie. "And that, unpleasant as it may be, is why we've got to protect Hitler."

He turned and picked up a briefcase on the desk behind him. "Okay, you've got the photos and info on the Mossad." He looked at Keegan. "You bother to go through that?" Keegan picked up the folder and began to turn the pages. He stopped halfway through. The picture was blurred, but it was him all right. PIPULSKI, NATHAN, COL. Keegan said nothing.

"They came through with that group that went to Palestine to help the Zionists," Fusco told him. "They disappeared two weeks ago, and I'll give you two guesses where they are now." He picked his jacket off the back of a chair and threw it over his shoulder. "Take it with you, memorize 'em, and keep an eye open." He started to walk out, but stopped at the door. "One more thing," he said, turning back to the group. "Desertions. Somebody split from the Tokyo office yesterday." He looked them over, one by one. "I don't have to tell you that if anybody tries that here I'll track them down. You'll be sitting up the line in a cell next to Singh, I guarantee it." He gazed at them for a moment before stomping through the door. "All right, get out of here."

There wasn't much conversation as the group filed from the room. Annie Mitshele left first, head held high, speaking to no one. She pushed Hendricks out of her way at the door, leaving him glaring after her and muttering to himself. Keegan sat for a moment, fingering the folder, then got up and followed them out.

The first group filled the old elevator, and Keegan found himself standing next to Aytrigg. He turned to the man. "Is Singh really still in prison?"

Aytrigg nodded. "Yeah, but not the way that Fusco wants you to think. They've got him under house arrest at the Institute. He's too valuable to lock up." He loosened his tie. "Got him working on transfer mechanics, same as before. He's tracking down other lines now. He thinks you have to go directly from one to another, like rooms in a house. He'll be back here eventually, to set up another transfer point."

"Working with Einstein," Keegan said.

"Yeah," said Aytrigg, smiling. "Working with Einstein." The elevator appeared and they got in. "I was there, you know, when we picked him up."

"In Princeton?"

"That's right. There he was, for six months, telling Einstein and the rest of them about quarks, black holes, strings, all that good shit. There was an incredible uproar after they found out that papers on the stuff had been floating around the physics community. Big historical change, they thought, but of course nothing happened. That's when they realized this wasn't the main line. Would have taken them years, otherwise. There don't seem to be any obvious differences."

The elevator reached the first floor and they stepped out. "Yeah, you can't go back," Aytrigg said. "It was the old man who figured that out. Along with Singh."

"You talk to him at all? Einstein, I mean."

"Yeah, he just wanted to know what year we were from. Singh hadn't told him."

"Did you?"

"Sure, he knew everything else." He stopped at the main door. "That's the attraction this era has for our people, the ones who desert. Singh wanted to work with Einstein, somebody else wants to be analyzed by Freud." He shrugged. "I can't see it, myself."

They walked out of the building and down the stairs. On the sidewalk, Aytrigg turned to him. "You're going to have a rough couple of days." He tapped the folder Keegan held under his arm. "Those boys play a hard game." He smiled and slapped Keegan on the arm. "But you know that, don't you?" He turned and walked down the street. "Take care of yourself, Keegan," he called back. Keegan stared after him for some time before leaving himself.

He had nearly gotten back to the cafe when the Israelis caught up with him. He was hurrying, wondering if Aytrigg's last remarks were what they sounded like, when two of them—the pop-eyed kid with the Brooklyn accent and the quiet, Arabic-looking Sabra—stepped out of a doorway. Keegan stopped. "Look, I'm not scheduled to meet you until Thursday."

Brooklyn stepped toward him. "Things change," he said. The Sabra moved to his side, and Keegan, looking back, saw a figure in the darkness a half-block behind. He shook his head. "All right."

They convoyed him to a touring car across the street. Brooklyn opened the door and Keegan slid inside. The old man was sitting there, wearing a gray derby and a

striped suit of the same color, resting his chin on a cane.
"Colonel Pipulski," Keegan said.

The Colonel smiled at him. "It seems that the Service
has identified us. I'm surprised it took them so long."

"That's right," said Keegan, handing the folder to
him. The old man took it, looked through a few
pages, then leaned forward and whispered something
to Brooklyn, who started the car and drove down the
street.

Pipulski closed the folder and tapped it against his
hand. "This adds some urgency. How much time do we
have?"

"They'll reinforce us by the end of the week."

The old man pursed his lips and nodded. "We'll have
to move by then." He regarded Keegan for a moment.
"Is it safe to assume that you're still with us?"

Keegan looked out the window at the passing buildings. He wet his lips. "We need to talk about that."

"Go on."

"You've heard about the Stalin assassination. Was
that you, by the way?"

The old man shook his head.

"Two of our people were killed in that attack. Now,
I don't care what happens to Hitler or the rest of them,
but I can't risk anyone else being killed, either in my
group or a passerby." He paused and took a deep
breath. "I'm afraid I can't go through with this."

He turned to Pipulski to gauge his reaction but the
old man sat unspeaking, staring coldly at him. From the
front of the car came a snort of disgust from Brooklyn,
and the Sabra shifted slightly in his seat. Keegan willed
himself to relax, and went on. "I realized today after
hearing about Stalin that he can't last. Too many people

have long knives out for him, both here and up the line. If you wait, it'll be done for you." He turned back to Pipulski. The old man was fingering his cane, his head resting on his chest. "Look," said Keegan, "I know how you feel. As Israelis, you think you have a better claim on him than anyone else. . . ." The old man raised his head, and the look in his eyes silenced Keegan.

"Oh, I do, Mr. Keegan, I do." He yanked back the sleeve of his suitcoat, then did the same with his shirt, ripping off the button in the process, and presented the bare forearm to Keegan. The crude line of numbers was faded but legible. "I was twelve," he said, his eyes fixed on Keegan. "I lived through the worst of them. Maidanek, Buchenwald, Auschwitz." He lowered his arm and pulled the cloth back over it. "My family," he said, "were not so fortunate."

Keegan sank back in the seat, raising his hand to his forehead and closing his eyes as Pipulski continued. "I took you to be a serious man, Mr. Keegan. I believed that you spoke to us, and failed to report it, because of a sense of shame, of dishonor, about your assignment. Perhaps I was mistaken about that. I should point out to you that this operation will continue in any case, and that the safety of your colleagues cannot be guaranteed unless you are present." He cleared his throat. "We would not be able to allow you to return, of course. You'll be held for a few days, and released after we are finished. Your superiors will believe that you have deserted and will not look for you."

Keegan lowered his hand and looked at Pipulski. "That's the way it is."

The old man nodded. "You knew that."

Keegan pushed himself forward in the seat. "Okay, I'll cooperate. But I have conditions." He leaned toward

Pipulski. "I okay all plans. Nothing is done without my approval. And if one of my group is killed . . . well, you have to go back to Palestine eventually."

"Understood," said Pipulski. He reached into his vest pocket and extracted a card. "This is our cover location," he said, handing it to Keegan. "The firm is legitimate. We bought it on our arrival. You'll destroy the card after you've memorized it, of course."

Keegan smiled at him, glanced at the card and returned it. The old man slipped it back in his pocket. "Shall we say six tomorrow evening? I think you'll find that we have a number of workable alternatives."

"I hope you do," said Keegan. He looked out at the street. They had been circling the neighborhood for the last fifteen minutes, and were not far from where he had been picked up. He reached over and tapped Brooklyn on the shoulder. "There's a cafe two blocks ahead. Drop me off in front of it."

They pulled up to the curb next to the cafe. As he stepped out he heard a short sentence in Hebrew from Brooklyn, answered sharply by Pipulski. He leaned back into the open door. "What did he say?"

The Colonel gazed at him for a moment before replying. "He said that you are going straight to your superiors. I told him I didn't think so." Keegan looked up at Brooklyn, who was glaring at him from the front seat, then stepped back and closed the door. Pipulski called, "Good night, Mr. Keegan." He nodded and walked away.

Yetta was nowhere to be seen when he entered the cafe. He collared the waiter, who nodded at him enthusiastically as if he had been waiting his whole life for someone to speak to him in broken German. He pointed the way Yetta had gone, and Keegan tipped him a few schillings before setting out after her.

He found her at the steps of the rooming house, rummaging through her purse for the keys. She turned away angrily when he approached. When she ignored his apologies and walked toward the door he stepped in front of her, arms raised as if in defense of the building. She stood silently in the glow cast by the old streetlights, keys clenched in her hand, not looking at him. She was silent as he told his story, silent as he made his excuses, silent as he asked her to say something. Then she looked up and was silent no more. He was a coarse man. He didn't know how a lady was to be treated. He cared more for the bald Fusco than for her. If he did care he wouldn't leave her alone in a cafe like a woman of the streets. People had looked at her and whispered. A drunken man had bothered her. The waiters had smiled when she left.

Keegan took her by the arm and led her away from the house, agreeing that he was no good, an American roughneck like the ones her father had warned her against. After a while she decided he wasn't as bad as all that, and they walked arm in arm through the streets of the old town. She had eaten at the cafe, and he wasn't hungry, so they stopped at a heurigen and drank some wine. There was a hotel nearby with a good orchestra—the girls at work had told her about it—and they went there afterward. As they approached the entrance, Keegan stopped her. "I wasn't going to tell you this, but I'm not going to be guarding Hitler much longer."

She grasped his hand tightly. "Will you have to leave?" He shook his head. She searched his face for a moment before speaking. "How can this be?"

"I can't tell you now, but don't worry."

She frowned. "Danny, don't get into trouble."

He chucked her under the chin. "Never happen. Now come on." He led her into the hotel, where they could hear music. It was what they called hot jazz here, not Ellington but not bad either, and they danced until the place closed, then walked home as the streetlights dimmed throughout the imperial city.

The next day passed uneventfully. Hendricks had been given a walkie-talkie, which went very well with his vintage suit. Fusco passed by a few times in a succession of unlikely cars. Hitler stayed in, as he had been doing for days, and there was no sign of him until late afternoon, when the curtains had parted and he had appeared, as if to give a speech. He had stood in the window for several minutes, staring into the distance, perhaps seeing the city, perhaps something beyond. Keegan had waved.

He drove past the Ring a few minutes before six and parked the car around the corner from Yetta's flat, in case someone from the Bureau should see it, then walked the few blocks to the Israeli office. He doubled back twice to catch any tails, but saw no one until he reached the building. As he was mounting the stairs, a man turned the corner and stopped, looking at him. Keegan paused at the door. The man called "Shalom," and Keegan nodded and continued inside.

The Colonel stepped forward and shook his hand. Brooklyn and the Sabra were gathered around a desk along with three others whom Keegan had never seen before. He walked over and looked at the papers on the desk. Street plans and photographs. The Sabra poured him a cup of coffee and Pipulski went over the plans.

The first gave him little more than a spectator's role and he rejected it out of hand, much to Brooklyn's

disgust. Pipulski outlined another that sounded much
better, and after a few modifications Keegan agreed
to it. They spent the next three hours hammering out
details until they were satisfied, when Brooklyn, who
had been chain-smoking all the while, changed his mind.
He walked around the room, trailing smoke and arguing
in a mixture of Yiddish and Hebrew until Keegan,
disgusted, slammed his fist on the desk and rose out of
the chair. "Look," he said, "this may give me more of an
active part in things than you'd like, but as far as I can
see, it's the only way to make sure that my crowd won't
be in the middle when you come in."

"I agree," said Pipulski, "I can see no alternative."

Brooklyn threw his hands up in the air and sat down
at a desk in the corner. Pipulski frowned, then turned to
Keegan. "Very well," he said, "Two o'clock tomorrow."
He looked around at the others, who nodded.

"Remember," said Keegan. "Nobody moves until I
fire. You don't hear a shot, you don't go in."

Pipulski rose from the chair. "I believe that is understood." He turned to the others. "Very well, gentlemen,
get a good rest." They filed out, Brooklyn last with a
parting glare for Keegan. The Colonel stepped from
behind the desk and put a hand on his shoulder. "If you
will, Mr Keegan." He ushered him into a private office
with massive bookshelves on the walls and a large teak
desk presiding. Pipulski opened a cabinet and took out a
decanter and two glasses. He poured a finger into each
and handed one to Keegan. "Brandy," he said.

Keegan accepted the glass. "How capable is Brooklyn?"

"Who's that? Oh, Heshe. He's quite good. A little
cocky." The old man sat down behind the desk, raised
his glass to Keegan, and drank from it. He put the glass

down and sat back. "I was abrupt with you yesterday, Mr. Keegan. I apologize. I hope you feel better about our mission today."

Keegan looked down at the glass in his hand. "I do."

Pipulski leaned forward and put his arms on the desk. "There is one thing that I should make clear to you. My personal desires are the driving force in this operation, but they are not paramount. Your country has changed this world, this continuum, for the better, but perhaps not as much as you think. The situation in Germany is still fluid. The coalition government is unstable, and the NSDAP is intact and operating underground. There is a large popular movement for the return of the Fuehrer." He raised a hand. "Oh. I realize that your country would never allow him back into power, but this leaves him much room for action. A coup attempt is not unlikely, or a pogrom." He put his hands around the glass, and stared into the distance, far beyond the walls of the room. "He is far from finished, and we know he is capable of anything. The blueprints for what was to be still exist in his mind. . . ." His gaze caught Keegan's and held it. "And that is why he needs to be destroyed."

"I understand," said Keegan.

The Colonel drained his brandy and poured another. "There was a man," he said, "who was dining in a restaurant in Berlin in 1932. It was shortly before Hitler became Chancellor. This man was a Communist functionary, a bodyguard, and always carried a pistol. He looked up to see Hitler being seated at the next table. As he ate the man considered shooting him then and there. He did not. He was sure that no one so clownish could succeed in politics." He ran a finger over the rim of the glass. "That man later spent eight years in the camps.

He cursed himself until the day he died over that one
lost opportunity."

They sat in silence for a few moments, each with
his own thoughts. Keegan finished his brandy and
rose from the chair. "Well, Colonel, we may not have
changed much on this line, but I will tell you this: that
man will never spend one day in the camps." He put on
his jacket and stepped over to the desk.

The Colonel nodded, still lost in memory. "Yes," he
said. He opened a desk drawer and removed a small
attaché case, then stood up and handed it to Keegan.
"You are to keep this. It contains fifty thousand American dollars. You won't be able to return home immediately, and it will take you far in this world." He regarded
Keegan for a moment. "You are not to consider this to
be a bribe."

Keegan took the case and slipped it under his arm
without looking inside it. "I won't," he said. "How did
you . . . ?"

The Colonel waved a hand. "It's counterfeit, by modern techniques, lasers and such. Not detectable in this
era. You'll need it." He smiled. "I understand there's a
girl. . . ."

Keegan extended his hand across the desk. "Thank
you, Colonel."

Pipulski took the hand in both of his, and Keegan
knew then how strong the Colonel must once have been.
"No," Pipulski said. "I must thank you."

Keegan turned and walked to the door. As he opened
it he paused, aware that the old man was still gazing
at him from across the room. But he could think of
nothing more to say, and after a moment stepped out of
the room and closed the door behind him.

Before he went back to the car he stopped at Yetta's rooming house. He rang the doorbell and waited as the landlady inspected him from the side window, making sure he wasn't carrying a machine gun, logger's axe or a squad of Cossacks under his sport coat. Finally she opened the door a crack and asked him what he wanted. It was his second attempt at asking after Yetta in two days and he had not improved with practice. The only immediate result of his guttural rumblings and arm-waving was to have the door shut in his face. He was standing there rubbing the back of his neck and wondering what to try next when the door opened and Yetta peered out, half asleep.

He pushed his way in and the landlady glared at him, muttering about the impropriety of men calling on young girls at this hour. She turned and grumbled off, leaving the two of them standing alone in the foyer. Yetta stood rubbing her eyes, dressed in robe and nightgown, her hair loose and tousled. She looked marvelous.

"It's so late," she said.

"I know, I'm only here for a minute." He took the case from under his arm and handed it to her. "I want you to keep this for me until tomorrow." She took it from him and held it in both hands.

"What is it?"

"You can look if you like." He reached up and grasped her by the shoulders. "I'd like you to do one other thing. Get ready for a long trip."

She frowned. "A trip? Where?"

He smiled at her. "I don't know yet."

"How long will this trip be, Danny?"

"Could be a lifetime." She stared at him, twisting the top of her robe, then stepped forward and put her head on his chest. "When do you want me to be ready?"

"Tomorrow at three." She looked up at him, a frown on her face. "That is too soon." He brushed her hair back from her forehead. "Is it?" She looked at him for a moment, then shook her head. "No."

They stood quietly for a moment, then Keegan kissed her on the forehead and stepped back. "I have to go."

She followed him to the door and took his hand as he opened it. "Danny, could you be hurt?" He looked at the floor and nodded. "Yeah, could be. If I am, you keep that case. Don't tell anybody about it." He kissed her once again. "But don't worry. I'll be back to you." As he walked out the door she stood watching him, holding the case in crossed arms. She stayed in the open doorway until he disappeared down the darkened street.

The day came damp and windy, unusual weather for this time of year. Keegan had barely slept and was out early, eating a large breakfast before taking up his post at ten. He brought along a thermos of coffee, which he finished in less than an hour, knowing it was a mistake all the while. He sat in the car, fidgeting, jittery with caffeine, looking at his watch every few minutes. He had checked it against every clock he had seen on the way over, half convinced that all of them were set at the wrong time and were off by, say, five minutes. After another hour of this he forced himself not to look and sat swivelling his head and tapping the steering wheel.

Shortly after twelve Hendricks strolled down from the corner, which was something new. He stopped to practice his German on the older Brownshirt, who listened stiffly for a moment before warming up. They stood there chattering while the new boy clenched his jaw and ignored them. Finally the old Nazi stepped back to his post laughing while Hendricks crossed the street to Keegan's car. Keegan rolled down the window and poked his head out. "You ask him where he got his uniform?"

Hendricks gave him a cold smile and sat on the hood near the windshield. The bulges of pistol, Uzi, and radio made him look like a gentleman shoplifter. Ignoring Keegan for the moment, he took out a cigarette case and selected one, a nasty looking brown thing. "You ought to consider it, Hendricks," said Keegan. "You'd look pretty good."

Hendricks sighed and lit the cigarette, tossing the match across the street. He took his hat off and studied it. "You're buddies with Mitshele, right?" He looked over at Keegan, who didn't answer. "Well, the dumb bitch deserted last night. Didn't show up this morning, and her place was empty. Ran off with some rich local, it seems."

"Good for her."

Hendricks pursed his lips and put his hat back on. "Anyway, there's going to be a nonfraternization policy from here on in. No contact with locals." He raised his eyebrows and nodded at Keegan. "That applies to you, right?"

Keegan turned to the windshield, teeth clenched. He took a deep breath before looking back at Hendricks. "Let's see if you can get your ass up the street before I open this door."

Hendricks made a face and slid off the hood. "Just thought you'd like to know." He stepped to the front of the car, stopped and elaborately butted the cigarette out on the hood, then continued on up the street, taking his time. The Brownshirts got a kick out of it; even the new one cracked a smile.

Petricci buzzed him, was disgusted when Keegan told

him what happened. They talked for a minute and rang off. Keegan sat back, checked his watch and thought about Annie. More power to her. Maybe they'd cross paths after all this was over. It worked out well for him also. Fusco would be running amok and wouldn't have time to show up and bark at him at, say, quarter of two.

It was that exact moment when the Daimler appeared around the corner. Keegan saw it in the rear-view mirror and froze. It stopped at Petricci's car for a short time, then rolled on toward him. As it came to a halt Aytrigg's gross face peered out at him. "How's it going, Keegan?"

Keegan breathed deeply and glanced down at his watch. "Pretty quiet," he said. "I hear things are hopping back at the office."

Aytrigg gave a high-pitched laugh. "Yeah, Fusco's out of his mind."

"I can picture it." Compulsively, he looked back down at the watch.

"I should sell tickets. Say, you want the right time?" Aytrigg slid over to the passenger window and held his wrist out. "Five of."

Keegan stared at him. "I've got ten of."

Aytrigg frowned and shook his head. "No way, I just set it."

"You sure?"

"Absolutely. You'd better reset yours." He slipped back behind the wheel and put the car in gear. "Gotta have the right time in this business, kiddo."

Keegan waited until the car turned the corner then held his watch up, counting the minutes until it reached five of. When he heard no disturbance at the end of the street he sat back and brushed the sweat off his forehead. Now why the hell did he do that? He considered calling the whole thing off but it was too late anyway

and he didn't have time to think about it. He looked up
and down the street once more. The Brownshirts stood
motionless, Petricci sat quietly in his car, and Hendricks
and Bosley at the other end of the street were out of
sight. He opened the glove compartment and took out
the can of mace, then picked up the Uzi by the strap and
hung it over his shoulder. He looked at his watch a final
time and got out of the car. The damp swastika banners
flapping in the breeze were the only things moving. He
glanced once more up the street, then turned and walked
toward Petricci.

He was a few feet away when Petricci rolled down the
window and leaned out. "Hey, Danny, what's—" he
began, and Keegan sprayed him full in the face. Petricci
recoiled and put his hands over his eyes. "Danny,
no . . . !" Keegan opened the door, pulled the pistol
from Petricci's holster and threw it in the back seat,
followed by his Uzi. At the end of the street he could
hear shouting and the sounds of a crash. He pushed
Petricci into the passenger seat. "C'mon, Frank, let's
go." Petricci's foot caught on the gearshift and he lifted
it over. He got in, released the handbrake and started
the car.

"Keep your head down, Frank, and you'll be okay."
He pulled away from the curb and gunned the engine.
The older Brownshirt took a step toward the street and
stared at the car, his arms held out from his side. As they
passed there was a shot and his head exploded. The
new boy screamed and scrambled over the railing, but
another burst caught him at the top and he fell in silence.
Keegan looked in the mirror and saw two cars pulling
up in front of the building, men pouring out before they
ceased moving. The tall Sabra knelt in the street, aiming
a rocket launcher at the window where Keegan had seen

Hitler. He fired, and it exploded in a shower of glass and masonry. They hadn't waited for his signal after all. He looked forward to see Hendricks racing around the corner, pulling the Uzi from under his coat. He hit the brakes and gave the wheel a quarter turn. The car slewed on the wet street, skidding onto the sidewalk and slamming into Hendricks broadside as it hit a wall. Hendricks was flung across the hood, and the gun, torn from his hands, clattered on the sidewalk. Keegan opened the door and reached for him as he went for his pistol. He dragged him across the hood, threw him to the ground and beat his arm on the side of the car until he dropped the gun. Hendricks tried to tackle him but one of his legs failed and they dropped backward into the street. Keegan threw Hendricks over him, then straddled him and gave his head a sharp crack on the pavement. He was rising when he felt the barrel of a gun in his back. He stood up and lifted his hands.

Hendricks pulled himself up from the street, shook his head dazedly and scrambled around for the pistol. He found it, limped down the street and stopped in front of the building, aiming the pistol with both hands. The gunfire inside ceased, but no one emerged. Keegan could see figures running over the roof in the back. After a moment Hendricks lowered the gun and began to curse.

Keegan turned around slowly. Petricci was leaning against the car, holding the Uzi in one hand while rubbing his streaming eyes with the other. He nodded at Keegan. "Never thought to let me know, did you?" He reached behind him and pulled out a pair of handcuffs. "I'm sorry, Danny."

At the office Fusco was sitting atop a desk, arms

NEW ERA Publications UK Ltd.
P.O. Box 110,
Tonbridge
Kent TN9 2TY

crossed, and rather calm, all things considered. He
pointed out a chair for Keegan, then got up. "Take off
the cuffs," he said. Petricci removed them without looking at Keegan, then turned and left the room. Hendricks
stood breathing rapidly, his face bloody, his suit torn.
He glared at Keegan wild-eyed. "I oughta blow your—"

"Get the hell outta here," Fusco said. He paced
around the office, head down, occasionally glancing at
Keegan. Hendricks left, muttering under his breath, and
Aytrigg walked in from the back office.

Fusco stopped at the desk in front of Keegan and
leaned over it looking down at the surface. After a
moment he looked up. "Well, how does it feel?" He
walked around the desk and stood over Keegan. "You
betrayed your oath, your country, and least of all, me.
You worked with another sovereign power to subvert
the policy of the United States. You caused the deaths of
twenty-six people. . . ."

"Twenty-eight," said Aytrigg.

"Twenty-eight people, and put the lives of your colleagues in jeopardy. You gave a black mark to the service,
and made our job here ten times harder. You feel bad
about that, don't you?" He put his hands in his pockets
and walked over to a window, shaking his head. "No
you don't. Not you. You're an idealist. You know better.
You rid the world of a menace, and that's all that matters." He turned back to Keegan. "Maybe you'll start to
feel bad when you find out that this was all unneccess-
ary." He gestured at Aytrigg. "You tell him."

Aytrigg sat down and crossed his legs. "We got word
from Washington this morning that the whole policy is
being changed. It wasn't very popular in the first place,
and the Stalin killing—the deaths of our people—
knocked down that whole house of cards. They're going

to let these people know what would have happened if
we hadn't intervened, what their future history would
have been. As a result, they're shutting down the guard
as well. Whoever's left . . . " He glanced at Fusco.
"Mussolini, I guess. Horthy, the clique in Japan, have
got two weeks to make their arrangements, then we pull
out." He took out his sunglasses and studied the lenses.
"If you'd waited, the Israelis could have walked right
in."

Fusco had not taken his eyes off Keegan once. "You
ought to be buried alive for what you did, but that's not
going to happen. We won't even interrogate you. We
know who did it, and we won't even touch them. They'll
be heroes when they get home."

"No," said Aytrigg. "We can't very well try a man for
being in on killing Hitler. But we'll have to be quiet
about it also."

"That's right," said Fusco. "So you don't go home.
You stay right here." He walked over to Keegan. "And
I'll tell you something else. Your career is over. We don't
want you." He put his hand on the arm of the chair and
leaned over Keegan. "You're an exile now, pal. You can
hit the road." He turned and walked back to his office,
and stopped at the door. "I don't want to see you when I
come out."

Keegan ran a hand through his hair. *Toss me in the
briar patch.* He looked at Aytrigg. "You knew," he said.

"Of course I knew. It's my business to know."

"That was a pretty shabby trick you pulled on me
earlier."

"Know any better way to find out when it was going
down?"

"Why didn't you stop it?"

"Why bother? We never approved of the policy in

the first place. It was a bureaucrat's daydream. Totally
unworkable, and we knew damn well that we'd be used
as a shield, while they schemed to get back in power.
Hitler was going to try a coup by the end of the year, so
the hell with him. Let the Israelis have him. Besides," he
said, "he made his bed." He walked to the desk behind
Keegan, picked up a set of keys and handed them to
him. "Here," he said. "You'll want wheels. The car's
pretty beat up, and we'll say it was destroyed in the
attack. Pick up some cans of gas from the garage. It'll
get you across Europe, and then you can sell it to some
English eccentric."

Keegan took the keys and got up. He held out his
hand to Aytrigg, who shook it and said, "Good operation, except you didn't guarantee an exit for yourself.
Keep that in mind next time. Now get out of here before
Fusco throws you out a window."

"Thanks," said Keegan. He walked to the door and
looked back. "I'll be seeing you."

"That you will," said Aytrigg.

He pulled up to the rooming house, shut off the
engine, and sat quietly for a moment. He looked around
the inside of the car. The Uzi was gone, as was the pistol
he had worn under his jacket. He unbuckled the holster
and shoved it into the glove compartment. The radio
buzzed, then spoke: there would be another meeting that
night. He leaned over and put a finger on the switch,
paused, and shut it off. A curtain on the first floor
window fluttered and fell back. A moment later the
door opened and Yetta ran out, clattering down the
steps toward the car. He got out and went to her.
She held him fiercely, speaking rapidly in Polish. She
stepped back, looking into his face. "It was on the

radio . . . I was afraid they had killed you. . . ."

He shook his head. "No. I'll tell you about it later."

Yetta looked back at the house. "All of my things are in the hall." She smiled at Keegan. "Frau Gelb is suspicious."

Keegan laughed. "I don't blame her."

And suspicious she was, looking him up and down as she gave him a rapid lecture in German that he was sure had to do with the care of this fine girl. He nodded and said "Ja" a few times and then walked back to where the suitcases rested next to the stairs. Atop them was the attaché case. He picked it up and studied it for a moment before sticking it under his arm, then lifted the suitcases and turned back to the door. Frau Gelb was saying a few quiet words to Yetta. She kissed her on the cheek and took out a lace handkerchief to dab her eyes. As Keegan passed she patted his hand, then followed them to the door, watching as they walked to the car.

Yetta waved goodbye as Keegan started the car and put it into gear. As they pulled away from the curb, she asked him, "Did you shoot anyone yourself, Danny?"

"No, I just set it up."

She smiled and put her hand on his knee. "I'm glad." She laid her head back on the seat and in a few minutes was asleep. He looked at her as he drove. She must not have slept at all last night. He looked at her hand, still resting on his knee, but turned palm upward. He tried to imagine a line of blue numbers across that wrist and could not, although it had surely happened to Yelizabeta Bronstein on the line that he called home.

They drove through the forest that surrounded the city and into the farmland beyond, leaving behind a thing that slowly stiffened on a slab, soon to join its partner who lay beneath the earth a thousand miles to the east. They passed quickly through villages and towns as the dusk deepened and the lights went on across Europe. Even on the old roads they made good time, and reached the border shortly after dark.

A Little of What You Fancy
by
Mary Catherine McDaniel

About the Author

Mary Catherine McDaniel *teaches literature and composition at Eastern Illinois University. She has learned to do what she teaches . . . learned it well. She is married, with a son, and, as of this writing, a daughter on the way. (In a science-fictionly world such as ours, she has been assured of this latter fact by sonographic techniques. Any cry of "It's a boy!" at the actual event will have invalidated modern medicine, but probably not Mary Catherine's notably cheerful attitude, which shines through her story like a grin.)*

The check for our story rights, she says, will probably be used to finance the event. "That's appropriate," she points out, "since both child and story, once only hot spots in my imagination, are now very, very real."

Please welcome into the world of SF a charming, charming talent . . . and a puckish one. . . .

When Fancy Briden died in the Spring, Roger Delgato did three unCapricornish things: he cancelled his appointments for the rest of the week; he took the train home early; and he locked himself in his study for three days, ignoring his wife so terrifically that she retreated after forty-eight hours, her knuckles raw, her voice hoarse, in deference to Willie Nelson and Chivas Regal. On the fourth day, he emerged. His eyes as red as a thirteen-year locust's, he carried Scotch bottles to the ashpit, resheathed Willie tenderly, and watered the plant that drooped as much for want of Fancy as he did. Then, showered and dressed, he took the train to the city, the address of Fancy's lawyer gripped in his hand like the dead woman's last kiss.

In the brownstone on Forty-Third, Thurman Madsen, senior partner at Madsen and Rhoads, met him in his offices' anteroom. Roger winced, feeling like a guest whose host would have preferred he use the back door. "This way, please," Madsen said, ushering him quickly past a secretary bristling at this breach in protocol. Inside, the lawyer perched on his burnished desk top, nervously twisting a potted plant. "Larry Briden asked me to take care of this affair"—at the word he blushed —"personally," he began. "And I asked you here, Mr.

Delgato, because of the rather unusual nature of Fancy's bequest."

Roger shifted in the red leather chair. "I don't understand," he said.

"Mr. Delgato"—Madsen pinched the creases in his trousers—"it appears that Ms. Briden left you in death what circumstances precluded her giving you in life." He handed Roger an inlaid wooden box. "Herself."

Roger traced the concentric hearts that covered the lid like ripples. After spending hours hidden away in the basement, choosing and cutting and fitting the wood, he knew the box, the way any craftsman knows his art, the way a mother knows each twin.

It was what was inside that he did not recognize.

The small heap of ash bore no resemblance to the woman he loved. Not a strand of auburn hair. Not a sign of the curve of her back. Not a trace of the flush his whiskers brought her throat when he kissed her there. No nails too short. No uneven breasts. Just a pile of dust, as easily the residue of some child's Fourth of July, the forgotten potroast, Mount St. Helens' phlegm.

But certainly no Fancy there.

"Mr. Delgato?" the lawyer was saying. "Mr. Delgato? Not a word of this to Mrs. Briden. For Larry's sake— not a word?"

Roger crossed back into the lawyer's anteroom, the box cradled in his arms. "No, of course not," he murmured, stopping for a second as if there were something else to be said. Some time later, the brownstone far behind, the box a portable casket that he held before him like a salver, he remembered. And now that I have her, he had wanted to say, what am I supposed to do with her? Like a desert nomad who prayed for shade

Illustrated by Rich Lynes

and found a sheet of paper wafting to his feet, he'd been given a form of the thing he most desired—a useless whetter of the appetite and not the thing itself. He dashed up the stairs to her apartment. It was not like Fancy to torment him so, he wept.

All he wanted was to throw himself on her bed and gather the pillows and sheets around him. There was no way that he, a man near enough their age to be invited home for bridge and expected to pat their daughter chastely on the head, could have known that when he turned the key in Fancy's lock, four eyes as grieved as his own would be staring back at him. He stood in the foyer, his raincoat wrapped around their daughter, extended his arm like a suitor on his first date and said, "I'm Roger Delgato." At which Mrs. Briden, an angular redhead who had not given Fancy her looks, threw up her arms and left the room.

"I'm sorry," Roger stammered. "I didn't know—"

Briden managed a wan smile. "Never mind. I guess it's natural that you'd want to be here. Carol just wanted to water the plants. We'll clear out in a bit."

Roger stuffed the raincoat behind him on the couch. "Get you a drink?" Briden asked, and Roger felt his animosity grow—it was, after all, his Scotch—until he watched Fancy's father pause to resteady his arm before he poured. "Who'd have thought it," he was saying. "You and Fancy. Can't say I ever got used to the idea, and my wife, well. . . ." He rolled his eyes and nodded toward the kitchen. "What it came down to was I loved my daughter. And when she told me she loved you, there was nothing more to say." The muscles in his back slackened and he stared into his glass. "Regardless of the circumstances, Mr. Delgato, you made my daughter happy. I don't harbor any ill will. I wanted you to know that."

Roger shook his head, afraid to try to speak.

"It's okay," Fancy's father murmured. "Carol?" he called. "You about ready?"

A small "hmmphh" came from the kitchen and Briden struggled to recover. "That girl and her plants," he said, gesturing at the green bounty in the room. "She surely had a way with them." Roger nodded, trailing them to the door.

"Good luck to you," Briden said as he stepped into the hallway. "It won't be easy for any of us. Just too few Fancies left in the world."

At that, too, Roger nodded.

When he woke, it was already dark. He felt none of the disorientation that the death of a loved one is supposed to bring: he did not find her pillow strangely empty; he did not call her name. Around him, the plants loomed and the wooden box cut into his ribs where he'd rolled onto it as he slept. He flicked on the nightstand light and opened the box.

He remembered his disbelief in grammar school science class: the human body, reduced to its basic components, worth a buck and a half. Surely not so much, he thought now, daring at last to touch the tiny dune. That this was Fancy was impossibly fantastic. This flake an ankle. This mote a wrist. And all of it a cubist jumble, no order, no use. In that exhausted emotionlessness which grief brings and crazy people covet, he knew one thing: if this was all his Fancy, he could no more free her in Bar Harbor than hoard her in the box. He wanted her near, in evidence, but to him alone and in a way Fancy would approve.

And when he finally quit ignoring the clues that fairly
leaped at him from every shelf and corner, he knew
exactly what to do.

"I thought you weren't going to put out a garden this
year!" his wife screeched, corseting her plump body in
a beige cotton bathrobe. "And why the hell are you
starting now? And where, for chrissakes," she said,
planting her stocky thighs in the doorway, "have you
been all day?"

He motioned for her to get out of his way. "Shopping," he said, pulling the patio door shut behind him.
He pressed his face against the screen. "Now run along
to bed, won't you, Nancy dear?"

He'd hired a cab to take him from Fancy's apartment
to the nearest nursery and home again, arriving at his
doorstep with a cardboard flat of garden plants on
either arm and two more to retrieve from the taxi's back
seat. And now, in the garage, he rummaged drawers for
last year's seeds. It was really too late to sow them.
They'd shoot up spindly and pale, the lettuce tough,
the radishes hot. In fact, with so little preparation, the
whole garden might be a disaster: he'd not composted
last year, plowed under the yard debris, trimmed the
oaks that had craftily encroached upon his beds. He
hoped, giggling to himself, that a little Fancy went a
long way.

His neighbors may not have heard him running his
tiller after midnight on the first of May. Their windows
shut to the night air, their ears closed habitually to
the traffic on the Interstate, they may have rolled or
mumbled but they did not get up to see Roger jerking
along behind the tiller, lit by his backyard floods and the
Moon, glimmering its blessing. Finished, he pushed the

machine aside and clubbed stubborn chunks of earth
with a garden rake, pulling the soil smooth in great
vertical swaths. The seeds came first, in patches, not
rows, to make the most of the space. Plants next, pep-
pers, broccoli, tomatoes; in hills, the melons and cukes.

The night was so still the willow on the ravine's edge
did not creak as Roger strode to the center of his garden,
a solitary pallbearer in the moonlight. He wanted to say
a prayer but he did not know any. And so instead he
opened the box and said the words he'd been reciting
while he tilled.

"Your father said there weren't enough Fancies in the
world. And I suppose most of us are lucky to be touched
by one in a lifetime. But, Fancy," he said, tilting the box
to the full Moon, "I love you too much to let it go at
that. This way," he said, "I can put back a little of what I
took."

And at that, he spilled the ashes on the earth and ran
to fetch the hose.

II

Salad came first. Radishes more red and sweet than
he could have wished. Spinach, dew-drenched. An ar-
mageddon of onions, translucent as babies' heads.

His wife detested vegetables. "Even if I could grow
fudge brownies, I wouldn't," Roger scowled, slamming
a bowl of radishes on the table. "These aren't just ordinary vegetables, you know. The least you could do is try
one."

Nancy lifted her nose in the air. Roger pouted. "Be
that way," he said. Popping a radish in his mouth, he
stormed out of the kitchen.

Nancy strummed her perfect nails against the table. In truth, she wanted to please him. His garden had become the talk of the neighborhood. An endless Eden of perfect produce. Not a wormhole in sight. Not a seed that failed to sprout. Everything glistening and veined, babies fairly bursting from their womb of earth. And all this from a man who subscribed to no garden magazines, used no sprays, pinched no shoots, a man who, in a lifetime, had tended to fruition three tomato plants and a houseplant that had shown up in his study two years ago. Even now, though his garden bulged so that a breeze sent peas like rockets to peck on the windows and the larder was so stocked he'd taken to abandoning the produce on doorsteps, even now he was more a garden watcher than a gardener. Nancy had seen him, knee-high in sweet corn, stockstill, as absorbed in each stalk as a time lapse camera. Sometimes, too, he talked. Once, home from her real estate office early, Nancy had caught him on his knees near the onions, speaking so sweet and low that a part of her expected to see a woman rise up out of the beans and take his hand. At the thought, an involuntary "Oh!" had escaped her, and Roger started like a guilty thing, pretending to pull weeds that did not exist.

Nancy grimaced at the radishes before she tossed one in her mouth. Lord knew she should eat food like this more often. She'd put on forty pounds since she'd taken over the office. Rushed, rushed, rushed from one whining client to the next, she juggled appointments with loan officers, patched cigarette holes and untangled cranky venetian blinds for sloppy sellers, soothed tempers when six month old water heaters belched and died, and carpeted hardwoods turned plywood overnight. No time to cook, no time to eat right. Doughnuts and

burgers and take-home fried chicken. Her body thick-
ened like an animal's set for slaughter. No wonder her
husband despised her.

She rolled the radish in her cheek. In truth, that
wasn't so. He didn't hate her. In the fifteen years they'd
been married, he'd really never said or done an unkind
thing to her. They were just two people with nothing in
common and no business being together. She'd considered giving him a divorce but there really was no need. It
was enough that they still slept in the same bed, that he
remembered her birthday, that he took her to sales
award dinners and tried his best to look proud. True,
he'd grown odd enough lately, like a man who'd made
the transition from Spring to Winter in a single afternoon. Poor Roger. She really wished she could help.

She chomped into the radish without realizing she
had. The taste was so unusual that she spit a chunk of it
out in her hand. It certainly *looked* like a radish. But it
was sweet, and the white yielded to her tongue like the
center of a chocolate cordial.

She ate another. This one, too, cool and sweet and
something more, a sensation she could only liken to the
feel of the firm hand that had pulled her, years and years
before, from the too deep end of a neighbor's pool.

III

The vegetables were disappearing. In the evening he'd
light on a half dozen tomatoes nearly ready to be picked.
Next morning they'd be gone. He did not begrudge the
filchers, exactly, but, like the minister of a faith he alone
understood, doubted their capacity for reverence and
preferred to do the harvesting himself. Thus when Harry

Melcher wandered up out of the ravine toward the middle of July, Roger decided to have a word with him. "Evening, Harry" was all it took: Harry, president of the local bank, was so embarrassed he offered to refinance Roger's mortgage. "I don't know what came over me," he said, sheepishly digging his toes in the tomato bed. "These vegetables of yours are just so good I get a kind of craving for them." Beads of sweat glistening on his brow, Melcher made Roger nervous. He snapped off two Big Boys the size of melons and placed them in the banker's hands. The man grinned like an idiot and disappeared back into the ravine.

Even Nancy had grown peculiar. She turned up her nose at double cheese pizza. Grew bored with Sara Lee. Instead, like a caffeine addict in a Mormon household, she sneaked to the refrigerator in the night, snarfing platefuls of spinach and buckets of unshucked peas. Face to face with the empty larder, she'd assert her innocence, claiming crafty neighbors; shown the tear of lettuce or the cornsilk pasted to her chin, she'd pale, as amazed by her own traitor tastebuds as her husband. Still, she was losing weight; on that account, the vegetables were doing her good. But she'd changed in other ways, too. She'd lost interest in her job, for one. Prowled the house, restless as a tomcat spying a jay from the windowsill. At the patio door every five minutes, she seemed not to know that she could open it and go out but stood staring at the garden and at him, moody as a locust shedding its first skin. For these things, too, Roger blamed her diet: a system weaned on Orange Crush and Ding Dongs might rebel at vitamins and fiber. Reasoning that the best thing to do was to keep her busy, he'd just considered asking her to join him in the garden when she in fact appeared, her long nails

shorn to the quick. She helped him plant turnips in the
space vacated by the lettuce, and then she simply watched, standing in the garden for hours, her dull brown hair
taking on a red cast from the sun.

He did not know what she expected to see. Prose-
lytized, most likely she played follow-the-leader. In ways
more obsessed than he, she borrowed books on home
canning, bought a pressure cooker, cleaned jars until
they sparkled.

She might not know why her husband's vegetables
had such a hold on her, but she could not bear the
thought of a winter without them.

IV

She did not know what was going on but she suspected it had something to do with the soil. He was too
protective of it. He would not clean his precious produce
at the sink but carried the hose to the garden instead. He
worked barefoot in the soil, wiping his feet afterwards
on a little mat which he shook back into the garden. He
even cleaned his nails outside. No ordinary soil
grew plants so big, so quickly, or yielded vegetables so
exquisite in taste, so impossible to refuse. Mrs. Summers,
a spindly widow with the looks and temperament of a
chicken, had called three times to beg for snap beans;
Mr. Forester, principal of the high school, was wondering if Roger would consider supplying vegetables to
the school cafeteria. It would do wonders for morale, he
had said.

But no one could attest to the vegetables' peculiarities
better than she.

Roger might not have had any previous experience growing vegetables, but at least he had eaten them. Nancy could not boast so. She'd been born spitting out strained carrots and mashed peas. She abhorred vegetables the way allergics do Spring. But it had been a losing battle since the very first radish. When she'd tried to resist, she'd awakened in the night to find herself grating coleslaw by the refrigerator light, a carrot dangling, long and obscene, from her mouth. She'd had no choice but to give in. Out of pride, though, she ate quickly and never in front of Roger. If he were bent on poisoning her, so be it, but she would not give him the pleasure of seeing her shame as she inhaled spaghetti squash.

She was being silly. The vegetables affected her, to be sure, and at first she'd been horribly afraid. She saw her husband too often in the garden, expectant as a lover awaiting a rendezvous. Herself she was losing, too. Like a menopausal caterpillar, she did not recognize her own reflection. But that, she conceded, was not all bad: the body she'd worn fifteen years ago was resurfacing; she was much less anxious about her work. Thus, even her fear was mixed with something else, as if the ground beyond the patio door held both her life and death. In the end, it again called the shots, and one morning she stumbled out of bed to find her once perfectly manicured nails jagged and split and covered with dirt. So she'd gone to it, not freely, exactly, but as a person with a nearly severed leg goes to the knife, knowing that win and lose were names for the same thing.

All she had to do now was hold on long enough to see whatever Roger was waiting for to happen, happen.

V

Lonely for Fancy, Roger slipped out of bed to walk in the garden. A pajamaed form lept into the ravine at the flip of the floodlight switch. Melcher, no doubt, in the throes of his addiction. For both of them the season's end loomed like a cloud of cicadas waiting for just the the right moment to descend and devour. For the piece of August left, there were potatoes to dig, onions to pull, cantaloupe to pick. And afterwards, the garden a grave again, six months and more. He wasn't sure that he could bear it.

Inside, he found Nancy crying. "I want to know what's going on," she wept on her side of the bed. "I see you look at that garden the way I'd always dreamed you'd look at me. I'm scared, do you hear? I don't even like vegetables, but look at this!" she screamed, drawing a handful of brussel sprouts out from under her pillow.

To laugh was not the thing to do, and so he strode to the window and let up the shade while she shook her sprouts at him like an angry fishwife. He could just see the garden's south end from here, the floods still on, as if a few bulbs and the wishes of man could extend the season. Once he knew he would not laugh, he turned to his sobbing wife to comfort her. The shade, flapping in the breeze, sent the light rippling across her auburn hair. He gasped. And then he did a thing he hadn't done in months—he pulled her to him. Her body, hot with tears, molded into his. He stroked the curve of her back, felt her breasts—the left one slightly larger—pressed into his own.

"Is it the soil?" he heard her saying, breathless now, as much with fear as with desire. "Am I in danger?"

"Shhh," was all her husband would say. And then he pressed a brussel sprout to her lips, realizing, as he should have long ago, that a little Fancy never hurt anyone.

How to Sound Like an Expert
by
Gregory Benford

About the Author

W.O.T.F. Contest judge Gregory Benford first appeared as an SF writer with a 1000-word short story that won Second Place in a Magazine of Fantasy & Science Fiction *contest. This capped a long career as an active SF fan, during which he co-published the legendary amateur magazine,* Void, *where many of his early stories and articles appeared.*

His Junior year in high school saw the launching of Sputnik, and veered him into a serious interest in science. This has culminated, so far, in a professorship at the University of California, where he heads a research group devoted to the study of plasma physics and a phenomenon he named, the "super-strong turbulence."

Re-awakened interest in writing then led him to also produce such landmark SF novels as Timescape, In the Ocean of Night, *and* Heart of The Comet. *So in the world of science he has been a Woodrow Wilson Fellow, a Fellow at Cambridge University, and a guest lecturer around the world. And in SF, he holds two Nebula awards. It's beyond a doubt that he knows what he's talking about when he tells you as an author how to sound like you know what you're talking about. . . .*

A scientist who writes fiction is as rare as a dancing bear. As Samuel Johnson might have remarked on seeing such a thing in the streets of London, one is not surprised to see it done well, but simply to see it done at all.

That gives anyone with a technical background an edge in writing speculative fiction. You have at your fingertips information that you can, with some dexterity, shape to fiction's needs.

I started writing science fiction while a graduate student working on my doctorate. My first few (utterly unmemorable) published stories used very little scientific information. I was so uncertain of my narrative strengths that I tried to stick to staple backgrounds and use the techniques I'd seen other, better writers deploy. This was a mistake.

I began to understand how bad an error it was when I finally did catch on to the obvious fact that scientists have some advantages. Like the dancing bear, you get the benefit of the doubt with editors. Up to a far-distant point, they'll overlook your thin characters, abrupt swerves, disconnected plot elements . . . *if* you have a "nice idea." A "nice" notion is one that strikes the usually nonspecialist reader as clever, striking, original. Like a ballet dancer's leap, this is an event that occurs in a glimmering, but takes long hours of preparation by the performer. SF editors love such moments in fiction, because they are the essential thrill in all speculative literature: something unforseen but instantly recognizable as *right*.

This means that the readership is paying you to dream in public. But these must be machine dreams, with gritty substance and some fact behind them. Having that, you can sin against many fictive commandments and still reach an audience.

Mind, this doesn't mean you'll be writing great fiction. That still requires all the attention to character, plot, imagery and narrative drive that all good fiction demands. But the simple advantage of knowing interesting things—or knowing where to find them, and mining those sources—can work wonders. There are magazines that run techno-talk yarns sometimes bereft of some narrative skills, and fans continue to read them because of the real meat they contain.

Of course, people don't read science fiction to learn science any more than others read historical novels to study history. There are easier ways to go about that.

Yet the fact remains that "hard" science fiction—the kind based on the physical sciences—remains the core of the field. The reading public persists in thinking of rockets, lasers and aliens as the central subject matter of science fiction. Writers like Robert A. Heinlein, Issac Asimov and Arthur C. Clarke—classic "hard" SF figures—now appear on the bestseller lists.

Similarly, most SF magazines yearn for more stories with a thorough grounding in science. Generally, it is easier to sell a short story with high scientific content than one which concentrates, for example, on social changes, or age-old conflicts in a futuristic setting.

The shortage is even more acute for book publishers. A prominent editor remarked to me recently that at least two thirds of the manuscripts he receives are fantasy, and much of the remainder is only nominally science fiction.

Why is this so? Because science is daunting, complex and hard to work into a story. Few writers have very much scientific training to build on, and the pace of scientific research is so rapid that you can be outdated while you're working out a plotline. Many stories of only twenty years ago look antique now.

This is a tough problem for even seasoned professionals. You can concentrate on the science and not notice that you're rolling out wooden, predictable stories. One reason some published hard-science fiction isn't very well written is that the editors can't get anything better, but they need some "hard" material.

For the enterprising writer, though, this represents a real opportunity. Speculative fiction is traditionally open to new talent and new ideas. The trouble with many incoming authors in the 1970s, though, was that their "new" idea often was simple doom-crying. It is always easier to see problems than to think of their solutions. Stories built on simple recognition of the unforseen side effects of technology have a sameness about them, a lack of inventiveness that bores readers.

This is an easy trap to fall into. It may be an unconcious choice; the current glut of fantasy novels (often trilogies) seems to arise from newer writers, who seem to share the anti-science sentiments of the middle 1970s. Of course, powerful yarns have been spun with this angle, and will be again—but it is a high-risk avenue to take.

So consider using not just dollops of science in fiction, but firmly basing stories on it. Admittedly, it's a help to have an extensive background in science or engineering. But even if your degree is in linguistics or animal husbandry, and you're interested in science, you can use your training.

The fundamental requirement, of course, is that you like "hard" SF in the first place. Trying to write something you have no enthusiasm or feel for is a ticket to disaster. If you have read hard science fiction for pleasure, and know the basic motifs, you have already served your apprenticeship.

There are several steps that can help you become an adequate writer of science-based stories and then go on to carve out your own individual corner in the field. They aren't hard-and-fast, of course, but I use them every day.

1. *Do your homework.* Everybody laughs when TV shows such as *Battlestar Galactica* routinely mistake "solar system" for "galaxy," use light-year as a unit of time, and make other howlers of that kind. Such blunders do seem to pass right by the mass TV audience, but in a printed story, even one can easily cause immediate rejection by science fiction editors and readers.

Science is replete with terminology (or, uncharitably, jargon). Using it accurately convinces the audience that you're telling the truth. If you need it, be sure you consult a reference. I keep my set of the *Britannica* nearby, but more specialized books are invaluable. A brief list from my own shelf:

The Science in Science Fiction, Peter Nicholls, editor; Knopf. The best place to start. Covers everthing, with many references to fictional treatments and nonfiction background.

Cambridge Encyclopedia of Astronomy, Simon Mitton, editor; Crown. A good overview, technically accurate and well written.

Isaac Asimov's Biographical Encyclopedia of Science & Technology; Avon. Tidbits of history and science.

The Quest for Extraterrestrial Life, Donald Goldsmith, editor; University Science Books. A collection of readings with many speculative ideas.

Black Holes and Warped Spacetime, William Kaufmann; Freeman. The best book on that subject.

The Seven Mysteries of Life, Guy Murchie; Houghton Mifflin. Observations on many sciences. You can pick up many "bits of business" here that lend atmosphere to even the driest facts.

The Science Fiction Encyclopedia, Peter Nicholls, editor; Doubleday. A thorough listing of major treatments of major SF ideas, plus much else of interest about the field.

This last entry is invaluable for trying out your newborn idea, to see if somebody used it in a famous story from 1938. Not that you can't re-use an idea, but you should *know* if you are; that affects how you treat it.

Don't pass up any chance to do some background reading, no matter how minor it seems. *Use* your natural curiosity.

A few years ago I was working on a novel using Greek archeology, *Artifact.* I had a character remark in passing, "The ancients were building elegant domes when *our* ancestors were hunting mastodons." After I'd typed those words, I realized I had no idea when the mastodons disappeared. A few minutes' checking showed that while they had been hunted to extinction in

Europe well before the Greeks, they lived on in North America until a few thousand years ago. I then used this fact later in the conversation, adding an insider's detail that an archeologist might plausibly know, but the casual reader wouldn't.

2. *Organize!* Technical material needs to simmer in your mind. Good hard SF demands not that you parrot material from an encyclopedia, but that you *think* about it and *develop* it creatively. I let my deep-down creative processes do most of my idea-making. I even go to the extent of lying in bed each morning, mulling over the science and plot of my current project, seeing if any idea has surfaced in the night.

To keep myself open to fresh notions, I keep my source material handy, so that I can review it whenever I want. That means accumulating clippings, photocopies, copious notes—and organizing them into quickly findable form, using headings like *Starship, Alien Biology,* and *Techtalk.*

I was browsing through this material when it suddenly occurred to me that an opening line in an already-written chapter could have two different meanings. The line was, "When he woke up he was dead." In the novel it meant one thing, but in the near future it could mean the man had his nervous system cut off. Why? How would he regain control?

Within a few minutes the material I had filed under *Advanced Medical* fell into place. I used the idea for a separate short story. Then I incorporated some of this new material back into the novel I had been working on, finding that this diversion had opened up new possibilities in the original situation. The back of the mind at work! Eventually these elements formed a crucial part of the novel *Across the Sea of Suns.*

3. *Counter-punch.* This is Damon Knight's famous tactic. It works well in quite technical matters as well as in the way Damon used it to write some of his best short stories, like "Not With a Bang."

SF is full of common assumptions that were once inventive but are now mere conventions. Time and again authors invoke faster-than-light travel so their characters can whiz around the galaxy, righting wrongs, with no more than a few weeks spent in travel. This is good for classic Aristotelian dramatic unity, but *not* using it can be an asset, if it leads you to a new angle. What would an empire be like if ships moved at a hundredth of light-speed? How would it maintain political unity? What conflicts would arise?

This policy of truly thinking through the ideas in SF can lead to major projects. Years ago I started thinking about time travel, and asked myself—as a physicist— how scientists would proceed if they discovered a particle that could move backward in time. Would they send a man backward, as their first experiment? Of course not—too expensive, too dangerous.

So I spent years writing a novel called *Timescape,* in which physicists do nothing more dramatic than try to send mere *messages* backward in time. This was more than enough to generate conflict and suspense, and I profited by not echoing the ideas of a thousand earlier stories. Asking how events might really happen, given the realities of our world, can always turn up unexplored avenues.

4. *Ask the next question.* This well-known motto, invented by Theodore Sturgeon, might well be the most important for any SF work. It's particularly germane for hard SF.

New technology and science appear everyday in our

newspapers and on TV. Much of it is obscure, or just another slight improvement of a particular widget. But some changes can alter the lives of common people, and these are the most fertile fields for anticipating the unseen effects.

The easiest things to anticipate are problems, but if developed no farther this approach leads to downbeat, hopeless stories. There are two ways out.

First, you can go for the really unexpected side-effect. For example, several years ago the news coverage of Barney Clark's heroic use of an artificial heart stimulated my imagination. Would the public always applaud such exotic medical technology? What if for 250 million you could buy not merely a replacement heart, but virtual immortality? I wrote a story about a dying man who could not tolerate the sight of a millionaire buying a whole new life. With nothing left to lose, what would this man do? Pessimistic, in a way—but the story, titled "Immortal Night," generated suspense which sprang from wondering just what the viewpoint character wanted.

The less risky way around the pessimistic-story trap is to see an unexpected *positive* aspect of what looks at first pretty bleak. For example, the Coming of the Computer. Will its ability to save and check information lead to a "surveillance society" where we have no secrets from the government? Think of a way computers can help thwart a police state—and show it in action. So many people fear computers already, such a story could key a surge of optimism and thus be very popular.

5. *Show the tip of the iceberg*. The most dreaded beast in hard SF is the Expository Lump. That's the long paragraph explaining how a new invention works, or what the ecology of a strange planet is like, or some other necessary but intrusive material. You have to ex-

plain a lot without slowing down the action.

Suppose your hero is on a low-gravity planet. Don't lecture your reader about it, dully cataloguing the mass and size and atmospheric details of your world. Instead, let your hero notice *in passing* that many kinds of large animals have wings for gliding or flying, that life in trees is more abundant, and that the trees themselves are taller and branch out farther. This colorful detail allows the reader to fill in much of the background himself.

This can work even better in near-future stories. In my novel *Timescape,* I dealt extensively with a runaway biological disaster. The foreground is concerned with scientists and how they work, but I realized I hadn't shown how advanced knowledge of manipulating the genetic code would affect ordinary life. How could I fill this in without devoting much space to it? My solution was to let a character notice that a road-filling job outside his laboratory was being done by apes. These animals had had their intelligence artificially enhanced until they could follow verbal orders and do manual labor. This, and one or two other quick touches, gave the background color I wanted.

Even if you're weak on science, you don't have to give up the hard SF story. The most important role of science in SF is establishing *setting,* and you can do that with reading or travel.

Years ago I sold a short story, but I couldn't put it out of my mind. Slowly I saw that it was the beginning of a novel—but the larger plot had to occur at the Jet Propulsion Laboratory in Pasadena. I didn't know much about how working space scientists talked or thought. So I used my journalistic and scientific connections to find out. I had written articles for *Smithsonian* and *Natural History,* so I cited these credits to line up several visits to J.P.L. There I got to know space-scientists and picked up those little nuggets of detail I later used for *In the Ocean of Night.*

Of course, there are some elements of technical detail that aren't really science, just engineering, or mechanics, or any hard-edged body of knowledge. But they carry the same freight of recognizable, "hard" information, and can have the same effect in establishing the writer's credibility. Look up Algis Budrys' remarkably compact "The Distant Sound of Engines," for a model example of working detail (this time about trucking) into a dramatic, understated story. It makes its points by analogy and works beautifully because you've been shown evidence that the author has done his homework and so is talking straight goods to you.

More than anything else, hard SF demands that you convey with assurance the *feel* of the future. Science is viewed by some as an embodiment of certainty. Certainty overcomes disbelief. Fine. Use that. Just as the whaling information in *Moby Dick* underpins the action, the science in SF commands belief. And that's my ultimate point:

To the SF reader, often the "bits of business" incorporating the atmosphere of hard SF are enough to convince him you know what you are talking about. Then he will go along for your voyages on whatever strange seas you have mastered.

In the Sickbay
by
R. V. Branham

About the Author

As you'll be able to guess from his story, R. V. Branham studied radiology in college and has worked as an X-Ray technician. But that does not begin to describe his background or his skills at various technical occupations.

His love of literature comes from his father, an English teacher who read to him from the classics. His insights into cultural conflicts, the ways of the world in general, and into the confusions that haunt the human heart, began with childhood in Calexico, a border town, and the heritage of his Hispanic mother.

His moody, relentless story here has gone through years of writing, re-writing, and resting between re-writes; another work had earned him Honorable Mention in the Contest before "In the Sickbay" won Third Place in the First Quarter. He is married to Moira McAullife, an Australian writer whom he met while both attended the Clarion SF writing workshop at Michigan State University. The two of them spur each other on. Everybody needs a friend in this world . . . on any world. . . .

These songs are not meant to be understood, you understand. They are only meant to terrify and comfort.
—John Berryman, "His Toy, His Dream, His Rest"

The Honduran-registered spacetug *Popol Vuh* screamed across the vacuum of space, unheard, unsensed. As it approached the moon Titan, the control module detached, like a sated insect after mating. Seven spacebus and cargo units in a rapid low succession fell inexorably, drawn to the ocean moon.

At the optimal moment their parachutes popped open.

Upon retrieval the two spacebus units were to be shuttled as quickly as possible to Mitsubishi-Dutch Shell Inc.'s Titan base. An internal elevator was to be inserted into each spacebus so as to facilitate transferral to the sickbay.

FASTEN $hFaArSnTeEsNs$ harness.

Marianna Held obeyed the flashing instruction above her seat; it would be at least fifteen minutes before unloading, perhaps another fifteen minutes after that

before the sickbay tranferrals would begin. Marianna
did not relish undergoing the treatment, but Earth and
L-side job markets were swamped, and being fresh out
of MIT she was not necessarily in the best of positions
for job shopping.

In many ways it was the best job in the Solar System—
salary-wise, for one. But there *was* a drawback; they had
to almost kill you with radiation sickness and then cure
you to bring you here.

Marianna looked out the porthole at the hostile sea;
no one could last for more than a moment out there. She
eavesdropped on the two men sitting to her right:

"I hope they cleaned up that mess in the south
domes."

Marianna, curiosity piqued, turned to him. "What
mess?" She was embarrassed by the panic in her voice.

"There was a chemexplosion," the other man explained. "No real problem; some workers were killed or
injured, though."

Jesus! Marianna had read, somewhere, that the base
was only a decade old. This was ridiculous . . . falling
apart after ten years.

"I wouldn't worry about it." The man next to her
smiled. "This must be your first time up here, huh?"

"Yes, it is."

"Look, I've been up here before. They've got this
system down pat."

Of the 148 passengers aboard (who'd just passed
through the ravagingly intense gamma-etcetera radiation of Saturn's orbit), an estimated 145 would only
need one treatment—a reasonable percentage by many
standards. And cheaper for the part of the haul than the
large fortune that installing full radiation shielding
would run.

Once transferrals were completed, the Feelgoods were called into action, Nightingales at the consoles, inserting silastic catheters, implanting them above each client's left breast. Then, to complete the process started by interstellar radiation, Cytoxan—an old and effective drug for treatment of aplastic anemia—was administered intravenously over a period of 48 hours. Only then, after all the bad bone marrow had been killed, could a marrow transfusion be administered.

Marianna came to, reluctantly rising to consciousness from her chrysalis of sleep. She felt a nascent tingling and cold nausea; par for the course, her Nightingale, Gemma, had warned her . . . two days ago—? Four?

She opened her eyes, turned her head, and stared at the pivoting vidcam monitor. She sighed, releasing all her fear and frustration, panic and exhaustion.

It returned with her next intake of breath. Calm down, she told herself. She and the other passengers could be here for 40 days, possibly, so it might be best to take it, not one day at a time or an hour or a minute, but second by second. The Cytoxin dribbled, drop by drop, from the plaspac through the tubing and into her catheter. Drop by drop.

She made a bitter attempt at wit: "Hello, silastic catheter . . . we're going to be such good friends."

Gemma had told her that the catheter passed through her subclavian vein and into her heart. "Your catheter can be used for blood samples as well as I.V., minimizing risk of internal bleeding," Gemma had said, trying to explain some of the procedures, alleviate any fears. The lecture had seemed like Attic Greek to Marianna, so removed and abstracted, so far from her specialty.

The vidfone discreetly buzzed. Marianna remembered what Gemma had said about vidfones being voice-activated in the sickbays, and answered.

"*Hullo, Miz Held.*" A smiling administrative assistant greeted her.

She fought back the urge to laugh, or be sick.

"*Just calling to remind you about your appointment with Andrea Butler.*"

"I've not forgotten—" Marianna winced at the pain. She would be glad when the apamorphine on backorder arrived.

"*She'll be in to greet you elevenish.*"

"Okay." It would take Marianna forever to adjust to Titan's timescale. "G'bye—" Her whisper triggered the vidfone and cut off the assistant. *Screw her, screw them all* . . . she nodded back off to sleep.

"*How're you feeling?*" Gemma was setting the controls on the Feelgood, which hovered over Marianna as it ran a laser scan from head to toe.

Marianna tried to be cheerful: "How am I doing?"

Gemma looked at her and caught her eye. " . . . Too soon to tell, really."

Marianna laughed. "No news is not always good news." She gasped, startled—the laugh had exhausted her.

Gemma tried not to look concerned. "But you're the statistician. You should know the odds are in your favor."

"Statistics," Marianna said, trying to be patient, "are never that simple." Then: "I hope that didn't sound patronizing."

"Don't worry." Gemma shrugged, smiling. "If you

get out of line I'll let you know."

The Nightingale continued: "Your platelets are too low to let your blood clot, so you can't brush your teeth. We can't have you hemmorhaging from bleeding gums, now can we?"

"So what do I do about bad breath?"

"Gargle." Gemma started to leave.

"Excuse me."

Gemma turned.

"Yes?"

"When will I know?"

"It could take anywhere from a week to three after the marrow transfusion. If you need another one, then it goes to Review——"

"Review?"

"Yeah—but don't worry; the corporation's not going to let you die; not after paying a fortune to bring you here. . . . Anything else?"

"Yes—No. It's just——"

"Do you have anyone L-side or Earthside?"

"An ex-husband on Earth. Then there's the folks on Neü Köln."

"I always have patients tell me the hardest thing about this—coming to Titan—is leaving your family behind."

"Exactly," Marianna said. "I'm an only child; I didn't want to hurt my parents——"

"Have you talked to them?"

"Yes." Marianna sighed. "My father's very encouraging. 'S name's Wolfgang . . . but we call him 'Wolfie'. . . . And mother . . . well, she's just a professional worrier."

"My father's like that, too."

"Encouraging?"

"No, worrying!"

Marianna and Gemma burst into laughter.

Then, an abrupt nervous silence. Gemma said: "Butler'll be here in an hour or so." The glass door opened and shut as she left.

Marianna nodded off, fell into a comforting sleep. She was awakened later by the whooshing of the glass door as it slid open, admitting a woman in a beige jumpsuit. *This must be Andrea Butler.* She looked as ubiquitous and unctuous as any other supervisor Marianna'd ever had to deal with.

"And how are *we* this morning, Miz Held?" Butler said in a cheerful tone, pulling an armchair near her bed.

"G'day. Wish I could be a bit more affirmative, but this whole adjustment——"

"Say no more." Butler cut her off, switched on the type-pad. "It took me six weeks to go through marrow tranfusions. Been here seven years. I really like it here. Last job I had was Earthside, with the L. A. Parochial School District Administration."

Marianna hated it when people prattled on about Earthside. "Yes."

"Well. I hate to bother you, but the forms containing your signatures were lost when one of our databanks went down in a chemexplosion last quarter-month." *Why can't Butler say 'week' like everyone else, instead of this quarter-month crap.* Butler reached over with a type-pad, for Marianna to sign the appropriate forms, which she did without bothering to read them over.

Some 24 hours later Gemma entered with a Feelgood-console. Marianna was anesthetized, rolled over by the Feelgood, and, under the skillful ministerings of Gemma at the console, scrubbed and sterilized for surgery. Review had only just now approved a second transplant.

Illustrated by J. Kenton Manning

The Feelgood made a laser incision above the buttocks, then suction needles were inserted to withdraw the diseased marrow. Repeatedly drilling through the same two holes in Marianna's back, they stabbed hundreds of separate holes into her pelvis, slurping up blood and marrow, sucking it out.

Gemma pressed a button. Fresh marrow, taken from Marianna a year before and cloned, was pumped back into her pelvis. The process, usually taking no more than ten minutes, was complicated by a slight drop in Marianna's pulse.

The transfusion wound up clocking in at 23.5 minutes, and an exhausted Gemma directed the Feelgood to post-op asepsis. Gemma hoped that this time it would take.

If it didn't, then it would be back to the Client Review Board, for a third transplant—a second request.

Gemma set the Feelgood to administer 100 milligrams of apomorphine, 50 of antihistamine, and RNA solution, through Marianna's catheter. She then pressed Monitor Mode, and headed out the glass door for the Nightingale Station.

In the showers she ran into Lisa, another Nightingale.

"How's it going, Lisa?"

Lisa turned her back to her, silently sobbing.

Gemma went to Lisa, embraced her tenderly. "Did the Ground Round Kid die?"

"N-n-no."

Gemma stroked Lisa's wet hair, normally thick and curly, now tangled and stringy. "Was—was it a Transfusion Client?"

"Yes." Lisa continued crying.

Gemma hugged her desperately, wanting to take on a

bit of her rage and pain, knowing it to be futile—but
wanting to help nonetheless.

"Lisa . . . want to do some bar-hopping?"

"What ab-out the Feelgood Counselor?"

"What about it?" Then, gently: "Lisa, I know coun-
seling's Good For The Psyche, and all that. . . . But
getting stinking blasted's better. Much better."

Five hours and four pubs later, Gemma was beginning to regret her suggestion. She'd never gone on a
drinking binge with Lisa before . . . nor would she ever
do it again.

Lisa was singing an old, old song. Having forgotten
the verses, she contented herself with endlessly repeating
the chorus in a voice as far from perfect pitch as hu-
manly possible.

"If you can't get laid on a Saturday night, you can't
get laid at all! If you can't get laid on a Saturday night,
you can't get laid at all! If you can't get laid on a
Saturday night, you can't get laid at all!"

Though the barkeep had gone hours before and left
the bar on Auto, though the few other people in the bar
were even drunker than Lisa, Gemma was flushed with
embarrassment. She downed her cognac-and-quinine
and went to the bar. Punched her credit number into the
keyboard. Ordered another drink. The holo of Titan's
surface, mounted above the bar, made Gemma shudder.

Lisa stopped singing long enough to shout, "Get me
one, too!"

Gemma had wanted to say, "Haven't you had
enough?!" But she didn't care for scenes. So instead, she
ordered Lisa another drink. And a sobriety pill. Gemma
plonked the pill into Lisa's drink before taking it back to
their table.

She sat down, silently pushing Lisa's drink toward her. Lisa nodded thanks, still singing. Gemma sipped at her drink—and almost gagged on it when she saw Butler approach their table. She nudged Lisa, who stopped her song in mid-syllable.

Butler spoke first: "Do you mind if I sit with you?"

"No," Gemma said. "Not at all."

Lisa agreed. "S-s-sit on d-d-down."

"Would you like a drink?"

"No." Butler shook her head. "I've had plenty. Thanks anyway." She grabbed a chair and pulled it up to them. Butler straddled the chair, leaning back, arms akimbo. The chair's back was digging against the table. Finally, Butler ventured a comment: "I really tied it on tonight."

"Taken a pill yet?" Gemma glanced sideways at Lisa.

Lisa had sobered up, and now sat there, bored.

"Twice." Butler leaned forward, her elbow against the metal of the chair's back, her face cradled in her hands.

Gemma gloated. "You'll have hell to pay tomorrow."

Butler smiled. "You should talk."

"Well, tomorrow's my day off."

"Want to trade?" Butler leaned back, grinned. "I'm just frazzled from having to deal with that new client, Held——"

"—Marianna," Lisa cut in.

Butler nodded and continued. "I'm not at all religious . . . but when I saw her, I thought—"

"There But For The Grace Of Ghawd," Gemma completed the sentence for her.

"But how do you two cope?"

Gemma and Lisa darted glances at each other, then at Butler. *Who says we cope?*

After a brief nervous pause, Gemma spoke: "Excuse

me, Andrea. But this is my day off. I don't talk shop on
my day off."

Lisa cleared her throat, spoke up. "It's late, and I *do*
have to work tomorrow." Then, to Gemma: "Walk with
me?"

"Sure." Gemma got up, and, as she went past Butler,
she impulsively brushed her hair, tousled it. "Good
night, Andrea."

Andrea looked up, forlorn. "Good night."

"Good . . . ni—night." Lisa's salutation was distended by a yawn.

"Andrea, do you want to walk with us?" Gemma
said.

"No. . . . I'll just sit here and mope and moan and
feel sorry for myself." Butler added a strangled laugh.

"You know you don't have to—" Gemma let her
sentence hang in the air, unfinished. She could feel it
float away. To hell with Butler.

Gemma dropped Lisa off and took the tube shuttle to
the southwest dome, where she subleased an apartment
on a quarterly basis. The apartment was only slightly
more expensive than a company-bachelor-unit and had
many more amenities: a bed-sit room, a bedroom with
walk-in closet, a kitchen and dinette, a *private* bathroom . . . and a *private* sunken bath. The apartment was
a real find. A friend of a friend had a friend who knew
someone who wanted to sub-lease.

The only thing she had had to agree to was to repaint.
Facing walls were a very soft yellow or orange. There
was a mirrored wall in the bed-sit room and a built-in
aquarium. All a company unit offered was a one-room
shoebox, painted white, with a galley, and communal
toilets and showers down the hall.

Gemma had lucked into this palace three months
after joining the colony; and though she'd often told
herself that, Contract be damned, she'd return to
Earth on the next outbound shuttle; and though she
counted-down often to the end of the previous tenant's
Sabbatical on Earth, she had gone ahead and made the
apartment *hers*. The tenant's pseudo-Early-American
furniture and Currier & Ives prints had been put in
storage. Some Scandinavian furniture had been leased.
Klee and Jackson Pollack posters had been bought, and
the walls now sported them along with her late Grand-
mother's Alicia Austin lithos of satyrs blowing on skin
flutes.

Home, Gemma rejoiced as she shut the door behind
her and sealed herself in for the night. She kicked her
shoes off and almost stepped on a small parcel that had
been sent through her mail tube and had ricocheted out
of the receiving basket. She picked it up and walked over
to her computer console and sat down. First things first.
She punched in for the Vivaldi mandolin concertos.
Second things second. As the "Concerto in G Major for
Two Mandolins" started its Allegro movement, Gemma
stepped into her kitchen for some chamomile tea. She
opened the grocerybay and found the week's order. As
she unbagged it, two packs of loose tea dropped to the
floor. She'd only ordered one pack.

She filled a straining spoon with some chamomile,
found her mug, and got hot water from the dispenser.
She was out of honey . . . *Goddamn, I forgot to order it*.
Gemma dropped the spoon into the mug, and let the tea
steep.

She returned to her console just as the Andante
movement began. A trio of strings, violins and violas,

gamboled to the rhythmically simple mutterings of the two mandolins. Gemma punched her grocery bill . . . scanned the screen and found she had only been billed for one pack of loose tea . . . punched in for a correction, and waited for the extra pack to be added to her bill. As the adjustment printed its way across the screen, Gemma punched for her correspondence. In addition to occasional notes from her addled aunt and namesake, she also corresponded with a Nurse Rochelle, who had trained her at UCLA Medcenter, Earthside. Also, the odd game of chess or Scrabble came in from her cousin, L-side. Today, alpha characters began to flit across the screen. It was a letter from her ex-husband. She punched *Erase* after two lines of some pathetic sob-story.

Gemma watched her aquarium; the lion fish danced to the Andante, their toxic plumage trailing as they chased each other. She remembered the parcel and opened it; inside was a vidgram cassette. The Finale Movement, Allegro, kicked in, with its trilling violins and violas and mandolins. Gemma loaded the cassette into her VCR attachment, and punched *Playback*. It was Ulrich, smiling his most charismatic smile. Violins, violas, mandolins. Gemma felt it all at that moment——*infatuation*lovehateanger*forgiveness*affection. Violins. Then, horniness*embarrassment*humiliation*lust*. Violas. And, finally, nausea*hungover*apathetic, somehow *dead*. Some part. Mandolins. Pouring down.

Uri spoke: "Hi, Gemma, how's my fave unrequited love?" He seemed just the same. Gemma had been teacher's pet when she'd been in his journalism class. Not only was he a teacher, but a fine journalist as well. He had won a Pulitzer Prize . . . then divorced his wife. Violins, like honey. Gemma was out of honey.

"Guess who's been offered a chairmanship at your

effing colony's college?" Uri still started with guess
*who*guess*what*, ever the journalist, ever the formulistic
bastard. He had even written a novel, once—gotten a
good sum of money for it in advance, but it had flopped
in the marketplace, and gotten apalling reviews besides.
Uri and Gemma had dated, for awhile. But, somehow,
never gone to bed. Violas, pouring down like honey.

"I just might arrive on the 28th," Uri concluded.
"Here's looking at you." He dissolved into dots of phosphor snow. Gemma had gotten sick of Uri, had even
changed majors. She really didn't have what it took to
be a journalist. So Gemma had chosen nursing. Had
gone to Neü Köln Hospice, for postgrad work and in
the trauma ward, leaving parents, friends, and even Uri
Earthside. Mandolins. Still. All the same, he had offered
good emotional support, a few years ago, when she'd
divorced.

The ritornello brought violins and violas and mandolins to a resolution, somersaulting to a happy ending.
If only life could be like good music. She got up and
stretched her back, well past her second wind.

Gemma drew her bath, waiting for the Recycle Mode
to start. She disrobed and looked at her body in the
mirror; not bad for 33. Not so good, either. She had not
done her sit-ups in ages, and was drinking too much.
Gemma closed her eyes and remembered Uri.

She sank into the hot bath, turned the water off. She
remembered something she'd entireley forgotten about;
once, at UCLA, she had arrived at Uri's apartment just
before a faculty party, and had had to use the bathroom.
Julie had told her to go ahead; she had gone in. Uri had
just been standing up in the tub and had been reaching
for the towel when she had opened the door and seen a
flash of him in the mirror.

Gemma shivered, opened her eyes. The water in the tub was tepid; she stood up, and looked in the mirror as she grabbed for the towel. She turned on the sunlamp and closed her eyes while drying; she laughed to herself. It would be exactly like Uri to come visit her when she was in a celibate phase. Her Feelgood-Counselor had reassured her that it was just a phase, that it was sometimes necessary, and would merely require forbearance.

Shivering under her comforter, she thought it might be a good idea for the Feelgood-Counselor to repeat this good news to Uri.

Marianna found herself feeling a bit better; but with 200 milligrams of apomorphine a day, *who wouldn't?*

This was Gemma's day off; and her other Nightingale, while competent, was hardly reassuring.

It had been six days since her second transfusion, and Marianna was beginning to get a bit worried.

This other Nightingale could only flit about nervously and say that Gemma would be back the next day to answer any questions Marianna had.

"All I want to know is if the transfusion took. Is that so much—?"

"—But—but—Gemma'll be here——"

"—Look, I'm sorry—but my birthday's tomorrow, and I'm expecting my folks to buzz me. I have to know one way or another."

The Nightingale injected the apomorphine. "You're late for your medication, aren't you?"

As the drug took hold and wrapped her fears in a soothing gauze, Marianna nodded. "Yes. Just worried." Then she floated off into her lucid high.

The Nightingale pressed Monitor Mode, then left.

Marianna was too raptly absorbed by the tiny dor-
mant dots on her vidfone screen to register the door
shutting.

A loud buzz and flicker of light from the Feelgood
startled Marianna, dragging her from her sleep kicking
and whimpering.

The door whooshed open and Gemma entered, trying
to project a cheerful and caring demeanor while she
fought a bad hangover. "Good morning——"

"Take that g'morning and stuff it!" Gemma was
taken aback. "I want to know what's happening, now!"

"And so do we, Marianna. If you can relax long
enough for a scan, we might be able to find out——"

"It's not working, is it? That's why Butler hasn't come
back; that's why I haven't had any visitors, isn't it?"

"You haven't had any visitors because we don't want
you to contract pneumonia." Gemma was at the console,
setting for Scan Mode.

The Feelgood whirred gently, scanned Marianna.

"Gemma, I am tired of being shunted aside, kept on
hold, given the runaround. I'm——"

"—You're sick." Gemma read the scan. "Sick, and
scared. Nobody likes being run through burning hoops,
but the odds are on your side. —Look, I went through
this . . . So did Butler, for close to two months——"

"—Next thing I know you'll tell me no one's ever died
from this no one's——"

"Marianna, I don't think you want to make yourself
a nervous wreck before your parents call."

Marianna looked at her Nightingale and fought back
the urge to vomit. "That is a free-fall-effing cheap shot."

Gemma squeezed Marianna's hand, looking at the life-line on her palm . . . unable to determine its length. "I didn't mean it to be one."

"I'm sorry—I know I use you Nightingales for punching bags."

"Don't be sorry for anything; you can't afford to be."

"Then can I have some apomorphine?" Marianna brushed a wisp of hair from her face. The entire lock of her hair simply fell. It slid down her gown. And then it landed on her blanket. Marianna was too stunned, too frightened, to do anything at all except ask for the apomorphine a second time.

After the patient had drifted off, Gemma checked the medication levels on the Feelgood. The medications for blocking menses and preventing fungal infections, okay. Antibiotics, low. Anticoagulant, low. THC, for nausea and insomnia, okay. Etcetera. Etcetera. To be on the safe side, Gemma wrote a refill for the antibiotic and anticoagulant. Most transplant clients never needed these medications for more than a week, at most. And of those who did, most of those did not need a second transplant. But Marianna—Marianna was going to Review *again*.

Marianna was riding the crest of an apomorphine high, her fear and dread rendered irrelevant, when the vidfone buzzed and an operator's voice spoke: "*Persontoperson—From Mr. and Mizzuz Wolfgang Held at Neü Köln, L4—To Marianna Held, at Titan Base—Do you accept——*"

"Yes!"

Marianna, giggling softly, turned to the vidfone as the phosphor dots began to assume shape, forming a message which read "PLEASE STAND BY FOR VIDEO PORTION."

"*Hi, Liebchen!*" That was her father's voice, as boomy as ever. She pictured him, all saltandpepper beard and bemusement, staring into a vidcam mount at his end . . . which wasn't transmitting at *her* end. "*—Me and Rebecca hope your job is working out fine.*"

There was a burst of static, and then her mother Rebecca could be heard: "*Ja! Happy birthday, Marianna!*" They began to sing, both of her parents, interrupted by static, which sounded better than they did. Marianna shook with laughter. She just knew they had a cake, that it was strawberry, her mother's favorite—not hers. Marianna hated strawberry.

Her mother started speaking again, but was interrupted by bursts of white noise. "*Karl wanted—call—but he—afraid—hangup.*"

Her father cut in, also interrupted by staticky bursts of white noise: "*I'm glad—didn't try; he—glad—didn't—your—year alimony option——*"

"*—Let's not—up that—is past——*"

Marianna was by now hiccoughing and hyperventilating from laughter, and, sighing, calmed herself. Mother and father hadn't changed a bit. She felt another burst of laughter coming on, knowing that half of it was from all the medication, and not caring either.

Then, just as suddenly, she felt utterly alone, frightened. She started to dry-heave. Too terrified to press the call button. Thinking the button might be broken. That Gemma might be with another client. That disaster might have killed all the personnel on the Base. Leaving her stranded. Sealed in a sickbay.

Her father's voice brought her back. "*Well, we've*

bored you enough, baby. So. I'm going to press the button, and we'll eat some of this cake while we wait for your answer."

They were done with the cake by now, Marianna was certain.

"*Oh yes. You should have been here for Oktoberfest— best we've ever had!*"

The "PLEASE STAND BY . . ." message imploded into a receding pinpoint. The voice of the operator came on:

"*If you'd like a response transmitted, say so. You have the option of erasing and starting over at any time, with only a 5% surcharge.*"

"Yes." Marianna hoped she would not regret it. Trying to compose herself, she turned to face the vidcam mount on her phone. "Hi, Mom and Dad . . . I don't want you to worry—I've got a bad case of influenza . . . there's a bit going around—My job's great—My supervisor, Andrea Butler, is just super—I'm getting to know all sorts of people—" Marianna tried to choke back the welling tears, took a deep breath.

"—Erase, please."

The operator came on, audio only: "*Repeat that——*"

"—Erase! ERASE!"

Marianna pressed the Call-button—but the Feelgood had beaten her to the punch, notifying Gemma the instant Marianna had started screaming.

The doors opened and Gemma entered, syringe loaded.

"Time for your shot. Sorry. I got tied up."

The injection done with, Gemma wiped the sweat from Marianna's brow . . . waited for her to calm down, to nod off.

Gemma's pager began screeching, so she rushed from the sickbay.

After several moments the operator came back on: "*Would you like to try that return call again?*"

It was another operator. This one was blonde.

Marianna said Yes, and proceeded to give a command performance for her parents' sake.

A faceless man entered Marianna's room that evening and climbed onto the bed. She observed him in dread fascination; was surprised by his lack of body odor . . . he was doing everything to excite her other senses. She felt as though they were melting into each other. A wonderful sensual ablution, being swallowed by a sort of lunar passion. She felt a wet-on. Coming on. It was so terrific that she began to dread the bubbles bursting inside her head, carrying her with them as they surged to consciousness.

She awoke. Still swaying into the rhythms. Her palm and wrist-bone rubbing against her. She felt a wetness and oozing. And, raising her hand, found blood.

It couldn't be!

They had given her medication to stop that. God, not that.

The Feelgood ran a scan on her. And, sensing the urgency of her problem, notified the grave-shift.

The next morning Gemma was at the Nightingale Station reading memos and savoring her first cup of coffee when the head grave-shift Nightingale sat down next to her. "Gemma, we nearly lost Marianna last night."

"What—?!" Gemma spilled her coffee.

"She's okay for now, but she lost a lot of blood."

"How?" Gemma reached for the paper towels.

"The Norlutate suction hose was corroded."

"The Feelgoods are idiot-proof." Then, catching herself: "I know, I should have checked it."

"You did . . . last week." The Nightingale coughed, then went on. "I think we should transfer Marianna Held to the Terminal. She's developing a liver infection."

Gemma and the Feelgood, now overhauled, accompanied Marianna aboard the tube shuttle, which was crowded. A muffled roar startled Marianna. "What was that?"

"Laser excavators working on the southeast dome."

"Isn't that where the accident was?"

"No. It was in the industrial unit."

"Gemma, can I have a cigarette?"

"I shouldn't." Gemma retrieved a No-Tar and a lighter from her satchel. "But. . . ." She stuck the cigarette in Marianna's mouth and lit it.

Marianna puffed on it, eagerly. "Thanks."

The shuttle came to a stop. The doors opened. People left. People boarded. Two men entered and sat near Gemma and the Feelgood. One of them turned to Gemma. "Excuse me, Ms., but this *is* the No-Smoke section."

"I'm sorry." Gemma turned to Marianna. "I hate to tell you, but you've got to——"

The men sitting by Gemma turned and recognized Marianna.

And she recognized them.

They'd been aboard the spacetug *Popol Vuh* together. The man who'd protested to Gemma changed his mind: "No bother. Forget it."

The other one muttered: "She must be going to Terminal."

Gemma and Marianna heard him. Gemma reached for Marianna's hand, squeezed it.

Assuming a deep and gruff voice Marianna spoke up: "*I've been here before, they got this system down pat.*"

The two men turned red and proceeded to do everything to ignore Marianna:

They spoke of the weather, nervously, back on Earth. . . .

They spoke of sports matches, fidgeting. . . .

They perused the Tri-D ads above the opposite seat.

The advert flashed, fading from capital letters to lower case. *SMOKE sKmOoOkLe kool.*

The two men got off at the very next stop.

Gemma spoke: "You know them, don't you?"

Marianna sighed. "I can't say I really blame them. I'd probably do the same thing in their position."

The suite in the Terminal was much larger than in the sickbay. Gemma checked Marianna in, set up the Feelgood, gave her her medication, and left her to sleep.

The next morning Marianna got to meet the Ground Round Kid. He was to be her roommate, as a laser cannon blast the day before had injured several people, making bed space for new patients a priority. Marianna had laughed when Gemma had told her that it was corporation policy to call transplant cases "clients", and other injured or ill people "patients."

It seemed a bit odd that they had stuck the Ground Round Kid with her, but when she got a good look at him during his dressing change she knew why.

After the Nightingale had left she spoke to him:

"I guess they're sticking all us rotting veggies together."

By way of reply, the Ground Round Kid groaned. He reminded Marianna of what a physiology prof in college had said about thresholds of pain, that at a certain point the mind just lost consciousness, unable to assimilate any further pain. He should have met the Ground Round Kid.

Gemma had told her that she found the nickname gruesome and cruel, distasteful.

Marianna agreed, up to a point. But she also found it to be apt.

That afternoon, or evening, Marianna dreamed of the Ground Round Kid: She saw his body from the waist up as a peeling onion skin, the third-degree burns and blisters covering every centimeter, all features burned, singed, eyes gone, lips gone, ears, nose, hair and follicles all gone. As the dream continued, a Nightingale ran the Feelgood over him, cleansing and debriding, cutting the dead tissue and opening the blisters, sonically bathing and drying him. She marvelled at his penectomy, covered with surgical dressing. Then the Feelgood sprayed him hourly with solution, removing and then replacing the dressing.

Marianna awoke to find the Nightingale again tending to the Ground Round Kid. Propping herself up, she watched. The Nightingale was taking something from a laboratory dish and spreading it onto the Ground Round Kid's burns, at which point the Feelgood would run a waldo back and forth over it, obscuring Marianna's view.

Finally, she had to know: "What are you doing to him?"

"Skin grafting." The Nightingale turned to her for

just a moment. "We've had to clone his healthy tissue to cover up the worst burns. Only problem is, he's burnt bad all over. We've only been able to work with tissue from the bottom of his toes. I feel like an American pioneer at a quilting bee." Then: "We had to wrap him in cadaver skins for weeks."

"But," Marianna wondered, "doesn't skin have *two* layers?"

"The trick's to do split-thickness, using dermis along with the epidermis."

"My name's Marianna. What's yours?"

The Nightingale answered without looking up. "Lisa."

Marianna, feeling slighted, let herself fall back down to her pillow. Lisa set the Kid's Feelgood on Monitor Mode and started to leave. "Excuse me, but what's his real name?"

"Yusin. He's from Free Palestine, L2."

Marianna shivered. "D'you know when Gemma will be back?"

"She's pulling duty in the other wing. She might be back here tomorrow; your medication's programmed."

"But——"

"If you have to talk anything out, or need anything, just let me know." Lisa's pager screeched. "Bye. Duty calls."

The Ground Round Kid's whimperings alarmed Marianna, but after her medication she calmed down and slept to the lullaby of his sufferings.

And I thought I had it bad.

Marianna woke up the next day feeling a bit better. She was ready for a big breakfast, until she remembered her I.V. She then looked at the Ground Round Kid, and a thought occurred to her.

"You can hear me, can't you?" No response from him. She coughed and caught her breath. "If you can hear me, nod once."

He nodded.

She thought of another question: "Do you mind being called the Ground Round Kid?" No response. "Do you—? One nod for no, two for yes." He nodded twice. "Okay, Yusin."

The door opened and Lisa entered, carrying a tray. "How are you doing?"

"Okay."

Lisa went to her patient's console, set dials, and then punched in a program. "Did he keep you up last night?"

"No." Then: "By the way, 'Yusin' is the name he prefers. He doesn't like 'Ground Round Kid.' Not one bit."

Lisa smiled condescendingly. "You talked to him——"

"He can nod. Twice for yes, once for no."

Lisa looked up from her console. "You sure?"

"*Look* at him if you don't believe me!"

Lisa turned and saw her patient nod twice, slowly. Deliberately.

"You're the first person to get a response from him. The scans didn't show brain damage, but we hadn't gotten any responses. We figured he was in some mental shock."

"You just weren't asking the right questions."

"Apparently not." Lisa punched a few more instructions into the Feelgood program.

"You running more tests?"

"Actually, he's having surgery—prosthetic and cosmetic."

"I thought you had written Yusin off."

238 R. V. Branham

"It's been touch and go, but he hasn't had any major infections, and the grafts are taking." Lisa pushed another button and curtains were drawn around her and Yusin. "Besides, his union's paying all the bills." Marianna could see the Feelgood hover into postion above Yusin, whir and bleep softly as it commenced.

"What sort of surgery is it?"

"Fiber optic implantation . . . better to be myopic and color-blind than no vision at all."

Marianna considered Lisa's answer, mulled it over. After a while she dozed off.

That evening, while Marianna slept, Gemma managed to knock an hour off her shift in the other wing and came to see her. She was surprised to find Lisa still at work, running the Feelgood over Yusin. "How's Marianna doing?"

"Holding. Did you hear about her getting through to the Ground Rou—" Then, catching herself: "Getting through to Yusin?"

"No." Gemma paused. "Someone said something about Yusin, but I was too distracted to listen." She checked the Feelgood console, looking at the spiral blips and bleeps of Marianna's vital signs. Gemma fought an oncoming yawn, lost.

"You should go to bed, Gemma. These double shifts are the double shits."

Gemma laughed. Then punched Monitor Mode. "G'night, Lisa." She left.

Half an hour later, Marianna's vital signs went haywire. Lisa rushed to the console, and, seeing the problem, phoned the other wing for a Feelgood respirator-attachment.

Gemma stopped in a bar. She ordered a drink and

went to a booth. In a nearby booth was Butler, sulking. *Over what?*

Butler looked up and saw her.

"Gemma! There's room over here!"

Gemma could tell by her expression that she didn't want to talk, not really. Butler just wanted someone to silently suck some psychic energy from . . . what else did administrators ever want? Well, Gemma had a question or two to ask Butler. She knew that Butler would not like the question—a question she'd been wanting to ask Butler for a few days now, though it seemed like weeks. Like months. Years. Like forever. It would be a shitty question, but, unasked, it festered inside Gemma. Sharing the misery would lessen the pain.

Gemma sat. Facing Butler. "What happened to the Client Review Board Appeal for Marianna Held—?"

"Don't ask that." Butler winced, turned away. "I knew you'd ask that——"

"And you also know Marianna hasn't the chance of a snowball in a cyclotron without at least one or two more transplants!"

"Look. It was the Bottom Line."

Gemma counted to ten. "I could've sworn this is about a human being. Marianna Held. Now the term's 'Profit Margin'?"

"The vote was 3 to 2 against," Butler pleaded. "I voted for—she's a good statistician—But you know about Review Boards."

Gemma wanted to throw her empty glass into Butler's face; Butler knew her mother had died when a review board postponed her liver transplant. "I'm sorry, Gemma, I didn't mean it that way. We have all lost someone who couldn't get approval for a transplant. I lost an uncle. . . ."

Maybe, Gemma thought, I should make her *eat* this glass.

Three days later, when Marianna came to, Gemma was with her. "I hate to tell you this, but we have to cut back your apomorphine dosage. There's. Another. Shortage."

Marianna was looking toward Yusin's bed. Empty. "Where's Yusin?"

"Puttering around in an airchair—he'll be back soon."

Marianna looked relieved. "The thing I hated about the other wing was being alone with that damn Feel good . . . not that Yusin is a better conversationalist!"

Gemma laughed. "They considered moving him; thought he'd bother you. Then Lisa gave her report." She looked at Marianna. With affection. With concern. At her burning blue eyes. Tried to smile. "It's been real close the last few days," Gemma said. "We almost lost you when your liver acted up."

"I'm going to die soon, aren't I?"

Gemma paused, for just a moment. "I'm not going to lie to you—it doesn't look good at all. Your chances of pulling through are very, very slim."

Marianna began to cry, her shoulders racked with fear and exhaustion. "I'm so scared."

Gemma tried comforting her best as she could. The doors opened, and Marianna sat up, trying to compose herself, to put a bright face on.

Yusin entered in his faintly whirring airchair. Lisa followed him.

He approached Marianna, attempted a smile.

Marianna was shocked at the changes the Feelgood and Lisa had wrought. He had eyes—hazel—and ears, and a bandaged nub of a nose. "Glad to see you getting better." She was glad for him and at the same time more than a little resentful. He nodded.

Lisa cheerfully announced: "He'll be out in no time." Gemma glared at Lisa. Lisa, realizing her mistake, tried to make amends. "How're you feeling, Marianna?"

"No better. But no worse."

Gemma spoke to Lisa: "Don't you think Yusin should get back into bed?"

"Quite right." Lisa took Yusin to his bed and with help from the Feelgood, set him into it, nice and blanketed.

That night Marianna began to go under. The Feelgood went into action, buzzed the Nightingale's pager, and, ministering to Marianna, made a laserscalpel incision in her trachea to allow breathing. Marianna screamed silently in agony, unheard, unsensed.

The Nightingale entered, rushing to the Feelgood console and punching in an order for apomorphine. The console replied:

"NIGHTINGALE'S ORDERS, NO APOMOR-PHINE."

She pressed Override Program, and the Feelgood administered the apomorphine through Marianna's catheter.

Marianna felt that surge again, and accepted it, calmly and quietly. She rode the solipsistic crest, objectified, yet frightened of the yawning maw of oblivion.

The Nightingale looked at the vital sign monitors in horror. The bouncing lines flattened into a horizontal green plain, the bleeps turned into hushed white noise.

Gemma stormed into the room—stopped in her tracks at the sight of the Feelgood covering Marianna's face with a bedsheet. She turned on the Nightingale: "What happened?"

"The client expired. . . ."

Gemma tried to calm herself. "I can see that."

"I punched Override, gave the client apomorphine, and she went into shock and expired."

"You *what*—?!" Gemma teetered on the verge of losing control.

"—It was at my discretion—I was trying to save her life."

Gemma took a very deep breath. Let it go very slowly. Then took another one. The Nightingale shut the Feelgood down. "By the way, I was wondering if you might write me a letter of recommendation——"

"You *stupid*—" That was much too much. Gemma lunged at her. "Stupid bitch! Goddamn cunt!" She had her hands on the Nightingale's windpipe, squeezing inexorably, full throttle. Suddenly, Yusin's Feelgood, hovering behind Gemma, injected her with apomorphine.

Marianna was embalmed and sent on the next outbound shuttle to the spacetug *Popol Vuh,* which now had full radiation shielding. She was to be transported to her parents at Neü Köln for burial. Also aboard was Gemma, who, having resigned, had been given a year's severance pay and three of her five company shares. Yusin was in the small sickbay, being transferred L-side for further surgery.

Things will be different L-side. Gemma repeated this to herself, also the fact that she would not be on Titan Base to welcome Uri. Relax, she told herself, it's a long haul.

A Day in the Life
by
Christopher Ewart

About the Author

Life is full of little surprises, as the characters in this story learn. It's a Fourth Quarter finalist, it has a certain air about it, and its author, we discovered over the trans-Atlantic telephone, has been accepted for admission to Edinburgh University, where he will study law. He is currently busy writing his high school dissertation on playwright Samuel Beckett.

Writing for publication as Christopher Ewart, he is a competition debater, has completed a tour in an anti-smoking play, and is taking a short course in creative drama. He has a strong interest in music. (His hero in that respect is Prince.) He enjoys writing "most forms of literature," as well as reading George Orwell, Beckett, and science fiction.

His entry emphasizes the international scope of the Contest. He lives in Kirriemuir, in the Tayside region of Scotland, which is the home town of J.M. Barrie, author of Peter Pan. Ewart is taking into account the fact that there has already been one world-class author associated with Kirriemuir. Watch out, J.M. Barrie—life is full of little surprises. . . .

"The Cowboys'll win."

"No they won't. The Bears'll beat them into the ground."

"Oh yeah? How many games did the Bears win last year?"

"Thirty-two."

"They did not! I'll be damned if it was more than twenty."

"That's a lie. The Bears won thirty-two games last year. I keep a record."

"Where?"

"In my head."

"In that case I wouldn't put too much store by your data. Where's the case from?"

"I don't know. I can't find it."

"What do you mean you can't find it?"

"What do you mean what do I mean I can't find it? I can't find it, okay? I've searched through my pockets and I can't find it. Are you sure you gave it to me?"

"Sure I'm sure."

"Sure you're sure you're sure?"

"Shut up before I kill you."

"Please don't, George, I'm not insured."

"Andrew, you're an immature little—"

"Hey, wait! I found it!"

ESCAPE TO NEW WORLDS
OF SCIENCE FICTION
AND IMAGINATIVE FANTASY IN
WRITERS OF THE FUTURE
—VOLUMES ONE AND TWO—

Read the award winning stories selected by Robert Silverberg,
Theodore Sturgeon, C.L. Moore, Algis Budrys, Gregory Benford,
Stephen Goldin, Jack Williamson, Roger Zelazny, Frank Herbert,
Anne McCaffrey, Larry Niven, Jerry Pournelle, Frederik Pohl and
Gene Wolfe in "Writers of the Future" (Volumes One and Two!).

"...one of the best collections of new science fiction I've ever seen."
ARTHUR C. CLARKE

"These authors can all tell a story, and that is all that matters in the middle of the night." **NEW SCIENTIST**

"...recommended as literally being the best, the very best, available to the public today." **MIDWEST BOOK REVIEW**

—ORDER NOW—
MAIL THIS CARD TODAY OR CALL
Tonbridge (0732) 361 082

NEW ERA Publications UK Ltd.
P.O. Box 110,
Tonbridge
Kent TN9 2TY

"At last! Right, let's check everything off. First: are we at the right place?"

"Errrm . . . let's see . . . category number . . . date . . . address of protestor . . . blah, blah. . . . Ah! Here we are; address of suspected offender: 2695 Doris Day Block."

"Well this is Doris Day Block, and this," George leaned forward and tapped the large red numbers on the door, "is apartment 2695. Is it the right date?"

"Ermmm, August twelfth?"

"That's right; and what are the precise instructions?"

"Follow up and, if necessary, deal with complaint."

"Okay then, let's go." George reached out and pressed the buzzer located just to the left of the doorway. He was glad of his bright yellow regulation gloves, as the button, the rusty grill of the speaker beside it, and a large area of the wall, were splattered with a sticky red substance that smelled of strawberries. He held the buzzer down a good long time to make sure the occupant heard. Andrew pushed a button on his watch.

Stepping back from the wall, George confirmed that this was indeed Doris Day Block. Every spare inch of the wall was plastered with murals of the woman herself, and ancient recordings of her songs were piped throughout the corridors. It was part of a local government plan designed to raise the morale of the occupants of tenement blocks, and try to combat the ever-increasing number of suicides. However, the dreadful squawking, thought George, was more likely to drive sane people to suicide than anything.

Deciding that he might as well make use of the waiting-time, George turned to check that Andrew was in correct uniform—he was generally a sloppy dresser and a discredit to the Force. But this morning he appeared quite smart for once. There wasn't too much muck on his canary yellow boots and gloves; the white helmet with the yellow and silver lightning bolts could stand a polish, but it would do; and the yellow-and-white jumpsuit was a little creased, but overall he was dressed better than usual. George was just about to deliver his standard lecture on creased uniforms when a voice came from the speaker.

"Go away."

George and Andrew looked at each other knowingly. Another tough one!

"Ahm, excuse us Mr. . . ." George dropped his voice to a whisper. "What's his name?"

Andrew hastily unfolded the form again, replied, "Wilson."

"Mr. Wilson, we're——"

"No," interrupted Andrew, "not Mr. Wilson, Mr. Teasmaid; his name's Wilson Teasmaid."

"Mr. Teasmaid, we're from the——"

"I don't care where you're from. I pay my bills, I don't do drugs, I don't want to buy a new toilet brush, and I don't care if God *is* the best thing since the compact disc; so go away."

"I'm afraid we can't go away, Mr. Teasmaid. You see, we're from the Police Force, Illegal Dangerous Automaton Section. We have a Search/Destroy warrant here, reference number 23——"

"My hands are over my ears and I can't hear what you're saying so go away before I call the police."

Andrew shouted into the grill: "We *are* the police, you awkward old goat. And if you don't let us in, we'll shoot the door down. So there."

"How dare you use abusive language to me. I will be

sending a letter of complaint to your superior forthwith. Who is your superior?"

"I'm his superior," said George through gritted teeth, "And if you don't let us in you'll be liable to prosecution."

"All right, all right. I'll let you in. But I am making clear my protest at your totally unprofessional conduct. Wait a moment."

There was a click as the intercom was switched off. George turned to Andrew.

"For Christ's sake, Andrew, did you have to insult him? If this thing turns mucky it won't look too good on the record."

"At least I succeeded in getting us in where you didn't."

"Yeah, into trouble if I know you. Just remember that I'm your superior, so play this one cool, okay?"

"A-okay."

"Right."

They stood for a few moments, not talking, both hoping that this job would prove a simple matter. Usually getting into the home was the biggest problem, and then it was a case of confiscating or destroying the robot, and leaving. However sometimes the owners were emotionally attached to their artificial friends, and then things could get tricky. Occasionally people were quite literally attached to their robots; it wasn't too uncommon to find that someone had used a computer assembly manual to build a computer brain onto his body—indeed it was quite a useful idea. But the Government said it was illegal. And the Government paid people like Andrew and George to see that no overintelligent robots were allowed to exist, and so that's what they did. George heard the lock on the other side of the door being rattled, and steeled himself, ready to launch into his "It's more than my job's worth" routine. The door opened a crack, releasing gobs of the sticky, strawberry-smelling substance which dropped to the floor. Next it opened a further two inches and a rusty security chain was pulled taut at eye level.

"Do you have a warrant?" Wilson Teasmaid called from behind the door. George replied that yes, they did and a gnarled old hand was extended round the door, its fingernails long and filthy, the whole hand lined with the black seams that come from a lifetime of work with oil, coal or dirt. Andrew took the hand and began to pump it up and down, saying:

"How do you do Mr. Teasmaid. I'm Andrew Moore and——"

The hand was snatched back behind the door. "I was not initiating an exchange of pleasantries; I was requesting the warrant so that I can validate it."

"I'm sorry, sir, but I can't do that. You may examine it while I hold it if you wish, but it is not our policy to hand over our Search/Destroy warrants." George had too often met the person who takes the warrant to examine it, and then destroys it in order to delay the search long enough to get rid of the evidence.

"If you don't let me see the warrant, I won't let you in."

"We can let you *see* it, but not take it. Look, here it is." George held up the piece of paper to the opening in the doorway. He saw a vague silhouette as a head was edged round the door behind the document just far enough to be able to read it. There was a pause, then the head was withdrawn behind the door again.

"You've got the wrong apartment. This is 2693."

"No, it isn't, Mr. Teasmaid. It states quite clearly that this is 2695. Now——"

"It's the wrong date. Your warrant is only valid for the twelfth of August; this is the thirteenth."

"I'm afraid it's the twelfth sir—you're going to have to let us in."

"Why did you say you were here?"

"We have reason to believe, Mr. Teasmaid, that there is an illegal robot in your home. If there is, and we find it, our job is to destroy it."

"Well in that case, gentlemen, I can let you in; because I am most definitely *not* harboring an illegal robot."

George and Andrew looked at each other in surprise. This was certainly a change of attitude! The door closed, they heard the security chain being removed, and then the door was opened wide. They stepped over the threshold and Andrew pushed the same button on his watch again, and looked at its face.

"Hey!" he exclaimed. "Twenty minutes and five seconds. That's nearly a record, George. Ain't our fastest around eighteen minutes?"

"Seventeen fifty-eight I think. Ah—Mr. Teasmaid?"

"Follow me, follow me. This way." The long corridor was dimly lit and George and Andrew could barely see or hear the little man as he scuttled into the darkness at its opposite end. Andrew moved to follow him, but George laid a hand on his shoulder to restrain him.

"One of the most essential rules for survival in this game is never to go anywhere without first checking for traps."

"Then why did we come through the door without checking?"

"Pardon?"

"Why did we come through the door without checking for traps?"

"Why did we come through the door without checking?"

"Yes."

"Well . . . that's a more advanced part of your training, Cadet Moore. You needn't concern yourself with it right now."

"Yes, George."

"Now, can you see any traps?"

"Erm." A pause. "Nope, none."

"Right, then it's safe to go forward." George moved forward two paces, tripped over a tripwire, and crashed to the ground.

"But I can see a tripwire."

"Then why didn't you say so?"

"I just did."

George, still lying on the floor, drew in his breath as though he was about to shout. Then he checked himself and said slowly and quietly:

"I will say only one thing to you, Andrew, and that is this: Your chances of promotion depend on my reports. Got it?"

"Right. You want a hand up?"

"No. I can manage." George got to his feet and dusted himself down. "It's too dark in here. Andrew, have you got the flashlight?"

"Yup." Andrew took out a small heavy-duty light from his upper left-breast pocket, switched it on, and sent a beam of light streaking down the corridor. It revealed five more tripwires. Andrew whistled in admiration. "Gee, this guy means business. He sure must want to hang on to his robot."

"Andrew, give me the laser gun."

"Are you sure about that, George? Use of a firearm takes us from a Grade 1 case to a Grade 3."

"Of course I'm sure! I don't want to fall over another of those wires and besides, it doesn't have to go on the record. Teasmaid won't know about it."

"Well, if you're sure."

"Sure I'm—" George realized what he was about to say and stopped himself. From where he stood, he took careful aim and with six quick bursts of the gun severed each of the wires. He handed the laser gun back to Andrew.

"I didn't know you could shoot like that."

"There are a lot of things that you don't know, Andrew; that's why I'm your superior. Now come on and let's get this over with." George took three echoing steps forward over the plastrete floor. On the third there was a click and three darts whistled out from the wall on the left-hand side of the corridor. One at head height bounced off his helmet, one at ankle-level struck his foot and fell out, and a third lodged itself firmly in George's upper thigh.

"Christ! This guy is beginning to be a pain in the ass." George yanked the dart from his thigh and held it to his nose. "Yep, it's poisoned all right. I hope you remembered to bring the poison kit."

"I think I did. Let's see." Andrew reached into his lower right-breast pocket, rummaged around, and withdrew a small cube-shaped object. Meanwhile George's knees gave way and he slid to the floor, dropping the dart. Andrew picked up the dart, slid back a panel on the poison kit and inserted the tip of the dart into it, saying: "I wonder if the poison's fatal. It probably will be. I mean, the guy's not going to shoot you full of darts

Illustrated by Bob Eggleton

and have you live to tell the tale, is he? I suppose what really matters is how fast-acting it is, and if the P. kit can come up with the antidote fast enough. It certainly seems to be a quick poison, anyway."

George was now moaning and rolling around the floor clutching his chest. There was a bleep from the poison kit and a message appeared on a blue screen on its surface. Andrew withdrew the dart.

"A-ha. The poison is Pentoxin 235-B and you've got two-and-a-half minutes from contact point to death. I'd better get it going with the antidote in that case. Oh damn, I've forgotten the code for antidote production. I can remember it starts with 276, but what comes after that? I'll try 8; I think it was a high number."

Andrew keyed the number in and the kit made a raspberry sound. "Hmm, that wasn't it, I'll try 9." Andrew keyed in another number and this time the device emitted a contented, gurgling bleep and began to make soft clicking sounds. "That's it! I got it right!" He looked down at George, whose whole body was jerking spasmodically. "Gosh, I sure hope it gets it done on time. I never had to deal with a death before, I wouldn't know the procedure. . . . I suppose I'd better get the syringe ready."

Andrew slid back another panel on the kit and took out a small syringe from the compartment beneath. Just then the kit bleeped again and dispensed a small red capsule into Andrew's hand. Andrew popped the capsule into the syringe and approached George, who had been jerking less and less and now looked close to death. With a quick jab to George's rear end Andrew administered the antidote. The spasms stopped almost immediately and Andrew was amazed that it had taken effect so quickly. Then a slow horror dawned on him. George wasn't moving at all. He had been too late! George was dead!

"Well you sure cut that one a bit short, Andrew."

"Oh. I thought you were dead."

"Thought? Or hoped?"

"Are you all right?"

"Yes, I'm fine now. The only problem is; how do we make sure this doesn't happen again?"

"What triggered off the darts?"

"I think it was my weight on a part of the floor. Maybe we should test the rest of the floor."

"What with? Have we got anything heavy enough?"

"How about you?"

"How about you?"

"How about the P. kit?"

"Is it heavy enough?"

"I think so."

"What if it gets damaged?"

"We'll go gently. And anyway, I'd rather it got damaged than me."

"Yes, but if you get damaged and it's damaged it won't be able to fix you."

"I'd rather damage it and not get myself damaged at all, thank you very much. Now, let's go."

And so they made their way down the corridor, foot by foot, placing the compact box onto the floor in front of them and advancing cautiously forward. Five more times they started as three darts sliced out of compartments on the left and clattered harmlessly against the wall opposite. Eventually there was just four feet of floor between them and the door at the end. The P. kit was by now very battered at the edges.

"Will we risk it, George? Six tripwires, six sets of darts: it should be safe. The P. kit won't take much more."

"Andrew, what is the first rule of survival?"

"Never shoot yourself in the head?"

"No, that's the third rule. The first rule for staying alive is never take unnecessary risks. Now give me the kit." George took the kit from Andrew and tossed it onto the floor just in front of their feet. There was a click; a barrage of darts shot out from both sides of the corridor and another rained down from the roof; a mesh of laser beams criss-crossed the area from the floor to the roof, sizzling a network of scars into the walls; a four-foot-square section of the ceiling, a foot thick, slammed down onto the floor three times by means of a pneumatic arm and was withdrawn back into the ceiling; three steel plates with razor edges slid sharply out of three different horizontal slots in the walls and withdrew. The laser beams disappeared and there was silence. The P. kit lay crushed, mangled and charred in a heap of poisoned darts. George pointed to it.

"That," he said, "could have been you."

"I gotta admit you were right this time," conceded Andrew, and he reached forward to pick up the P. kit. As he did so the four foot section of floor slid back and the P. kit, along with the darts, was dropped into a deep vat of acid below. There was a fizzling sound and clouds of fumes began to be given off as the section of floor slid back again. The door in front of George and Andrew opened a crack, and a frail old bespectacled head, lined with years and covered with a smattering of clear white hair, was poked around it. Wilson Teasmaid smiled.

"Gentlemen, what took you so long? Come in, come

in." He opened the door wide and stood there in a
black-and-white jumpsuit, waiting for them to come in.

Andrew advanced a careful toe onto the floor in
front of him, and eased his weight down on it. Nothing
happened. He jumped through the doorway and George
followed quickly, Teasmaid closing the door behind
them.

The room was large, with white decor and black
furniture. Teasmaid sat down in an armchair and motioned George and Andrew to sit down on a couch
opposite. Andrew was about to sit down when George
stopped him and pointed to the cushions and the couch.
Out of each stuck the point of a dart.

"We'll stand, thank you, sir," said Andrew politely.
"Now——"

"About this investigation, Mr. Teasmaid," interrupted George. "Our scanners have indicated that you
have a robot which has an intelligence above the legal
safty limit in your home. Do you comfirm or deny this
charge?"

"I have, as you well know, already denied it."

Andrew exclaimed: "Do you also deny the charge
that you attempted to poison, incinerate, slice and dis-
solve two police investigators?"

"I don't know what you mean." The old man looked
blank.

"Excuse us a moment," said George to Teasmaid, and
he took Andrew by the arm to the other side of the
room. "Look, Andrew, we want this case to be as quick
and as clean as possible, right?"

"Right."

"So don't antagonize the guy. The only goods we
need on him is the robot. We don't want him to have any
complaints against us, like false accusations."

"But he tried to kill us!"

"Can you prove that?"

"No."

"Then shut up and let me do the talking." George walked back toward the armchair where Teasmaid was sitting pretending not to have been listening. "Sir, the procedure is very simple. I have a device which will tell me if there's an illegal robot in your home, and if so exactly where it is."

"Very well, if you insist on being so official."

At no apparent signal, a panel in the wall behind George slid up and what looked like a tray on wheels carrying a percolator, a jug of cream, a bowl of sugar and three mugs with spoons trundled through the opening and came to a stop between George and Teasmaid. "But do let me offer you a cup of coffee."

"I'm sorry sir, but we're not allowed——"

"Oh, I insist. Tell me, just how intelligent does a robot have to be to qualify as illegal? I have made several robots for my own personal use, but I am not aware that any of them are illegal." The coffee trolley had extended a pair of arms and was pouring the coffee.

"A robot is a danger to the state, and to humanity, if it is intelligent. That is if it can carry out analyses, draw conclusions and act on them when they are not clearcut. And if it can augment its original programming. Such a robot could easily become very powerful—too powerful. Thank you." George took the mug which was extended to him by the trolley and swallowed a mouthful. "Mmm, two sugars. Just the way I like it."

"But George, we're not supposed to—" Andrew started forward.

"Don't worry, Andrew. Drink your coffee and enjoy it." George seemed very calm and at ease. "This is good coffee, Mr. Teasmaid. What brand is it?"

"Brazilio. It is good, isn't it."

Teasmaid drank some coffee. George leaped over, smashed the mug from Andrew's lips just as he was about to take a drink, grabbed the laser gun out of his pocket and fired a long, continuous burst into the trolley. The trolley exploded. Wilson Teasmaid collapsed, choking, onto the floor and died. George clutched his stomach and sat down heavily on the floor. Andrew leaned over him, in a panic.

"George! What . . . ? Why . . . ? How was . . . ?"

"My training, Andrew . . . didn't let me down . . . the coffee machine . . . acting too intelligently . . . instinct . . . knew it was the . . . robot. Teasmaid probably . . . told it to poison our drinks . . . only it did his, too . . . megalomania . . . affects all clever robots . . . ugh!" George's face contorted as the poison took effect.

"But why did you drink the coffee? Didn't you know it was poisoned? Isn't detecting food poison through aroma part of advanced training?"

"Yes . . . knew it was poisoned . . . had to keep Teasmaid . . . off his guard. Now . . . I'll never know who wins the game."

"It'll be the Cowboys, George, it'll be the Cowboys. They're the better team. I know that now." A tear trickled down Andrew's face.

"Good," said George. "I'm glad to hear you admit that." He stood up and handed the gun back to Andrew. "Did you really think I'd drink that coffee if I knew it was gonna kill me? I only pretended to drink it. I just wanted to hear you admit that the Cowboys are the better team. Now let's get moving; our next case is scheduled for half an hour from now and it's the other side of town. We'll have to hurry." George set off back down the corridor, leaving Andrew kneeling on the floor.

"Hey, George!"

"Yeah?"

"You really had me fooled there—I mean with drinking the coffee and acting cool and all."

"All in a day's work, Andrew. You've got a lot to learn."

"I guess so," said Andrew to himself. He stood up, dusted himself down, and followed George out of the apartment.

Old Mickey Flip Had a Marvelous Ship
by
Lori Ann White

About the Author

Lori Ann White was sent to the Clarion workshop some years ago by the "Moscow Moffia" of Moscow, Idaho—the writing club to which W.O.T.F. writers Nina Kiriki Hoffman, Dean Smith, John Gustafson and Marianne Nielsen also belong. The Moffia has a rigorous workshopping program, and then raises funds for formal tuition when a member's considered ready. In our eyes, it's a model for how to do it.

Then in early 1986, Lori was one of a small group of W.O.T.F. winners and high finalists at our first invitational workshop. We used L. Ron Hubbard how-to articles from writers' magazines, and applied proven study techniques developed by him. Carefully gauging their results, the students and instructors participated in the first test of what we think is a major advance in teaching writers. What we did not know at the time was that Lori's most recent Contest entry was simultaneously being judged a winner.

She is in her twenties, has acted in college theater, and currently lives in Oregon, where she continues to produce further work. It's a real pleasure to have been watching her talent come into its first flower, and to know it will continue. As for where she was in the second Quarter of 1986, here's the story. . . .

When the cold, thin-edged voice interrupted Eli Golden's concentration, he was squatting on a futon in a Port Security waiting room, with his arms akimbo and his head between his knees. He was watching the carpet and waiting for it to move.

"The ship will speak with you now, young Free-Sir Golden." The voice was followed by two square-toed boots that stepped into his circle of vision and drew his gaze up the armored body of a PortSec guard. He stopped to examine his reflection in the guard's chest plate. It ballooned and dipped crazily in the shock dimples, picked up an oily black sheen from the reflective coating, and when he grimaced, his features fit together much better. Above that, the guard's face was split neatly by mirrored goggles. Both sections were equally impassive. Eli sighed.

"That's nice," he said. "What am I supposed to say to her?"

The guard allowed the corners of her mouth to curl up. "Your discretion, Free-Sir."

Eli glared at the guard, then at the floor, then at the walls of the tiny, windowless room. They did not glare back; though slick and smooth, the light stroking them was mild, and overpowered by holos floating in the corners, depicting all manner of flight: birds, shuttles, ships, stars. Eli thought them quite ironic.

"My discretion. You people are the ones who are so damned discreet. Has your Supervisor—what's her name——"

"Marcus."

"Has she even acknowledged my request for an audience?" Eli, thinking his fear showed in his voice as nothing more than petulance, shook his head and cleared his throat. "What's wrong with the ship? Why has she summoned me here? And where's her Pilot?"

"If you wish to find out, I suggest you follow me." The guard stepped back, and something in the movement (a hunching of the shoulders, a drooping chin) spoke of regret. Eli slid his feet on the floor and hurried after, before the smell of peppermint grew too cloying. Perhaps, after nearly a year of his Jaunt, he should have grown accustomed to all the strangeness on other worlds, and be able to take delight in what was yet to reach his home world of Villanel. But he could still consider the carpet as nothing more than a bio-engineered slime mold bleeding a too-strong scent onto his bare feet.

When they left the PortSec offices, Eli scuffed his feet against the cream-colored tile of the Port's main concourse as he looked around. He was allowed only a quick glance before scurrying after the guard, who was striding implacably toward a tube access.

Eli only needed one glance. The Port of Camber's Folly looked the same as it had one Standard Year before—a third-rate port on a marginally profitable trade lane. The corridor, ten meters wide but only two-thirds that in height, still arced overhead to an uncomfortably low ceiling. The walls were still blank, the air dry, warm, and devoid of character. Stolen glances to either side told him not even the faces had changed: whether male or female, Race Pure or Survival Variant,

all were emigrés who huddled against the corridor walls
and watched Eli with the same wary look, their hands
cradled protectively against their stomachs, as though
he meant to steal from them their last assets—the tickets
off-world tattooed across their palms.

Eli looked away and noticed his face again, this time
reflected on the guard's back and always receding, as
though he were being taken away from himself. In a
sudden moment of near panic, he inhaled deeply, testing
the air for an aroma that he could not find. One Standard ago, Eli had sniffed the faint cinnamon spoor of an
X-T, an extraterrestrial Patron, here in this very corridor. He had felt justified in expecting great happenings
at the Port of Camber's Folly. When they did not materialize, he had expected even greater happenings from
the rest of his Jaunt. Now he was back on the only world
where he'd even caught a hint of X-T, on the last leg of
his wandering, with no chance at an off-world calling.
Next stop: his home world, his father, his failure. It must
be enough. It would never be enough.

Unfinished business first. Eli brushed past the guard,
who had paused at the request board to notify PortTrans
that they needed a capsule. He looked back through the
open door and frowned.

"Something wrong, Free-Sir?" asked the guard.

Eli could not decide whether to shrug or shake his
head, and finally combined both into a complex movement that left him looking at a bare wall. "No, I—
I just expected to see something. But I must be
disoriented—"

At the same instant, as though choreographed by
a precise and perverse god, the buzz announcing the
tube capsule's arrival sounded in one ear while his other
ear was buffeted by a suddenly risen squall of childish

laughter. Eli turned toward the young, tuneless voices, and saw a flood of 'Course Kids spill from a cross corridor. They were the children of emigrés, abandoned at the port by parents who could not afford their tickets off-world. They ran the corridors in rowdy packs. Eli knew them, cherished their innocent cunning, and blessed the opportunity to drown himself in the energetic tide.

Even as he raised his hands to hail the children, the PortSec guard grabbed his upper arm and yanked. Eli swung around, cursing at the shock, and slammed into the guard. He ricocheted off her armor, and with the help of a neatly placed hand on his chest, tumbled backward through the open door of the tube capsule and into a seat. He came up with fists clenched and teeth bared. "What the hell do you think you're doing?" he asked, in a voice so shrill that it hurt.

The guard merely climbed in, sat opposite, and reached across the aisle to punch in their destination. Eli had one last chance to look out through the door, and his last sight before it slid neatly closed was of one particular, well-known 'Course Kid: a tall, solid girl whose eyes were wide with the sight of him and whose broad face was crumpling into tears.

The tube ride out to the Private Port was silent and tense. Eli glowered, rubbed his arm, and would not look at the guard. He stared out at the tube walls blurring by, and let them provide a screen for past follies and future fears. Included in both those categories was the summons that had brought him back to Camber's Folly. It had been in the name of both the ship, X-T-H Skimmer the *Seventh Veil*, and her Pilot, Mickey Flip, but he was certain neither of them had worded the transmission. Cold and efficient, it simply had asked him to come. He could not refuse their names. And besides, it only took a very small detour to get to Camber's Folly from his planned route home. Hunched in the capsule, Eli closed his eyes.

Upon arrival, he had been politely but persistently "escorted" to the PortSec offices, told nothing, and left in the waiting room with the smelly carpet. And now he was tubing toward the Private Port, toward his interview with the ship like a pulse across a synapse, on its way to change a thought forever.

Eli and the guard disembarked at the Private Port, which was smaller and more comfortable than the main port; the carpet in the single Security room was synthetic and Eli could look the foyer attendant in the eye. The guard showed something to the attendant, who smiled at Eli and said, "Come with me, now, Free-Sir." Eli did, simply glad to get away from his own face. Though he was as appreciative as any woman of his honey-colored hair and his long-lashed hazel eyes, the distorted reflection peering back at him from the guard's armor made the skin on his back itch. As she walked away, though, Eli could not shake the feeling that she took some part of him with her, and he could not think of how to get it back.

"Wait," he called, and cleared his throat. She turned around, straight, tall, a meter-thick wall of polished steel. "You said the ship would see me," he said softly. "Won't the old man be there, too?"

"No," said the guard, speaking as softly. "No, he's not there anymore."

She turned away. "But, wait—" The door hissed shut behind her. Eli stared at the door, then dragged in a great, convulsive breath. "Take me to the ship, then," he said, and the solemn attendant nodded. He led Eli through another door at the end of the long room. As

they walked by, Eli caught glimpses of other rooms to
either side, offices decorated in what he'd always called
"natural" colors, though from what he knew of the
planet's surface the sedate browns and grays had nothing to do with the bubbling, fiery reds just past the
Port's walls.

The attendant led Eli to the P-Port hub (crystal,
flashing on twilight-blue ceilings) where a private guard,
looking familiar and friendly in a simple cloth jumpsuit,
ushered him down a spoke toward the berth of Mickey
Flip's ship.

Another P-Port guard stood at the entry lock of the
Seventh Veil. And Mickey was a beggar, Eli could not
stop himself from thinking. He shook his head. The old
man had an X-T Patron who provided a Skimmer ship,
and yet he had to beg in the corridors.

The new guard was an experienced hand-eye-voice
man who would not clear Eli until all prints checked.
Then he waved the boy into the tiny airlock. It cycled;
the *Seventh Veil* stayed always space-ready, though
Mickey could never qualify to lift her again. The guard
shooed Eli on with a hand-wave at the outer view port;
his audience was to be private, then. Eli waved back.

As soon as the inner door hissed open, he scooted
through, over the catwalk, and onto the webbing that
enveloped the entire inner sphere of the ship. The zero-
gee webbing was not safe in gee land, but that had never
fazed Mickey the experienced pilot, so Eli gritted
his teeth and crab-scuttled his way up the curving under-
belly of the *Seventh Veil* until he found a hatch and let
himself into one of the two tiny staterooms. It was
sparsely furnished; Eli could not guess if he had entered
Mickey's room or the spare. Situated on the ship's top
hemisphere, the stateroom curved upward, narrowing.

It was shaped much like a flaring pie-slice, as were all
the compartments not part of the great circles around
the ship's body. The great circles themselves were the
exercise track and the hydroponics section. All the tips
of the compartments formed the central command core.
Eli decided to wait until he reached it before talking to
the ship. He needed every drawn-out moment to choose
his first words.

The door to the command core hissed open, and he
pulled himself up. With a last shimmy, he was all the
way inside. Eli thought of old man Mickey doing this,
day after day, and then wondered sadly how long he
would cling to such pieces of his past life. He gained a
foothold on the nearest strut and hoisted himself into
the command chair. At least gimbals kept it level at all
times.

"The *Seventh Veil*," Eli called softly. His heart
thumped in a painfully syncopated beat. "Sevvy, come
talk to me. Tell me why you called me here."

A long moment passed, divided into many misgiv-
ings, before the ship finally answered. "This is X-T-H
Skimmer the *Seventh Veil*, of the port of Camber's Folly,
responding to query. Please give current legal
identification—"

An instant's pause, and, "File-search shows—" was
interrupted by a low cry that throbbed from all six
speakers. "Eli. Oh, Eli, you're more welcome than any
new world the Rim may hold. I was so afraid you
wouldn't come."

Eli covered his eyes with one palm, in part to let her
mellow voice sweep over him from all sides, in part to
hide the stinging tears. Her monitors were ever efficient.
"I'm only sorry I took so long. Your message has been
chasing me for three worlds' worth of Jaunt. What

happened? Where's Mickey? What's the secret? PortSec wouldn't say a word."

The ship's voice wavered, gained ugly mechanical tones as her emotional analogues threatened to overload and cut out. "It's horrible, Eli. Mickey is dead."

Eli flinched.

"But that's not all. He was murdered, Eli. Murdered. And the Port Authority is accusing me. I could be shut off, Eli. I could die."

Even an Eli Golden newly lifted from Villanel had been able to take in the port of Camber's Folly and sum up the interests and wonders it held for him: none. There was nothing out on the surface. That was why it had never been terraformed in the first place. No self-made men or First Family members from any Homeworld ever came here, so the entertainments and organized vices were practically nonexistent. There were also no special accommodations for other Races, so Eli doubted the opportunity to ogle a Graftling or a Spenser's Pharisee would arise. So much for the major chances at a little diversion.

Camber's Folly was a place to make connections. That was all. But must it take a whole day before his ship to Bombilay was ready to depart? He only had a Standard Year for his Jaunt. He hated the thought of wasting time.

Perhaps he should just go back to his rooms and study the planets on his itinerary. He must be prepared. If he was reduced to using his father's money for this Jaunt, he'd better purchase something memorable with it.

A faint, sharp cinnamon smell cut through the dead air and stopped Eli in his tracks. He swung around, nostrils flaring, as he tried to determine the direction the smell came from.

There. Out of that side corridor. Eli drifted nonchalantly across the prime corridor, his feet whispering over the cold tiles. Men and women noticed his round face, his simple but well-made clothes, and smiled at him as they brushed closely past. Eli ignored them. He had a purpose, now.

He stopped to casually look over the sign at the mouth of the cross corridor. BEGGING STATIONS, read the legend, and the arrow pointed—the way he was going. He followed, trying to still his excitement, wondering what an X-T was doing in this Godforsaken port, praying to round the next bend and meet the Patron, which would immediately make its inexplicable choice—him. Then Eli would never have to return to Villanel again. He would learn the Flip, and take a Skimmer of his own to the Rim, and find worlds of such riches —

A pack of 'Course Kids be-bopped past, jostling Eli's elbows and making him lose his place in his daydream. Their ebullience made a loud contrast to the wise, aware faces of the watchful beggars poised above hats, bowls, and more modern 'Course Credit changers lining the corridor walls. Eli tried to ignore the Kids, thinking as he did that he was following his nose toward his certain destiny, but they surrounded him and swept him this way and that, in a waist-high wave of bodies. Kittenish Apocalypse.

The Kids flooded with Eli in their midst toward a particular unfrequented beggar-bubble, and he balked. He was more than tired of feeling like a bit of plankton here or at home or anywhere. He tried to stop and watch a woman from—probably Balloon, Eli decided. Her bubble encompassed a personal environment as well as a damper field, and she did her low-gee tricks with a certain flair he found intriguing. He applauded as she pleated her body like a paper fan, and turned toward the nearest wall access to exchange some Credits for Beggar Chits.

The Kids cut him off. "No, Free-Sir," they chorused, a dozen shrill voices reaching for a harmony. "Come with us. We know something you'll like a lot better."

Eli looked back at the woman, who caught his eye and shrugged. The boy swallowed; the slow smile she gave him next was a sensuous gift that turned her from a clever and flexible cartilaginous body into a warm, impish woman, and he felt a sudden queasiness rise from the pit of his stomach. He swallowed it back down. "Villanel," he murmured. "It's just off the beaten track, is all. I'm getting away."

The Kids grinned gap-toothed grins at him. "This way," said the tallest girl, blunt-faced and loud. "You'll like this lots better. Mickey's real fun to watch."

"Mickey?" echoed Eli. "Mickey who?"

A hush descended, old and reverent. "Mickey Flip," said girl. "That's who." Her hand swept up in a gesture that condemned Eli's ignorance.

In the last bubble before the corridor split to go its separate ways stood a man who looked quite authentically old. He tucked a fiddle against his shoulder as if it were the head of a child, and played with a manic tenderness that struck Eli even through the bubble's dampers. Eli did not need to hear the old man play; he need only see how Mickey's white hair flared out about his head like solar prominences, and how every line of the old man's angular body met and married with the fiddle and the bow. The Kids swept Eli along in their surf, so swiftly that Eli's first step into the deadening of the beggar bubble came as a surprise. The damper field was only two paces wide, but Eli heard a smooth increase in sound from step to step, like one of the ore transports back home swooping down. He ducked reflexively.

Nothing broke Mickey's concentration—not even Eli Golden stepping through the thin skin of his private world. Close now, Eli saw how delicate was the skin of the old man's eyelids—bluish and insubstantial, wrinkled with effort below a taut forehead. The children drew Eli that last step forward, and into a wild song; then they established themselves in a tight, elliptical orbit with the old man at one focus, Eli at the other. They joined hands and commenced a hilarious circle dance, spinning around Eli and reaching out to slap at his legs. The music was wild, but evidently familiar; the tallest girl swirled out of the dance and held up her arms. Her eyes glittered in the harsh light. At a sudden discord, both arms swept down. "Now," she cried. The children exploded into song:

"Old Mickey Flip had a marvelous ship,
In his marvelous ship Mickey sailed the sky.
Went out on a lark, came back in the dark,
And Mickey, old Mickey, he never said why."

"Why, Mickey, why? Where'd you go, what'd you find?"

"How, Mickey mine, how'd your ship make you blind?"

The music screeched to a halt, a thousand bag-cats hooking claws into a thousand skitter-mice. Eli lost his breath and could not find it again for the life of him. The old man straightened from his protective crouch

Illustrated by Greg Petan

over the fiddle and raised his face to the ceiling, letting the lights etch into his skin like the tracks of an acid spill. He shuddered, and swung his head toward Eli. He opened his eyes. Both glinted mild white, with no pupil or iris. The children sang true. The old man was blind.

"Quiet, Sev," said the boy. "Settle yourself and explain."

"The Port Authority is charging me with murder," said the ship evenly. Eli sighed. He'd rather talk to her while she was composed. But, oh, how she hated to lose her emotions.

"First question," said Eli, "and don't be upset, since it is the obvious one. Did you do it?"

"No, I did not." Eli winced at the empty voice.

"Then why do they blame you?"

"Several reasons, Eli." Her rigid vocal control gained an obsessive quality as the emotional segments of the *Seventh Veil* tried to regain ascendancy. Eli had always thought it terribly unfair that a part of her could feel, but not too deeply. "One, he did die an unnatural death," Sev continued. "He was tubing back from the beggar stations when his capsule lost a seal."

Eli pictured a hurtling capsule suddenly opening inside its tube, rebounding from the walls, exploding its contents into the vacuum, trailing a growing plume of debris that had once been something else.He thought to hide his expression, but the ship was all around him. He watched his fingers twist in his lap and hoped the old man had felt no pain.

Sev was saying: "It's a matter of Port Engineering's negligence. I'm sure of it, Eli, but they need a scapegoat. I'm the only Skimmer docked, and since we're recognized Sentients, if they can convict me they can have their culprit and not a human hurt. Except Mickey."

Eli wrapped his hands tightly around the contoured grips of the chair's arms and pulled in a deep, shuddering breath. He thought he tasted the faintest tang of X-T in the air. "Where is your Patron? Can't it just repossess you?"

"It says this is a human matter, Eli, and—" her voice cut out. Feedback whined.

"Wait a minute." Eli clapped his hands over his ears. "Sev, listen to me. Just stop thinking for a moment, and listen." The ship might show her turmoil in a different fashion, but Eli recognized all the signs. She was throwing as grand a tizzy as his mother ever had, and he must calm her down. "Why don't you throw up a nice holo on a viewscreen, any orientation, and pipe in your favorite Copeland—"

"Stewart or Aaron?" Eli let his relief trickle out in a sigh.

"Either one. Be ready for me when I get back."

"Where are you going?"

"The galley. I'm starved."

Eli slithered out of the chair and lowered himself toward the hatch as the skyline of New^2 York flicked on overhead. He grinned wryly. The damn ship was so enamored of things human. She really had no choice; as Mickey had explained the year before, it was built into her.

The Skimmer Ships were one result of a deal struck three hundred years before by the X-Ts and a quorum of Earth governments, both political and economic. The X-Ts were an old, cold, aloof race with little interest in continually exploring, expanding, staying vital. But they did not wish to succumb to resource depletion, either, and sink back to the mud of one world. So they enlisted the humans to explore for them.

The Skimmer Ships the Patrons provided set humans free. Every Standard Year the known boundaries, the Rim of pilots' boasts, widened. Humans were also quite welcome to try to plumb the principles underlying the Flip and other X-T mysteries. Thus far, the humans had had only limited success.

X-Ts seemed content to collect their tribute and observe their agents. They studied humans as well as employing them; that was part of the deal. The results of their studies were incorporated in the programming of the Skimmers, which they then gave to humans for use during the humans' lifespans. Often their choices seemed completely random.

Offer me Sev next, Eli begged an unknown X-T. Let me be a Skimmer pilot, teach me the Flip, and I'll find you more worlds than you know what to do with.

He lowered himself out of the private cabin and onto the inner-sphere netting once again. Sevvy and her kind were not very efficient in a gravity well. But that was not her rightful dwelling place, and if he had her, they would both be where they belonged. His knuckles showed as white as the cool mesh he gripped. He would be out with her, skimming the Rim, finding worlds more perfect and glittering than Villanel. And they would be rich, so rich his father would stand in shame. And Eli would leave the worlds exactly as they were.

He swung himself into the galley, too hard, and thudded against the bottom wall. All the little bones in his feet told him to slow down. Eli winced and nodded, then tried to think of something quick to eat. She should calm down soon, soothed by her human music, distracted by her man-made vistas. He wished she did not

long so ardently for the label "human" when she herself
was much more wonderful.

Eli touched a light pen to the first item on the menu
that caught his eye. The chicken breast was vat-grown
but would be succulent and well-seasoned, he knew; Sev
took as much pride in her cooking as in her quantifying.
It was part of being people.

The steaming chicken slid out and he dropped it into
a carry bag, sealed it, and slapped it on his chest for the
climb back. Grabbing a skin of wine from the reach-in
cooler, he slapped that against his tunic next to the
chicken and hoped they'd both stick. His clambering
around the sphere of the ship had left him far from the
command core and he lowered himself gingerly. Mickey
had been accustomed to such monkey-work, but Eli was
strictly a passenger, and an occasional audience for his
uncle Steven, a ship's outfitter. Mickey had known Sev
well, in all orientations.

Mickey. Eli paused, and laid his forehead against the
backs of his hands, his fingers curling around the webbing. Damn the old man anyway. Why did he die and
leave Eli with such a mess? The boy shook off the first
pain of Mickey's death. He'd held it off this long, he'd
hold it off a little longer. Long enough to tend to Sev.
He climbed.

Back in the command core, Eli lowered himself past
the bright lights of the city and into the command chair.
He rescued his wine as it peeled away. Sev held her peace.
She still listened to the music she'd chosen: Aaron, this
time. "Fanfare for the Common Man." Horns flared
out at him from the cardinal points of the cabin as Eli
strapped in. They shared the dying notes. Eli's eyes were
wet.

"I'm sorry, Eli."

"Why?"

"I should have had something ready for you when you got here. I'm sorry I've been so rude."

Eli had to laugh. "Sevvy. You've had your own worries. But now it's time to stop worrying and start thinking our way out of this one." Eli settled back and bit into his chicken. He felt calm now, and ready. And glad she'd called him. "About these charges. What exactly happened to the tube? How do they claim you rigged it?"

Sev blanked out New^2 York and replaced it with random swirls that colored Eli's supper with soft pastels—her concentrations, she called such patterns. When she spoke, her voice, though tight with pain, was calm. "They've got it all figured out. They say a charge was planted on the inside of the capsule. It blew when Mickey was about half-way down the tube." An edge cut through her voice, cut across Eli's cheeks. "Do you want to pay your last respects? He's in an urn in the upper stateroom."

"Sevvy, please." Eli dropped the chicken and it plopped on the hatch below.

"I'm sorry." The ship was as instantly contrite as she had been instantly bitter. "It was messy, and it was sudden, and I'm sorry, Eli."

"How were you supposed to have planted a charge? You'd need a human for that, or didn't PortSec notice?"

"I bribed a 'Course Kid. That's how." Her voice started losing its emotional overtones again, but not before Eli identified them as anger. "I'm convenient, Eli, and so PortSec has decided. It's just like you humans—"

"Wait," Eli cried, and flung up his hands. His wine followed the chicken, and he spared a hope it would not seep into circuits. "I don't believe them. I believe you."

The silence was impenetrable. Eli cleared the running
lights and raised normal illumination in the core. He
examined the tiny room, instrumentation crammed into
every cranny, its red, green, and amber tell-tales faded
by the incandescent wash, the largest clear spaces left the
meter-square viewscreens at the cabin's cardinal points.
Eli had often, over the past Standard Year, thought back
to Mickey's ship and tried to picture how she would
look as a woman. Sometimes he saw a slender young
girl, sometimes with long black hair. Sometimes he saw
his mother's twin. None of them ever clicked in with a
feeling of rightness. Sevvy was an alien ship. No matter
how sophisticated her analogues, no matter how much
the X-Ts had learned.

"Motive," he said.

"Anger. Frustration." A sigh whistled around him,
from speaker to speaker. The lights dimmed again. "Do
you mind?" she asked softly. "I don't want anyone to
look at me right now. Not even you."

Eli murmured something and wiped his palms over
his hair. "Were you angry? Were you frustrated?"

"Yes, and yes." In the waiting silence that followed,
Eli succumbed to an odd, quiet little fear that his pounding heart would shake him out of the command chair.
He tightened the chest straps, and as he smoothed the
crossed webbing, he watched his fingers tremble.

"I'm a Skimmer, Eli." The speakers above, behind,
and below cut out so all her voice came at him, low and
urgent, from somewhere near the level of his eyes. "I
was built to explore, to uncover, to skim across the Rim
like a flat stone over water." Eli saw a woman with her
eyes closed, sitting cross-legged on a floor and swaying
back and forth. "I'm not meant to sit in a Private Port
and serve as nothing more than an obscene little house.

I'm very patient. I can wait. But Mickey—"

"Mickey what? Wouldn't get R 'n R'd?"

"No. He would not put in for Repair and Rejuve, no matter how I tried to reason with him. And as long as he was alive, I had to stay with him." Nothing in Eli's own future had prepared him for such hopelessness, and he shuddered. "I had to stay with him" said the ship. "I had to."

"If only he hadn't been blind," offered Eli.

"No," said the *Seventh Veil*, her voice laced with acid. "If only he hadn't seen so much."

The old man's head swung away, and the bands binding Eli's throat slackened. He slumped forward and gasped. "All right," said the old man. "Tattie, front and center." His voice was big and warm—bigger than the voice of his fiddle, yet deep and soft enough to hold the most delicate subtlety. Not to mention the wildest 'Course Kid, Eli thought, as the tall, broad-faced girl was deposited in front of Mickey. He reached out surely and laid a broad hand, all knuckles and bluish veins, on her head. "Are you responsible for that dubious lyric?" the old man asked.

The girl squirmed. "Yes, Mickey."

"Do you really want your question answered?" His voice plummeted to a whisper so low she had to search the floor for her reply. She shook her head, once.

"Then don't ask." The old man spun her about and bent to give her a little encouragement with the flat of his palm, but she did not need it. The rest of the Kids followed, each shooting through the bubble with an audible pop, and when the last one scampered around the far bend, the silence felt like it did not belong.

Mickey chuckled, took a measured step back, and knelt beside his fiddle case.

"Must you put it away?"

Mickey squatted back on his heels and braced his forearms on his knees, hands dangling down between. He sucked a tooth and cocked his head, letting Eli's words mix well and settle into more expressive meanings. "Why, boy?" he finally said. "Do you really want me to play another song?"

"No," said Eli. "Not really. I can't breathe when you play. But I've never seen a fiddle close up before."

"Is that true, now?" A deadly pause, during which Eli first noticed the trickle of sweat that was making his cheek itch. The old man's face looked powder dry. Finally, Mickey shrugged and laughed. "Come look at it, then," he said. "May the fiddle strike you as breathless as its songs do."

Eli sighed, smiled, and squatted next to the wild-haired old beggar. He reached out tentative fingertips and drew them gently down the soft layer of air above the soundboard. The fiddle was beautiful, rich reds and golds, hand-rubbed, oiled with exotic oils, the swirls of the grain like glowing gas clouds that would part in the next instant to reveal—Eli drew back.

And smiled at his own foolishness.

"Shame we don't have those back on Villanel," he murmured. "I might have sat still for my music lessons if I could have played something like that."

"Touch it, boy. Hold it. Take merely as much care as with your only child, and you'll be fine." Eli clutched the fiddle as it was thrust at him, but two twanging strings warned him to ease his hands the rest of the way. An incipient frown on the beggar's face eased into a smile.

"Like that. Ah, you're good, you'll make a fine papa someday."

"How do you know I'm not one already?" asked Eli, stung by the beggar's quick knowledge. He'd always thought, if only I didn't look so young. Now, it seemed he must find something else to blame.

Mickey snorted, leaned back against the wall and raised his face to let the light pool in his eyes. Eli looked back down at the fiddle.

"What kind of wood is this?" he asked. "It's so warm."

Mickey shrugged. "Can't really say. Didn't wait around for them to name it."

That caught Eli; an incredulous suspicion sparked. He leaned forward. Old Mickey sensed the move, chuckled, and slid his fanny to the floor. "Never could sit that way for very long," he said. Eli wiggled into a more comfortable configuration, and as he scooted closer to the old man, he caught a whiff of cinnamon. He bit his lip, his suspicions crackling in his head.

"What's your name, boy?"

"Eli. Eli Golden."

After a moment's careful consideration: "That sounds about right."

Eli snorted.

"No harm in having a name to fit. Birth or chosen?"

"Both." Eli bit the inside of his cheek. By a careful trick of his eyes, he could almost see the fiddle's graining sweep along like warm honey. "From the womb. I think that's the only time they understood me."

Mickey clucked and Eli thought he must have failed, once again, to keep out all the bitterness from his voice.

"Then, allow me to introduce myself." The old man

laid a feather-light hand, all crepey skin and sinews, on Eli's shoulder. "Birth Name: Michel Phillipe Gaston Louis Charles Julien D'Evigny." He chuckled, and after a moment, Eli joined in.

"And your parents' names?" he asked.

"Jason and Julia Devers."

Eli's chuckle grew to a full-throated laugh.

"They were First Family of Enterrat," said Mickey, "and much more concerned with that than the weight of their name on a boy. I sundered myself as soon as I decently could, and hit the trade lanes. Never looked back. I got out. I got out."

Eli shifted and cleared his throat. "Looks like you've made it to a lot of places," he said softly. The unspoken offer that hung between them began to slide away, and something inside Eli shrivelled just a little more.

Mickey nodded once, brusquely, and took his hand back. "I guess you might say that, boy. That fiddle, for an instance. I had it made from the finest wood available on the first quality planet I and my ship found."

Eli shivered and the fiddle thrummed in sympathy.

"Here, boy. Stop that now. If you won't quit, I'll have to take my fiddle back, if you please."

Eli hugged it to his chest and scooted away. "You're a Skimmer pilot, aren't you?"

Mickey stopped in mid-reach and settled back. "Was, boy, yes, I was."

"Tell me about that. All about it. Please? You can have all the beggar-chits I've got."

Eli's offer hung, suspended in the quiet. He examined it and felt his cheeks start to burn. "I'm—I—God, sorry. Here." He thrust the fiddle toward Mickey, and when the old man sat motionless, cursed himself for insulting Mickey's blindness as well as his integrity. He must really be making a fine impression, as a first-class, prime grade bumpkin. He heard his father's voice whisper in his ear, and wanted to cry it back to some permanent grave.

"Here, boy. It's seldom enough that I get to tell my life story to some unsuspecting Jaunter. You are on a Jaunt?"

Eli nodded, surprised to find he could still move. "First planetfall from home," he said. "But I already know what I want. I want to be a Skimmer pilot, too."

Mickey grinned and smoothed splayed hands down the front of his coveralls. "Maybe you should give me back my fiddle, boy," he said. "If you want to pair with a Skimmer, you're a bit too unstable to be holding it."

"You did it."

"I've friends who didn't." Vexation cooled the edges of his voice. He reached for the bow, which he'd left in the case, and played it across his fingers. He could not seem to sit still. "Listen well, boy. There's something in those ships, and the space they Flip through, the some-thing the X-Ts won't tell us about. That something will take you across the galaxy faster than a wish. But some people, their bodies go and their minds stay behind. I've seen that, and it ain't pretty. That's why you came here in cold storage."

"Won't know until I try."

A stubborn silence stepped between them.

Finally, Mickey clapped Eli on the knee and rose. "Come on," he said. "You've got a life story to hear."

Eli scrambled to his feet. "Where are we going?"

"I'm an old man; my story's long. We might as well be comfortable. And yes, you can carry the fiddle. But put it back in the case, first."

Eli grinned and did as he was bid, swearing to himself

to become a recording machine, soaking up everything
the old man had to say.

"—What was that?"

"I said," said Mickey, "dust off your company manners. My ship's quite a lady."

"Your ship?" Eli was sure he'd died and made his
own heaven.

"That's where I live." The wry amusement in the old
man's voice told Eli he was missing nothing, but the boy
didn't care. "I may as well introduce you two. And I
need her to keep me flying right. She says I tend to
explore uncharted areas every time I re-tell my stories."

Who will tell of your blindness? Eli wondered, but
did not ask. He had already tasted his foot too often that
day, and the flavor would not get any better.

"I won't let anyone hurt you," Eli murmured. He
stirred in the chair as memories faded. "I promise."

"Do you, now?" she said sharply, and in that moment
sounded much like one dead old man. "They've made
up their minds, Eli. What do you think you can do?"

"I don't know," Eli said. His hands and face tightened and grew hot. "If you thought I was of no use, why
did you call me as your rightful witness?"

"I'm sorry, Eli," she said. "I wanted a friend near.
I—wanted you near."

"Why, Sevvy?" Eli asked.

Long silence. "Besides," Sevvy cried, bursting out
from every speaker, "Mickey left you his fiddle."

"What?" Eli jerked against the straps. "Are you
sure?"

"I can't very well make a mistake about this." A dry
touch crept in. "It's recorded. All I have to do is play it

back." Eli plucked at the webbing across his chest. The ship went on. " 'Seventh,' he said—he was always formal when he was serious—'Seventh, make sure Eli Golden gets my fiddle. He talked back enough to deserve it.' "

The instrument tell-tales blurred before Eli's eyes and when he flung back his head, the swirls of Sevvy's "concentrations" jewelled the moisture in his lashes. "I accept. Thank you. But is that the only reason you summoned me?"

"I told you. I want you with me."

Eli spat the next words. "You've given up. I'm telling you I'll help you fight, but you've given up."

"Eli, the humans of the Port Authority want to shut me off. My Patron isn't going to stop them." Her voice cut out from speaker after speaker, until it emerged, thin and cold, from only one. "I am a novelty. It wants to study the socio-economic implications. But don't believe I've given up."

Eli froze in the chair, only partly because of the ice in her voice. "Sevvy, what do you intend to do?" he whispered.

The ship did not answer.

Eli scrabbled at the webbing with clumsy, urgent fingers. He dropped onto the hatch below, and knelt in the puddle of wine beside it to un-dog it. A faint click stopped his hands, and as he jerked his head up, a whole series of clicks rattled off around him. He squatted back and decided not to try the hatch right away. "Eli," said the ship, "Please, don't leave me."

Eli looked around, wondering how so many shadows could gather in a round cabin. "I'll only be gone for a little while, Sev," said Eli. "Please. I swear I'll come right back. I need to stop at the 'commodations 'course and get my things, if I'm going to stay with you, don't I?"

"You can send for your clothes from here," said Sevvy stubbornly.

Eli ran his hands through his hair. His mouth had turned dry; he needed to swallow twice before he could speak again. "Sev," he said. "Where's the fiddle? I'd like to take it with me and visit the begging stations for a while." He closed his eyes and waited.

"In the personal effects compartment at the head of Mickey's bunk," came a cold, wholly electronic voice. "Upward stateroom in my present orientation."

Eli reached for the hatch, but the expected click did not come.

"This isn't fair," said the ship. "You swear on that fiddle that you'll be back?"

"I swear, Sev."

The ship sighed. "Oh, Eli. Sometimes I don't want to be human after all, but what's left?"

"I don't really know," Eli said. "I'm still working on that myself." The hatch opened easily, and Eli shivered. The sweat drying on his back was chilling him.

He took the exercise track back up to Mickey's stateroom and lowered himself down, kicking aside the bed, a hammock slung across the middle of the cabin. Lights flicked on. Sev was watching. Eli would not have known which was the head of the bed if a round door, about half a meter in diameter, had not popped open behind him.

There was little in the compartment except darkness. Take away the fiddle case, and there was nothing left, really. Just a small, slick gray urn. Eli could not shake the thought that he was about to take the only thing left of an old man's life and leave the death behind. He eased his hand past the urn and wrapped it tightly around the neck of the case.

He pulled the case from the compartment and cradled it against his chest, stroking the soft, black leather. By what felt right to Eli, the case should stay beside the urn, but Mickey had given it away. Mickey seemed to have given away much of his life—his eyes, his pilot's rights. He could have gone to any R 'n R facility. Repair and Rejuve could have given him back his eyes, erased the years. Instead, he'd huddled on this little planet like a crab in a rock crevice, hiding from the light. Which was his right, but he had no right to do what he'd done to his ship.

Eli frowned as he slung the case over his shoulder for the climb out. Sev had something planned. He would have to help her in spite of herself. But he had to get away from her first, clear his head, find out more information. Could the Port Authority truly be so blatantly unjust? How much had Sev not told him?

A mix of anger, frustration, and confusion spun through Eli's head as he picked his way back to the airlock. Just what had blinded Mickey, so long ago? Eli could say to himself that he would not have run from it as Mickey had, but he knew the truth: not even the most fantastic worlds he conjured up in his fantasy flights could match Mickey's reality.

Music flooded around Eli; something soothing and monotonal. Kaufman, another one of her favorites. Eli ducked into the lock and paused before rapping for the P-Port guard. "Sevvy," he called softly. "Sevvy?"

He had just decided she was not going to answer when a slow "Yes, Eli," reached him.

"Sevvy, can you see me?"

The ship chuckled, warm and intimate in the tiny

space. "Of course I can see you, Eli."

"What do I look like?"

"Like a human, of course," said the ship more sharply. "Why? Why do you ask?"

"No reason, Sev. Just wondering. I'll be back soon." Eli rapped, and stared down at the dull gray of the deck, waiting for the guard to open the door. Sevvy thought he looked like a human. Just that. Not like a young man, a—boy, and not tired, sad, and more than a little frightened.

Eli could no longer be sure who was blind and who could see.

Eli had missed connections twice, and ships did not follow each other closely into Camber's Folly. He had received a heated and somewhat irrational 'gram from his father, to the effect that if his son wanted to spend his money gallivanting around the Galaxy, he'd damn-well better gallivant and not sit on his duff in some sink-hole of a solar system, and Christ, if the boy could not even jaunt correctly. . . .

With a burning face, Eli sent his love to his mother, then told his father he was traveling farther than the man dared dream. He showed up at Sevvy's airlock promptly at eight every morning, Port Time.

The *Seventh Veil* captivated Eli from the first. Everything about her, from her round little ball of a body to the piercing tones of her voice when she sang, like clear shards of mountain glass across his palm, held the boy in thrall. Mickey took him all through the ship, explaining what he could, improvising what he had to, and tied it all together with the threads of a dozen fantastical stories.

Afternoons, Eli tagged along to the begging stations

and listened to wild fiddle music until he felt he held so much it would burst through his skin if he could not fling it out in a dance. Just then, Mickey would stop, and Eli would gasp for breath while Mickey laughed at him. They would count the money they never made— astronomical sums, always—and head back to the ship in tired, companionable quiet.

The wildness seemed to infect Eli, and his questions grew bolder. His last morning on the ship came, though he was given the scant comfort of not realizing that until after the fact. Eli was tucked away in a corner of the tiny, pristine galley while the old man, nude, baked bread. "Ultimately less messy," he'd explained briskly at Eli's first bark of laughter. The old man was a sight: coated from head to foot in rust-red iron-wheat flour, chin up, eyes seemingly locked on a personal demon, his fingers would search the dough. Then he'd pummel it into submission, raise up the whole blob, and slap it smartly down on the bread board. Good yeast smells filled the cabin. Mickey talked, as always, but this time Eli let the words recede to a drone while he pondered how to phrase his own questions.

". . . So, I had Sev pop us into a pretty loose orbit, one easy to duck out of, you see, because damned if the place didn't give me the willies, for no reason I could tell. Then I took the pod down, and damned if I wasn't right—"

"Mickey," said the ship gently, "you knew all along of the anomalous sulfur content in the atmosphere. I'd told you about it when I took my first readings."

"Hush, girl." Mickey laid a forefinger across his lips, leaving a dusty stripe down the middle. "Do you want the boy to find out I'm just a dray horse in this operation? He thinks you need my brain for more than just making the Flip. Boy, do we have him fooled—"

"Mickey," said Eli, raising his chin from his cupped palms. "Why are you blind?"

"Who said I was blind, boy?" the old man asked easily. "Let's just say I choose not to see."

Eli squirmed. "You know what I mean."

Mickey popped two small loaves into the oven. The installation of the oven was the only acknowledgment Mickey had made of his permanently grounded status— that, and ensuring that every cabin had at least one level surface on which to stand. Eminently sensible concessions, both of them, in Eli's consideration.

"Yes, boy, I know what you mean." Mickey scrubbed himself with a cling-cloth, and his own pale flesh emerged from beneath the flour, one broad swath at a time. Sev directed him to missed spots. "I hear your words very clearly," he finally continued. "But you won't listen to mine."

"Then explain them better." Stubbornness sharpened Eli's voice.

"Nothing to explain. It would be a simple matter to get new eyes, but I will tell you (and this is more than you deserve) that on my last trip I saw something the likes of which I'll never see again, so why be foolish and replace it with a lesser vision."

"But—"

"But me no buts about my choice, boy. Sev understands, don't you, girl?"

"Yes, Mick," came back too quickly, Eli was certain. He leaned back and fumed.

The old man reached for his coverall and shimmied himself into it. "You coming, boy?"

"What about the bread?"

"Sev will watch it. We'll have it with supper."

Eli straightened in his chair. Silly; the old man couldn't see him. "You still have to get the fiddle, don't you? I'll meet you at the airlock."

"Got a question for Sev, have you?"

"Yes."

"One you don't want me to hear."

Eli straightened until his spine hurt. "Yes."

Mickey nodded once, more to himself than to Eli, and swung toward the upper hatch. He paused as though to speak, but Eli thought his expression more cutting than anything he could say. Mickey shrugged. "At the airlock, then." He left.

"Whew." Eli slumped down.

"What's this mysterious question?" asked Sev.

"Oh, Sev, don't you be harsh to me, too. I just want to know why you let him do this to you."

"He's the pilot, Eli," said Sev. Her voice held infinite regret, and longing, and perhaps even a touch of anger. "He chooses. I'm his Skimmer, true, and we're supposedly partners, but I'm a ship. I'm only a ship."

The trip to the begging stations was suffered through in silence. When they reached Mickey's bubble, the old man bowed the boy through first with a sardonic grin. Mickey did not need to see, Eli thought. He could probably feel the heat radiating from the boy's cheeks as Eli stepped past.

Eli gathered himself together in the seconds before Mickey followed. Hands clenched, shoulders hunched and straining the thin fibers of his tunic, he waited for soft footsteps behind him. "Mickey, introduce me to your Patron."

"No," said Mickey smoothly, and flipped open the case with deft and tender hands.

"Why not?" asked Eli, trying to shift into a mood

that matched Mickey's for casualness.

"It wouldn't want to speak to you," said Mickey, and settled the fiddle against his shoulder.

"Well, why did it ever want to speak to you?"

A slow flush colored Mickey's high cheeks, and Eli told himself that this was the man who kept him from what he most wanted, kept the ship from what she most needed, turned his back on what was most worthwhile. This was the man who kept Eli around simply as an uncracked vessel into which he might pour himself as his stories, before he dried up into dust.

"I don't know," said Mickey. "I don't know why my Patron chose me. But when it did, I wasn't down on my knees begging to be saved from a life I didn't have the guts to just turn my back on and walk away from."

Eli's clenched fists rose up and hung—then he slammed them against the wall, again and again, while his rage consumed the air around him. But he had to stop; soon there would be nothing left to breathe. He let his hands fall, and when he could speak once again, all he had left was the simple truth. "You don't understand," he said dully. "My father . . . it has to be big, you see, because he thinks I'm so small. . . ."

When Mickey found Eli's hands and gripped them tight, the pain from his bruises and scrapes felt very far away. "Boy, you must learn it's the simple decisions inside yourself that make the difference." Eli took in a deep breath and with it held the tears down. Mickey sighed. "Ah, boy, I hope you can learn that."

"I'm leaving tomorrow."

"I thought you might come to that, boy."

"Give Sevvy my love."

"Will do."

Still, Eli did not pull away, nor Mickey release his

hands. The old man bent down and kissed Eli gently on the forehead. "May we meet again on the Rim," he whispered, "and share visions."

Eli ran. He ran past the beggar stations, through the Prime Corridor, and all the way to his rooms. Had he stopped before then, he would have turned back.

Eli's first stop off the tube was a fax booth. But his request for all the news concerning Mickey's death was interrupted. He swore at the test patterns on the screen and punched at the "Reset" button, then rolled his eyes and settled back. He hadn't long to wait.

"Supervisor Marcus," he murmured.

The goggled security officer nodded at him from behind her wide, bare desk. "Free-Sir Golden."

"You're impeding a lawful request for information."

She allowed herself a tight smile. "I am the law. But that's neither here nor there," she added hastily as he raised a hand into her field of view and let it hover over the "Disconnect" button. "I would like to make you a quite hospitable offer."

"Listening."

The supervisor gathered herself, as though against some force of nature. That is what I'll be, Eli thought. One of the summer winds from back home. The Flaying Wind. "Would you care to come to my office, so I may explain in a less impersonal setting exactly what happened to your friend?"

"Why now?"

"I beg your pardon?"

"Why are you offering to explain now, when I asked for an audience three times before I first went to the ship?"

"We felt you would appreciate the opportunity to

hear the ship's side of it first."

"Don't hand me that shit." Eli watched with immense satisfaction as the supervisor's mouth fell open, then snapped shut. "How stupid do you think I am? You were hoping that Sev would tell ignorant little Eli something that you people didn't already know."

Marcus shrugged.

"Where's the bug?"

She hid her mouth behind one gauntleted hand and coughed. "On your feet."

Eli smiled. "I'm going to watch the fax casts now."

"Wait. Please." She pulled off her goggles and toyed with them, looking down. Eli stopped. He wanted to see what color her eyes were. "Will you believe what you see?"

"If I can't think of a reason for you to lie."

She looked up. They're the same color as mine, was Eli's first startled thought. "You are very determined, aren't you," she said. Her eyes, he noticed next, were also sad.

Eli frowned at her, wondering at her change. "Why should my curiosity concern you?"

Her goggles clattered onto the desk as she clasped her hands under her chin. Her gaze made him dart a nervous glance over his shoulder. "Several reasons. Purely professional reasons. The friendship between X-Ts and humans is long and strong. This must have no adverse effect on the relationship."

" 'This'? What's 'this'?"

"The death of a human as a result of the premeditated actions of an X-T-H Skimmer."

Eli carefully slipped his hands out of sight and clenched them into fists. "I am still not certain that anything like 'this' has occurred to disturb our long, strong, and profitable friendship."

Pain tightened her face, giving her a skull-look under skin-tight black hood. "Watch the fax casts, then," she said softly. "I know what she told you, but she did it, my friend. Why else should she try so hard to keep you with her? She didn't want you to find out the truth. I'm sorry, and you're right. Our relationship with the Patrons is very profitable. Nothing must interfere with that."

"What will you do to her?" Eli asked harshly. Sev was right. They had decided.

"Oh, boy," the supervisor cried. "You sound like we're going to string her up in a dungeon somewhere and wire her for pain. She's a ship, damnit. Just a ship. So, we'll try to understand why she did it, and when we can't we'll scrap her. Yank her brain and send the parts back to the X-Ts and does that answer your question?"

Eli stared at Marcus. She bit her lip, threw herself back in her chair, swept her goggles to the floor. "I'm sorry, Free-Sir Golden. I looked you up, you know. I know what you're doing. I just want to say that I tried, too. I know what she means to you."

Eli closed his eyes.

"But you'll go home and find—something. After a while, you'll feel better, and later on you'll even come to realize she's just a ship."

"Just a ship," Eli echoed.

"Just a ship," and Eli had never heard so hollow a voice. She tried to stay firm when he opened his eyes to her, but her gaze faltered.

"Show me everything you've got," Eli said. "And not the sanitized fax casts, but the tapes your own people made."

"Free-Sir, there's no doubt—"

"I have to see."

"Yours is an unreasonable request. Those tapes are classified." She ducked down to scoop up her goggles, fiddled with them, dropped them in her lap. "I could lose my job."

"What's your name?" asked Eli.

"My name?"

The supervisor touched a button and the view panned back to include a precisely rectangular, highly polished name plate on her desk. "Supervisor Marcus," it read.

"Supervisor Marcus," said Eli. He smiled at her, not without calculation; he knew what his full, glowing smile could do. "I'd hate to have a name like 'Supervisor.' I'd be very upset with my parents and pick a chosen name as soon as I legally could."

"Madeleine, damn you," cried the supervisor, and in one glorious instant Eli knew that the hair trapped under the tight hood of her uniform was long and curly and black; that she liked to travel but never seemed to find the time; that she kept pets instead of lovers. He could be wrong, but still he knew, and the objective truth did not matter. And he knew for a fact that she was not very happy. "Watch the tapes," she said. "I'll feed them to you from here."

"Thank you," said Eli softly. She was shaking.

"Don't," she said. "Now, leave me alone." She blinked off as though swallowed by the circuits. But no, thought Eli, she would always be with him now.

Later, much later, Eli pushed himself away from the booth. He was shaking. There were more tapes, but he could not watch them. Supervisor Madeleine had told the truth. The *Seventh Veil* had murdered Mickey.

Eli walked blindly down the concourse, and people

who saw him moved away. He walked faster and faster
until he was careening down the corridor, all direction
lost. He believed the fax casts, believed them utterly;
they were too detailed to have been faked. The damage
to the chute tube was real, the interviews with the
'Course Kids were real.

They hurt the worst. Eli could not shake the image of
the tall girl with the broad face. Two little ones clutched
at her as she answered questions, their faces buried in
her sides. Her bewilderment turned to anger, turned to
pain as she slowly came to understand that the joke the
ship had convinced her to play on her friend had killed
him, so dead he could never be put back together.

Eli's steps slowed, and he started to drift, taking turns
and twists as they came to his feet. Inevitably, though,
he came to familiar places; he did not even pause to
glance at the other beggar bubbles he passed, but walked
straight to Mickey's. No one had claimed it yet, and Eli
popped into the quiet, set his back against the wall, and
slid to the floor.

He unwrapped the fiddle from its case and cradled it
on his knees.

Something else fell from the case and clattered to the
floor. Eli watched it, slow to move. He felt so dull and
tired. But curiosity finally prodded him toward it on
hands and knees, and he scooped up a small, clear
message marble. It warmed in his hands and Mickey's
face slowly took shape.

"Play the fiddle, boy," Mickey said.

Eli had to laugh, though it hurt to hear. "Play
the fiddle?" he said. "What do I know about playing
fiddles?"

"Play the fiddle, boy," Mickey repeated. That was all
he'd recorded. "Play the fiddle, boy." Eli dropped the

sphere and it rolled away. "Play the fiddle, boy," faded as it cooled.

Eli looked down at the fiddle laid across his thighs. It still glowed, just as he remembered it, still shone warm and rich and soft, and he still handled it gingerly, not wanting to disturb whatever sounds it waited to sing next. Play it? He could barely even bring himself to touch it. But the old man had asked him to, and Eli had watched him often enough to remember how a sound was made. . . .

Tuck the fiddle against the shoulder, thus, and hold the bow like so, then draw the bow across the strings, this way—

A low, mellow tone flowed out, surprisingly pure and calm, and playing, he was sure, just for him.

"Not like the stuff I played, eh, boy?"

Eli almost dropped the fiddle. Mickey grinned down at him, and Eli was sure the old man could see. But the image was only an image, wavery and weak, and Eli's heart dropped back into place.

"Time for a lecture, boy. Of course, you can stand up and leave, but do a dead old man the courtesy of listening to his last speech."

Eli settled back warily, fiddle still tucked. He watched the holo and drew the bow across the strings again.

"Since you're watching this, you must have gotten your hands on my fiddle. And since you got my fiddle, I must be dead." Mickey laughed his deep, secret-laden laugh. "Not funny, right, boy? At least not from your side of the question. Maybe in eighty years you'll laugh, too.

"But something that truly isn't funny is why I'm dead. If I didn't choose to go, I'm assuming Sevvy did it."

Eli tried to look away from the great, empty eyes. His throat closed tight, and he had to swallow before he could breathe properly. The holo of Mickey did the same.

"Don't feel bad, boy. It's my doing. You live with someone for fifty, sixty years and you think you know her. Especially if you have a little tag to put under the pictures you see in your mind's eye when you say her name under your breath. Tags like 'lover,' 'friend,' or even 'ship.' That's pure conceit. Whatever I called her, I always assumed she was mine. I should have thought of what my decision would do to Sev. And yet," he shook his head, sending white hair flying, "I don't know what good that would have done either. I could never give up Sevvy, and I could never go back to the Rim. I know how you feel about that, but I tell the truth. After what I've seen, I couldn't become a transport pilot, carrying frozen bodies that wake into frozen minds. But I can't go back to the Rim. I'd lose myself if I went back. I'd fly apart, try to fill the void."

Mickey shook himself and laughed again, but it had gained a strain. "I know what's coming, but I can't leave Sevvy. Stubborn old fart, I am. Not afraid, either. Lived a long time, seen a lot of wonders, and Sev will make it quick. But I'm worried as hell about her." The milky eyes sought him out, and Eli held still. One last time. He'd listen to the old man one last time.

"She'll be scrapped, boy, if the Port Authority gets her. But she's not mean. Only . . . sick. Get her to an X-T outpost. Please."

"But I thought—" said Eli, and frowned.

"Now, I suppose I'd best warn you I spoke true when I said not everyone is cut out for the Flip, and you'd have to Flip to get to the Patrons. They're that far away.

But it's Sev's only chance. It's also your decision, now. You decide." He sighed. "She's such a marvelous ship. I haven't done right by her. She deserves better."

"You bastard," screamed Eli, and swung the fiddle viciously at the hologram. It sliced clean through, slammed against the wall behind, and exploded in a shower of sparks. Eli recoiled from the sharp pain that slid up the fiddle's neck and under his fingernails. It embedded itself in his skull, somewhere behind his eyes, or was that pain caused by the back of his head thudding into the wall? Eli did not know. He could not see, could not hear, could feel only a great vexation.

When Eli's vision cleared, he was calmly watching one hand pluck splinters from the other. Judging by the number of bloody dots on his skin, he'd been plucking out the bits of wood for some time. The pain in his head receded a bit more with each splinter he yanked, until, as he pulled the last sliver of wood from the web of skin between thumb and forefinger, the pain vanished completely. But it left behind a hint, as though it lurked in the bones of his brow.

Mickey was gone, for good this time, swept away in a shower of splintered wood. Eli forced himself to look at the ruin of the fiddle. He let a hand hover uncertainly over it until his hesitation changed to desperate haste and he scrabbled through jangling strings until he found a long, slim sliver that still held some warmth. He tucked it away and left before the desolation could strike.

Eli returned directly to the *Seventh Veil*, dismissing his belongings. The words of other people twisted his thoughts, tangled his steps: "She's just a ship." "She deserves better." "Not everyone is cut out for the Flip." "You'll find something. Things get better." "I expect you'll limp home at the end of a year when you've had your fill of the nothing out there and the con men who sell it."

The same P-Port guard stood watch, and smiled at Eli, who brushed past without a word. The guard hurried after him, and stopped him as he reached for the airlock hatch. "I was given a message for you, Free-Sir, and told to suggest you read it before you go inside." The guard moved a discreet distance away, leaving Eli to stare dumbly at the message marble dropped onto his palm.

It warmed. "Supervisor Madeleine," Eli murmured. The goggles were back, but Eli could see past them, now.

"Please," said the supervisor, "listen to me for just a moment. We—I had hoped that letting you speak with the ship would calm her, but we have reason to believe she's even more irrational than before your arrival and re-boarding her at this time would be extremely dangerous. I ask you to leave quietly."

Eli joggled the sphere in his palm. Why was she asking, and not ordering? He closed his eyes. "I tried, too," she'd said. He smiled.

"She's just a ship," he told the marble, but it simply started to repeat the message. He dropped it and ground it underfoot as he stepped through the hatch.

"Eli," Sev called. "You're back. Oh, I—I was starting to wonder. But I shouldn't have. Listen, Eli, love, I've been thinking, and I've got plans. You must want to hear them, or you wouldn't have come back. Am I right?"

Eli almost turned and walked out. He hung suspended on Sev's words and opened his own mouth, wondering what would come out. "What are your plans, Sev?" he called. The hatch behind him clanged shut. He climbed into the spare stateroom on his way to the core.

"You can be my new pilot, Eli. I have it all figured out. I'll teach you everything you need to know, and I'll take good care of you, and we'll find so many new places, we'll run out of names for them all. How does that sound?"

Eli stopped and leaned his cheek against the cool bulkhead. "Sounds just fine," he whispered. "Oh, God, it sounds wonderful, Sev."

"I promise I'll take better care of you than I took of Mickey," said the ship in a distant, chilled voice. "To tell you the truth, Eli, sometimes I didn't take such good care of him. But he always forgave me."

"Wasn't that human of him?" muttered Eli.

"I don't know," said the ship, "was it? Maybe I should forgive Mickey. Would that make me human?"

"Sevvy, please," said Eli. He jerked away from the sudden vibration in the netting and almost lost his grip. The vibration was accompanied by a low, steady rumble. Sev was readying the sub-Light engines.

Eli pushed himself away from the bulkhead and resumed his climb as Sev went on:

"I think he'd like it if he knew what we're going to do. He liked you, did you know that, Eli?"

"No, Sevvy, I didn't."

"I like you, too. That's really why I waited, because I didn't have to. I can leave any time I want. But I like company. Are you glad I waited for you? Are you glad?"

Her voice bounced around him giddily, and Eli swallowed against the bile burning his throat. "Yes, Sevvy, very glad."

"We'll reach Flip-point ten minutes after we leave the station. Less if they chase us. But I've already picked our first Flip." The ship's voice was so painfully eager, and it would not stop. "Would you like to know where that is?"

"Tell me, Sev." Eli swatted his way past the hammock and reached for the command core hatch.

"The last place I went to with Mickey. I don't mind telling you, because you're my friend. When you left, you sent me love."

"Tell me what, Sev?" Eli spoke carefully; tears had finally come after a long, broken year.

"I've always wondered why Mickey and I both saw the same thing, and he went blind, but I didn't."

The command core was locked.

"Oh, don't worry about a thing, Eli. Just go strap yourself in, and I'll take care of everything. It's always bothered me, because we not only saw the same thing, I saw more of it, if you understand me."

"Not really, Sev," Eli said, trying to steady his hands.

"All we saw was a huge, glowing nebula, a big, shining, gold cloud of gas, and of course I had the light adjusted so it wouldn't hurt Mickey's eyes. But he kept asking me to let in more and more light, and I thought he knew what was best. Then he screamed and couldn't see anymore."

You bastard, Eli thought again, but the heat was gone. He was too busy trying to pry off the access plate to the locking mechanism, trying to remember every trick picked up from Uncle Stephen, the ships' outfitter.

"So, I want to go back and see if I can't see, if you understand."

"Yes, I do," Eli said. "You have to find out what you are."

"Exactly!" squealed the ship. "I knew you would understand." Eli blinked back the sweat stinging his eyes. "Are you strapped in, yet?"

"Not quite yet." Each word was spaced with a grunt,
Eli prayed Sev would not catch on. At least he screened
his own machinations from her monitors with his body.
But as soon as he touched the wiring, she would know.

"You'd better get strapped in. You're not strapped in,
yet, are you? Why are you still by the hatch? I'm going
to take off now." She did.

She's going! Eli thought in amazement. Then he
screamed. The sudden acceleration dragged him off
the ladder and slammed him to the floor. He had pried
loose the access plate. It was plastered to his chest like a
lead weight. "Sevvy," he gasped. "Compensate. Compensate."

Pressure eased as the weak artificial gravity cut in.
The X-Ts had never bothered to perfect the feature, but
it allowed Eli to roll, coughing, onto his knees. The plate
clattered to the floor. He stared at it, vision rimmed in
red, and dragged in a great, burning chestful of air.
Almost forlornly, he reached for the ladder and began to
climb again.

"I'm sorry, Eli, but I said you should strap in. And
you'd better do it now, because we're being pursued. I
may have to accelerate again."

"Sevvy," Eli moaned. He clenched every muscle in his
body that he could still feel, knowing full well what
would happen. He pried one hand off the ladder and
reached into the opening. The door slid open.

"Eli, why did you do that?"

The artificial gravity faded away, slowly settling every kilo of a three-gee acceleration onto his joints. His
shoulders hurt the worst, as if his arms had been nearly
ripped from their sockets. They might be yet.

Don't think about that—

What to think about, then? He hugged the ladder forehead pressed against a plasteel rung. He had to climb.

How far must Sev lift before she could attempt the Flip? But she needed him for it, anyway; Eli was quite sure of that. She needed his nerves jacked into the system. So, what would she do when she could not Flip? Or could she Flip, but not come back? Eli climbed the first rung.

Centimeter by centimeter the boy fought his way up the ladder and into the command core. He could barely breathe; each rib lay across his lungs like an iron bar. He pulled himself through the hatch until his waist cleared, then let his upper body thud to the floor. He was afraid to look up at the command chair, too afraid the weight of his own head would snap his neck.

"I'll be Flipping in two minutes, Eli," said the ship, and he sobbed onto the deck.

"Sev! You need a pilot in the chair!"

"Not this time, Eli. I'm the pilot. Don't you think you should do as I say? I really do know best this time."

The chair. Eli felt upward with every sense toward the chair. He had to get to it and jack in before Sevvy tried to Flip. But damn, he could not look up, and his senses were . . . stuck, overloaded with stimuli. Vision was a uniform blur, sound a roaring in his ears. Smell was acrid sweat, taste was bile, and feeling . . . Eli moaned, or thought he did . . . feeling was weight, heavy and hot, his eyes like lead shot. She's only a ship, he thought, and the next thought followed so natural and swift he knew it had been waiting for him all along. Then what am I? He pushed his body up, swung one arm blindly, and heaved.

"One minute, Eli. I have to Flip, or they'll catch up. I

don't have the reserves for a prolonged sub-light chase."

As Eli hung under the command chair, he saw a vision; he saw himself suspended in a space too great to comprehend. It was a convoluted space, with folds and eddies too large to touch in whole. He could only guess at what lay far away. He could only guess, and weep his frustration.

Instead of a path under his feet, empty space invited a catastrophic fall. Instead of wants and dreams before his eyes, a void mocked his hope of choice. Then he saw himself make little, fumbling, blind grabs outward. His hands touched and his eyes discovered and his heart wondered instantaneously. He dragged himself over the arm of the chair and let his face fall onto the seat. In his vision, everything he touched flowed into him, made him bigger, lengthened his reach. He found a window he could wrap around his eyes to clear his sight.

"Forty-five seconds. You really have me worried, Eli."

Eli tried to pull himself the rest of the way into the chair, but his body would no longer obey. He was getting worried, too. He concentrated on one hand, his right hand, and willed it to move. It grudged him a few twitches. He spoke to it, cajoled it, whispered extravagant promises if his hand would only slither its way into the little compartment set into the arm of the chair and pull out the soft mesh skullcap inside. His right hand wriggled about, undecided.

"Thirty seconds. Eli, you're being very stubborn."

Eli's hand gave in. Eli was so glad he yanked himself all the way into the chair. He could not see what his hand held, but he did not need to. Who needed eyes? He settled into the chair with a great gasp, spread the skullcap wide with two docile hands, and slid it over his head.

"Fifteen seconds. Eli, cut out of the system. You don't know how to do this."

Eli did not care. As soon as the mesh settled against his scalp, his body disappeared. He wanted to cry out with relief. He wanted to sleep. He wanted to laugh until the tears came. But Sevvy was there, waiting.

As long as you're here, she said, *this is where we want to go.* She showed him a sight so dazzling he shied away in panic: a golden, swirling cloud that threatened to suck him in and spin him around like a tiny sea bird that had just missed the eye of the storm.

No, Sevvy, please. I don't want to go there.

Then where do you want to go?

Eli thought, and suddenly realized the fiddle had been trying to play a world to him as he drew the bow across the strings, and the dying scream of the instrument had slammed that world home like a spike between his eyes. He did not like it—it looked cold and ancient— but: *There. I want to go there.* The countdown hit ten and thudded monotonously along behind him.

No. Sevvy suddenly materialized. He could see her now, and she was not a dark, mysterious woman. She was a little golden-haired girl. She looked like him.

Five—four—three—two—one

Sevvy pulled, and Eli pulled, and something snapped.

The first time Eli was not quite sure he had awakened. He felt nothing but a great, cold numbness. But he could smell. He smelled cinnamon. He was pleased.

The next time Eli awoke he was sure of it, because he could look around, and he looked right into the eyes of a young woman who was looking back. She was not much older than he, wore a simple beige coverall, and had a ready smile. Eli liked her. She also had something in her eyes that Eli thought Mickey must have had when his own eyes were still clear. Eli raised his head and regretted it immediately.

"I think you've just found out you shouldn't move much," said the woman with a grin. "You must be sore all over." Eli grinned back and found that even his face hurt. The woman shook her head and laughed out loud. "Boy, that must have been one wild ride."

"Yes," said Eli. There. Just moving his lips was not so bad. But what would he do when his nose itched? He decided to let that take care of itself. There were more important matters to attend to. "Sevvy," he said.

The young woman's smile dropped away. "Your ship? She'll be all right. I think. The Patrons don't really tell us much. Not that they keep secrets, understand, but they don't communicate very well. They try to keep the Skimmers as go-betweens. And this is a case not even the ships know much about— Well," she said, and shrugged, "you'll find all this out."

"I will?" Eli tried to sit up again. If he could drag himself into the command chair against umpteen-zillion gees, he could damn-well sit in about a half-a-gravity. And he did, with the help of the woman, who clucked at him when she saw him move, but eased his way when he showed he would not quit. "When will I find out? Will a Patron come and talk to me before I leave?"

The woman laughed. She smelled good; clean and sweet, different from the X-T spice. "You're not leaving for quite a while," she said. "The training program takes two Standards to complete. And if the *Seventh Veil* is your ship, you'll have to wait until she recuperates before you even start. I won't mention that you're not in too good a shape yourself."

Eli's head spun. "Wait a minute," he said. "Who are you? And where exactly am I, anyway?"

"Right where you wanted to be, I thought," said the woman. "My name is Jessica Lampert, and I'm a second-year pilot-designate. You are on the World of Hard Knocks, aptly though somewhat whimsically named, and the home of the only Skimmer pilot training program in existence.

"You're kidding."

"No," said Jessica, her full brows raising and fuller lips twisting, "I most certainly am not. I was told you Flipped to these co-ordinates as though you'd been doing it all your life."

"Mickey, you old bastard," Eli murmured.

"What's wrong? Isn't this where you wanted to be?" Eli luxuriated in the feel of the cool, smooth sheets spread over him as he took the measure of the room in which he lay: clean, neat, cozy, and holding a pretty, smiling woman. He grinned, but a sudden cloud passed over, and left a shiver.

"What's wrong?" Jessica asked again, leaning forward to tuck him in more securely. No one had done that for him since the first time he had returned home from boarding school. Eli decided, through his embarrassment, that he liked it.

"I'm fine, really," he said. "But you did say you thought Sevvy would be all right too, didn't you?"

"I think so, yes."

"Then I'm right where I want to be," Eli sighed, and lay back. "I'm exactly where I want to be."

Time and Chance
by
Eric Heideman

About the Author

Eric Heideman is a man who cultivates a scholarly, serious air, and edits an ambitious SF literary magazine for local writers in the Twin Cities. He is a dedicated SF fan who long ago formed the ambition to turn professional, and has now made it. In addition to his story here, which has been a long time in the polishing, he has sold a long story to Alfred Hitchcock's Mystery Magazine since winning First Place in the first Quarter of the contest year.

His approach to a writing career is one of the ways of doing it rationally. By contrast, some writers seem to simply follow a guiding intuition. Either way works, and there are others equally effective. One wonders, sometimes, as one sees that there are other ways for other individuals, how it would have felt to be some other writer, pursuing some other path. Ambrose Bierce, of course, eventually disappeared during America's 1912 effort to control border banditry. Some say he went off with Pancho Villa. Edgar Allan Poe, now. . . .

*After all, what is it?—this indescribable something
which men will persist in terming 'genius'? I agree with
Buffon—with Hogarth—it is but* diligence *after all.*

Poe, *"The Literary Life of Thingum Bob, Esq."*

Gambler, n. A man.
Ambrose Bierce, *The Devil's Dictionary.*

On a clear, bright Indian Summer
afternoon in the Autumn of 1865, a young man
in a stiff black suit rode through the tobacco-
scented air of Richmond, Virginia, reining in his horse
outside the gates of a stately mansion at Fifth and Main
Streets. As the man dismounted, a black lad of ten or
twelve appeared at the gate to lead the horse to stable.
With a nod of appreciation the suited man strode up the
pathway, past trees swelling with birdsong, smelling and
seeing on both sides of the house a garden bedight with
fruit and vegetable, flowers and twisting vines. As he
commenced mounting the steps the wide, fine-framed
door was opened by an aproned woman, round face
smiling. "Are you Mr. Bierce?" He stopped, the step
beneath her, and half bowed. Perhaps both pleased and
flustered, she said, "Mr. Allan is expecting you." He
followed her through a spacious, crimson carpeted hallway, its silver-tinted walls decorated with paintings of

landscapes realistic, landscapes imaginative, and several portraits of men and women.

He was conducted to a parlor, where a lady rose to greet him, dainty and fine-featured, with a touch of the sprite for all her silver hair. "Mr. Bierce, we are very happy to meet you. My husband is out on the portico— Edgar! ... I regret that our son cannot be here, Mr. Bierce. I am Elmira Allan." The young man kissed her outstretched hand; then raised his eyes to see, standing behind her and before a bust of Dante, the unmistakable figure of Edgar Allan, humorist, editor of the *Stylus,* poet laureate of the Confederacy.

The visitor held out his hand. "Ambrose Bierce, sir."

The contrast between the two men could scarcely have been more marked. One, introducing himself in clear Northern tones, was dressed all in black. He was blond, youthful, ruddy-faced, strong of jaw, clean-shaven save for an upward-curling yellow mustache. Standing nearly six feet in height, his entire frame seemed to vibrate with a barely leashed and near explosive vitality. The older man now taking his hand stood perhaps five feet eight inches, deeply tanned, with flowing dark brown hair going to gray, a nose broad but delicate, a chin whose want of prominence was largely countered by a finely moulded goatee. Though the eyes of both were gray, those of the visitor were sharp, piercing, tinged with blue, while the eyes of Edgar Allan were large, soft, and dark. Where Bierce's features all had the symmetry of Greek sculpture, the proportions of his host's head were unbalanced by a huge expansion in the region of the temple, as though he were veritably bulging with brains.

Dressed from neck to foot in white, in the 'vanilla ice cream suit' that had become his emblem, Mr. Allan

Illustrated by Brian Murray

bespoke relaxation and courtly ease. "Is it *Lieutenant* Bierce—or *Mister?*"

The young man looked down, blushing, at the suit he had so purposefully worn in place of Union blue. "Lieutenant." At the sounds of light laughter, seeing the twinkle in his hosts' eyes, Bierce chuckled himself. In this house at least, for this hour, he was not to be made to feel an invader.

"Mr. Allan has *so* been looking forward to your visit, Lieutenant Bierce," said the lady in her lilting Southern voice. "I shall leave you gentlemen to discuss literature." Bestowing a kiss on her husband's cheek, she withdrew from the parlor.

Allan beamed at the young soldier. "Who can find a virtuous woman? For her price is far above rubies." Motioning the foot-shifting Bierce to the settee, Allan went to his liquor cabinet and poured him a glass of wine. "I remember how a young man loves his afternoon sherry," he said with a wink, sipping his tea.

Bierce surveyed the parlor with its white, finely textured carpet decorated with small, green circles; its white curtains, silver wallpaper interlaced with a faint green zig-zag cord; its bust of Dante and portraits of General Lee and Benjamin Franklin. It was simply but finely furnished with the settee, several chairs, and a round table with a few elegant books. At several points of the room were vases brimming with fragrant, vari-colored flowers. "Your wife has a fine sense of decor."

Allan nodded. "If I correctly recall your letter, Lieutenant, you were a surveyor in the war?"

"Yes, sir. A cartographer."

"Since which time you have been in the business of *finding* Confederate cotton for the United States?"

"Yes, Mr. Allan, with rather indifferent success.

Many a cotton grower would rather see his cotton go to the swamp than to the United States." They both chuckled.

"And now you must determine whether to make surveying a career, or whether to instead employ your pen in the making of literature."

"Precisely. I have received an invitation from General Hazen——"

"A general, I am told, as stubborn in his resolves as he is courageous in their defense."

Bierce grinned. "—An invitation to accompany him on an inspection tour of military posts in the West. In San Francisco a Captaincy should await me—if I decide to accept it."

"Unless you choose to turn to writing. Well, the two professions might be followed simultaneously, the one providing security for the proper maturation of the other. I once contemplated such a course myself." Stroking his beard thoughtfully, Allan rose from his chair. "Come." With their respective drinks in hand the two men walked out on the portico.

The portico extended the full length of the house, undecorated save for a few cane chairs and a luxuriant grapevine which, rising from the ground, apparently continued its climb above them to the roof. No decoration was needed where such a view could be obtained, for beneath the porch's pillars could be seen the sweep of the valley of the James, with its woods and meadows, streams, islands and bridges in the distance, and the James River winding sinuously through all.

Allan inhaled deeply of the clean, flower-scented air. "Virginia! Seek where he will, where else can a man find such beauty, such life-renewing grace!"

Bierce raised his glass as in a toast. "Indeed, sir. My

regiment was camped among the Alleghenies four years ago. The memory still lives with me from day to day. It is a land of waking dreams."

The older man drew himself to his full height. "Virginia, Lieutenant—seat of the Republic. In my student days I dined with Thomas Jefferson: for all the wild impracticality of some of his theories there never lived a more learned man, nor a finer gentleman. Two centuries and a half after Jamestown, a man must still turn to *Virginia* if he seeks the center of Art, of Knowledge, and of gracious living on this continent."

"The people of the South are very noble," Bierce said, "refusing to be bowed down no matter what the hardship. Regrettably, I myself have been in occupation."

They were silent for some moments; then Allan sat and motioned Bierce to join him. "But your time is limited. To literature, sir." He rested his chin on his right fist. "Tell me how you came to fancy a career in writing."

Bierce drained his glass and set it on his chair arm. "Some of my experiences in the war made me think of turning to writing. Many things happened that seemed full of irony." His eyes wandered reflectively over the landscape, then fixed upon Allan. "I knew two brothers from an old and influential family. The older of the two was studious and responsible, a model soldier. The younger was a wild and thoughtless ne'er-do-well. Both had been rivals for the same woman's affections, and now both served together, although I suspect that coincidence had been arranged by the elder brother, who hoped to keep the younger alive through careful supervision.

"One night two years ago he got his opportunity to do that. The ne'er-do-well had volunteered to carry an

important message through enemy lines. Shortly before
he was to leave he bolstered his courage by consulting a
Scotch bottle. The older brother looked in on him and
seeing how it was, that the messenger-to-be would not
stand a chance, he bound and gagged the drunken man
and slipped out of the camp in his stead. He delivered
the message and returned, gravely wounded, and died.
The younger brother recovered from his hang-over and
soon enough returned home to wed their mutual love.
Since then, I have heard, he is making very free with the
fortunes of both families.

"Such incidents made me think about the great part
that chance seems to play in human affairs. Had the
younger brother gone on his mission and the older survived, who can guess what changes might have been
wrought—in the lives of thousands. . . ?"

Allan frowned thoughtfully. "None can guess. Praise
our Lord! With all the struggles of *this* existence, let us
be thankful that we need not concern ourselves with
struggles that never came to be!"

The soldier shrugged. "Mr. Allan, I have lived many
years in the hope that I would be able to speak to you
one day about your work. How does the *Virginiad* fare?
Will we have it soon in its completed form?"

"As it is the work on which I expect such reputation
as I may have in later years to rest, it will continue to
occupy me for at least two years—perhaps for as many
as five. I shall submit additional selections from it to the
magazines from time to time."

"The parts you have already published are magnifi-
cent! It is a work as stately and dignified as its protago-
nist. Of living men only Robert E. Lee has the dimensions to fit him for an epic."

The poet nodded his agreement. "Mr. Lincoln was

also a man notable for strength displayed through moderation. Had he survived, the South might not have had to endure occupation. Perhaps Mr. Whitman might yet discipline himself in writing a cluster of sonnets about him."

During this last the soldier's eyes had darted to his coat. They fixed again on Allan. "What of the *Stylus?* When will it resume publication? Will you be removing to a different city for the editorial duties?"

"It *shall* resume next Summer and I *shall not* move. I will remain in Richmond—" Allan smiled. "And to Richmond those who aspire to a place in the magazine may submit their work."

"Good, sir! Now more than ever the myriad states need the unifying force of a national magazine of literature." Bierce leaned forward. "You know, Mr. Allan, I think the work of yours that truly lasts will be your short humorous tales."

Allan chuckled softly. "An amusement, sir, not a craft. Despite the fine efforts of my late friend Mr. Hawthorne, the tale has never fully evolved into a distinct art form. In the area of the *novel,* certainly, there has been fine work, especially that of Scott and Thackeray and our own Cooper and Brockden Brown." He gesticulated, one finger slicing the air tutorially. "Of course the best and purest writing in all epochs has been done in the field of poetry. As to my short tales—I have devoted many more hours to the verse. The acclaim with which a work is greeted seems to bear a direct proportion to the number of hours spent upon it. In tales one is free to ramble; in poetry each word is significant."

He paused to sip contemplatively on his tea. "But choose your field of writing, whether verse, or the drama, the novel, travel book, or the essay, even the tale—bear this in mind. Literature is the most noble of professions. In fact it is about the only one fit for a man. It is grueling, *arduous* work—to learn to discipline your lines, or your sentences, *purging* them of all infelicities. You must look into your *heart's core* so that you may write as well and as *truly* as you are able. When you learn to do that—I say *when* for I see that you are a very clever young man—your work will be accepted; no, acclaimed! It will not happen tomorrow—it may not in ten years—but patient industry and dedication will reap their rewards. It is the seven eighths of an iceberg that are never seen, but without them the eighth part would never rise above water. Look to *Franklin,* sir—Leonardo of our continent! 'Diligence is the Mother of Good Luck,' and 'God gives all things to Industry!' Advice on writing, sir? I give you none save this: practice!"

Bierce's hands, which had lain still through the poet's discourse, now rose from the chair arms to dance in front of the soldier as though bringing up the advance guard for his own words. "You speak of application, sir. But while hard work will suffice in the excavation of a ditch, is not something more required in composing a sonnet? What of the role of talent—of genius? In suggesting that *any* man may approach your own achievement if he but work hard enough, you too much deprecate yourself, Mr. Allan."

The poet smiled broadly. "My talent *is* my capacity for work. Certainly I do not suggest that any common day-laborer may write competent verse. Intelligence is needed, and a broad knowledge of the literature of the ages, and, if I may speak thus as one gentleman addressing another, good breeding. But I repeat: although one time in a millennium a *Shakespeare* may, though deficient in education, rise above the whole tribe of poets through this ineffable thing called *genius,* nonetheless, for we other ten thousand, simple dedication to our craft will suffice, as it ever has. Do not trouble yourself about genius, Lieutenant! If you are possessed of it, it will make itself manifest ere long. Put your nose to the grindstone and I *guarantee* you will succeed."

"But, sir, beside talent, beside dedication, is there not a third factor requisite to success in art as in all other things? What of *luck*? Even in your case, Mr. Allan; the fortune to be loved by a good woman, the respect of your contemporaries—no man is guaranteed these things. You do not *know* from whence all your words spring, nor how they would have differed had your experiences been different."

"Pshaw, Lieutenant! Nonsense! All life's necessities come in time to he who will not permit himself the luxury of failure. It is a matter of *will*."

Bierce's eyes and nostrils flared; he spoke in slow and measured tones, with the hint of a drawl. "I have stood in an open field in which thousands fell around me in the space of minutes. The will to live did not protect others of my comrades who did *not* escape the bullets whether they were courageous or cowards. What of the will of the *South* to triumph? Robert E. Lee epitomized the will to succeed. His will and his virtuous application are without flaw, sir. You know this yourself. He was not lacking in intelligence or courage—it was an *accident* that Stonewall Jackson was killed; how can you call it otherwise?"

Allan looked at him, fingering his chin thoughtfully. Quietly, he said, "Mr. Bierce——"

"*Mister* Allan, on the night of April 14th last, John Wilkes Booth was uncertain at which theater in Washington President Lincoln was in attendance. Apparently a *lucky* guess brought him to Ford's. Had he guessed otherwise, there might not now be Federal troops in Richmond." He stopped and for a full minute both stared silently into the valley.

Bierce rose, taking out his watch. "I have imposed on you for longer than I had intended." They walked together through the parlor and down the hallway to the door. The young man turned to his host. "It has been a great honor speaking with you."

Allan inclined his head gravely. "The honor has been mine. You are a thoughtful young man." They gripped hands. "I shall not forget this conversation."

Edgar Allan stood in his doorway watching his visitor ride away.

II

They who dream by day are cognizant of many things which escape they who dream by night. In their grey visions they obtain glimpses of eternity, and thrill, in awaking, to find that they have been upon the verge of the great secret.

Poe's "Eleanora."

Edgar Allan returned to the parlor, turned the leaves of a folio volume of Shakespeare's plays on the table, closed the book, extracted the sherry bottle from the cabinet and filled up a glass. He ascended the staircase and entered Mrs. Allan's and his bedroom, passing through it to the upstairs portico. He took a small sip of the sherry; inhaled the scent of blossoms; stood motionlessly amongst the peace and silence. He smiled at the porch's telescope—How many visiting boys had yelped for joy at the sight of it!—and put his eye to the glass. Far away in the valley a line of blue-clad soldiers was drilling.

Stroking his beard with his free hand, Edgar Allan wandered back inside to the upstairs hallway, finding himself facing the alcove that led to his son Auguste's room, the room he himself had inhabited in the far away days when he had been just short of becoming a man. He opened the door and sat himself down on a venerable, soft-cushioned sofa.

The bookcase had once been his, and that table . . . he raised his glass to the framed portrait he had drawn so long ago, and drank to those soft girl-features of Myra.

All this . . . all this. The kindest and most helpful of wives, a son to be proud of, a good daughter (grandchildren soon!), warm friendships, a fine estate. And, central to all these, supporting them all, his work. Well, Poor Richard; He that hath a Trade hath an Estate—a Calling, an Office of Profit and Honor. At the Working Man's house Hunger looks in, but does not enter. He had always believed those things, indeed, his life was a proclamation of their truth. Though his blood-ancestry had been sound Revolutionary stock, the two that birthed him were struggling itinerant actors who left him an orphan before the completion of his third year. But he had struggled with his difficulties; he had persevered; finally he had won the respect and, yes, the love of his contemporaries.

Could circumstances have taken a greatly different turn? Well yes, he could and should have done better. If only he could have given Aunt Maria more of the help she so desperately needed much sooner, Cousin Ginnie would surely have lived far longer than her five and thirty years.

He took another small sip of the sherry, savoring its taste slowly with his tongue. How unlike those care-

laden University days, when he would seek an evening's
oblivion in tossing-off a glass of foul "Peach and
Honey" at a draught! An oblivion it seldom denied
him; all his life long he had been constitutionally un-
suited to handling more than the smallest amount of
drink—for which, praise the Lord! His brother Henry,
with a somewhat stronger stomach, had drunk himself
to an early grave. What a blessing, Temperance; even
these few swallows made his head swim slightly.

  . . . But the fact was, he was *not* his brother Henry,
nor was he any of the others he cared for who, although
showing great promise, had stumbled from the main
path through lack of will. The pathway to success was
perhaps a narrow one, certainly full of obstacles; all his
life he had faced obstacles. But it had ever been a
straight and a steady path for those who *chose* to see it
and to follow it.

  Still: give the young Lieutenant his due. He was an
intelligent man, and it could not be said, despite his
youth, that he lacked experience. . . . Edgar Allan once
more brought the glass to his lips. Could the essentially
successful pattern of one's own life be laid to chance?
Might all the foundations of patient application and
work rest upon some early series of *accidents*?

  Go back to the earliest memories, of Mother
coughing out her life in a dingy room; a new home and a
new, loving Mother and a Father of sorts, stern and
austere. Then the years in Britain, Scottish countryside
and that incomprehensible maze of a school building in
England. The return to Virginia, swimming and wild
country rambles with the boys, writing fluffy schoolboy
poetry to charm the ladies. The warmth and comfort of
Ma and Miss Nancy, the sympathy and understanding
of Mrs. Stanard, with her tragic death; then the after-

noons singing in the parlor, and the long garden strolls, with Elmira. Adolescent infatuation deepening to love, the secret engagement; and a tear-filled parting as he left his lady (but to return!) for a first term at the University.

Hideous year! The man who had taken him under his roof when an orphan child, who had raised him in full expectations of the life of a gentleman, now sent him to the school of Thomas Jefferson with too few funds to cover even the immediate costs of board and tuition! He had written home apprising this Not-Father of the situation and received an additional sum still far short of the required minimum. Thus was he, the seeming foster-son of one of the richest men in Virginia, reduced to pauper's status at the outset of his university career. What could be done? Why, he had done the only thing possible to a young Virginia gentleman faced with such circumstances. He had . . . he had . . .

He had gambled.

There it was. He had gambled, and he had won. Not consistently; in his early months at the University he had gone into debt at the Loo and 7-Up tables and been forced to pay with suit-coats purchased on credit from the merchant-chiselers of Charlottesville. But Dame Luck had at last turned his way, enabling him to recoup his losses, cover all other expenses and more still to spare. In the flush of victory, that late August of 1826, with some hundreds of dollars in his pocket, he had ridden a coach unannounced back to Richmond.

For there was more afoot than mere money troubles. During his six months away there had been no word from Elmira, nary even an acknowledgment of his beseeching letters. Could she have neglected him so cruelly, or had some mischief been done? Suspicious as he was, he had not wanted either family to know of his return, so he had contacted Myra in proper seventeen-year-old fashion, by pitching pebbles against her window. They had met in their magic garden, where the truth was puzzled out soon enough. Each had written the other many times, and been frantic at not receiving a reply; during all of which Mr. Royster had encouraged his wounded daughter to accept the wooings of one Barrett Shelton. Clearly Elmira's father and Mr. Allan had intercepted letters and otherwise conspired together to prevent love from following its normal course.

So, young and foolhardy as they were, they had eloped! A quick message left in her bedroom, some days hiding in an inn 'til boat passage could be obtained, then with a bundle of her clothing and the residue of his money, off to England! England, and privation; struggle; then at last recognition, a modest but sufficient income, and growing mastery of his craft. And the return to America after seven years, his fame preceding him, no doubt aiding in the deathbed reconciliation with John Allan, who above all, good Scotchman that he was, admired success.

Would any of this been possible had he not won at cards? What if he had *not* returned when he did—how long would Elmira have held off the advances of an attractive rival, especially thinking that *he* had deserted her? Or even if he had returned, having *lost* at his gambles, would he have been in any position to offer her marriage? Would she have accepted? If he had not been in England when Ma died would John Allan have still married Miss Nancy—she who had applied her jolly wiles every day to softening her new husband's attitude toward his sometime foster-son—or might he have re-married someone altogether different and altogether unsympathetic? In short, had Dame Luck played him an

Illustrated by Brian Murray

entirely different hand, what man might he have been?

He downed the last of his sherry, his head now swimming madly. "Well, sir." Had *he* spoken? He gazed upon a man standing all in black like young Bierce, somewhat seedy where Allan was fastidious, younger than Allan but older far in years of dissipation, with but a clipped mustache to Allan's luxuriant goatee. For all these differences and many more he could not deny that this man in both his external lineaments and in his overall bearing could only be a grotesque caricature of himself.

Edgar Allan stood; and looked into the steel-gray eyes of—Edgar Poe.

III

With every day, and from both sides of my intelligence, the moral and the intellectual, I thus drew steadily nearer to that truth, by whose partial discovery I have been doomed to such a dreadful shipwreck; that man is not truly one, but truly two.

Robert Louis Stevenson, *Dr. Jekyll and Mr. Hyde*

The man in black motioned to the sofa, himself sitting down on the bed. "Edgar Allan! Make no obeisance for *me*—a mere airy phantasm, an undigested bit of beef as Dickens would have it."

Allan reclaimed his seat and spent some moments in the contemplation of this specter. On such inspection the seediness of Poe's appearance could be seen to owe more to the worn and tattered state of his clothing than to any inherent defect in bearing, for even seated thus informally on the bed of one's son he had something of the carriage of a gentleman. The suit and shoes had been good ones, in their day; the hands were fine and delicate, though emaciated; the face, dissipated and unfocused, was not unkind. Having said his introductory phrases he now sat in quiet patience, much as if to say, *You summoned me, Edgar Allan; what do you propose to do with me, now that I am here?*

"You would appear to feel quite at home, here, Edgar Poe," Allan said at length.

"Indeed, Edgar Allan, this *was* my home, if only for a few, fleeting months. There I threw my cap, there I stretched out to read. . . ." His eyes fixed upon the portrait of Elmira. Rising from the bed, hands limp at his sides, he spoke in a distant, just-audible voice:

"Thou wast that all to me, love,
For which my soul did pine—
A green isle in the sea, love,
A fountain and a shrine,
All wreathed with fairy fruits and flowers,
And all the flowers were mine."

Edgar Allan beamed. "Very fair lines, Poe!"

Allan's visitor half-turned towards him, a puzzled expression on his face. He swung his head about the room, his voice croaking, "Where am I? What madness is this?" He lurched forward and nearly fell.

"For shame, man! Are you drunk?"

Poe turned fully to face Edgar Allan, but he seemed to be gazing quite beyond him. He spoke in a formal, quiet, steady voice, which slowly grew in volume as it gained in momentum: "Ladies and gentlemen, I have much—very much which it would give me the greatest pleasure to communicate: of the incomprehensible connection between each particular individual in the Moon with some particular individual on the Earth—a connection analogous with, and depending upon, that of the orbs of the planet and the satellite, and by means of which the lives and destinies of the one are interwoven

with the lives and destinies and inhabitants of the other;
and above all, if it so please your Excellencies—above
all, of those dark and hideous mysteries which lie in the
outer regions of the Moon—regions which, owing to the
almost miraculous accordance of the satellite's rotation
on its own axis with its sidereal revolution above the
Earth, have never yet been turned, and, by God's mercy,
never shall be turned, to the scrutiny of the telescopes of
man. My general proposition is this:*In the Original
Unity of the First Thing lies the Secondary Cause of All
Things, with the Germ of their Inevitable Annihilation.*
Let me declare that, as an individual, I feel impelled to
fancy—without daring to call it more—that there *does*
exist a *limitless* succession of Universes, more or less
similar to that of which we have cognizance, to that of
which we *alone* shall ever have cognizance, at the very
least until the return of our own particular Universe
into Unity. *If* such clusters of clusters exist, however, *and
they do*—it is abundantly clear that, having no part in
our origin, they have no portion in our laws. They
neither attract us, nor we them. Their material, their
spirit, is not ours—is not that which obtains in any part
of our Universe. They could not impress our senses or
our souls. Among them and us—considering all, for the
moment, collectively—there are no influences in common. Each exists, apart and independently, in the *bosom*
of its *proper* and *particular God*."

Allan snorted his disgust. "I see that you are not
merely *drunk,* Poe. Not drunk, but *mad*!"

Poe seemed once again to take cognizance of his
surroundings. A slight smile crossed his weathered face.

"I have often amused myself, Edgar Allan, in fancy-
ing about the fate of an individual gifted, or accursed
rather, with an intellect *very* far superior to the rest of

mankind. As his manner of thinking and mode of observation would differ from that of all others, so would his
way of speaking—his matter-of-fact reportage of the
truths of his elevated existence—seem to them bizarre.
The verdict of mankind upon such a creature would be
quite universal. They would call him mad."

"I see that I am to deduce from this latest that if there
be Madness in your discourse, still there is Method in it.
Very well, Poe. Granting you for argument's sake the
Genius you have so generously assumed to yourself as
your portion, why do you not set it to some ennobling
purpose instead of thus babbling? You speak of universes
beyond all ken, prating about multitudes of gods like
some Hindoo. But look to your *self,* man—while you
thus disport amongst Cloud Cuckooland your clothes
have fallen into rags; your health itself seems to cling to
you by the veriest thread. *Take* your clusters of clusters!
It is the business of all men to attend to *this* world while
they are in it—even if they be geniuses!"

Poe's eyes narrowed. "Those are strange, harsh words
from one claiming the sobriquet Poet. I have heard their
counterparts many times, for nowhere but in America is
a man so despised for being poor. A man in shabby
clothes is likely a scoundrel—certainly an idler and a
vagabond. Heaven forbid that in America, ruled over by
that most wise and beneficent monarch, *Mob,* anyone
should be found working himself to the bone, year after
year, from morning to night, and still unable to provide
for his family! Unless, perhaps, that struggler should
have the audacity—the insanity—the monumental
folly—to think his nation quite as good a one in its way
as any of the nations of Old Europe, and therefore quite
as deserving of a National Literature worth the name,
guided by a fearless and unsparing literary criticism. If

such a *blockhead* could be found, perhaps even America could permit him and his the honor of starvation."

"Your words are eloquent, Poe, and your logic has a fair seeming to it. Indeed you could almost persuade me that I have stood in callous opposition to the goals you so nobly propound. But nothing could be farther from the truth. Those goals have guided my life as surely as your own. Indeed I daresay that in my case they seem to have been kept more *steadily* in view. I have made some little contribution to the literature of my land, as both editor and writer. Nor have I found those things to be inconsistent with keeping a family clothed and housed. . . ."

"You speak *thus*, Edgar Allan? *You*, the principal heir to one of the richest estates in all Virginia, dare to denounce a man not so blessed for his inability to bridge the difference in our fortunes through the mere frantic scribblings of his *pen*? You, with a strong and healthy family to give you solace, with this splendid mansion to recline in and servants to bring you sustenance when you are tired from a half hour at your writing desk. . . ." Poe's eyes grew wilder with each word spoken, and his hands flailed about him. "You speak of *reality*, Edgar Allan. Step out of your fine mansion for one moment and *see* reality—the reality of peddlers and weavers, lepers, and most poets. Walk *my* streets, ere you judge me."

Perhaps a trick of tired eyes, the outlines of Auguste Allan's room had seemed to grow hazy by imperceptible stages; now, with a grand sweep of Poe's arms, Edgar Allan found himself seated not on cushions but on the hard stool of a tavern. Poe, propped by his elbows on the bar counter, looking at him in amusement, tossed off a glass of port wine then walked, beckoning, to the doorway. Allan, as if under a compulsion, followed.

Without was a night-bustle of the lame, the drunken, the stealthy, tired, fearful, and the frenzied. Edgar Poe turned from the throng, his face ancient, and something cold and dead looking out from his eyes. "*This* is real, Edgar Allan. Here is the home of those who are turned out of great houses, to fend as they may. In a cottage too small for your notice *my* wife *died* by inches, coughing and bleeding, for *five years.* Damn your finery and your smug wisdom, rich man!"

Allan hunched up his shoulders in defense against whatever madness surrounded him. "I have known these streets and many like them, Edgar Poe. Our opportunities have not been so very different as you make them. I, too, know what it is to be cold and friendless. I have starved. But I had *won* my battle long before I came into possession of the house you make so much of. Had no inheritance ever come, my career would still have been in its essential elements the same. I kept a steady course, Poe—avoiding the debilitating effects of liquor and bad company. I have succeeded because I *chose* to, following the hard path of determination, not the easy byways of madness and despair. I affirm *Life,* Poe—if Death *you* choose to celebrate, then Death shall surely be your portion."

"*Enough!* Indeed, even an American writer may succeed if he leave his native country for England, submitting his attitudes completely to the binding yoke of the Mother Country. Your wealth is great and your fame wide—but what of that? Even *with* all of your advantages you have written nothing of true—of lasting worth. In thirty years' time scarcely a line of yours will be on any lips. But, Edgar Allan, as for me; I who have starved, and despaired, who sometimes drank, who suffered the shame than which there is none greater of being *unable* to provide food and clothing for my dying wife—I, Edgar Allan *Poe,* have written words and raised up demons that will haunt the brains of men as long as the things that I have said speak truly of their souls." Now the crowd and the tavern vanished from Allan's sight as an impenetrable white mist suddenly engulfed all save the midnight form of Poe.

Without another word Poe turned from Allan and stepped into the mist; Allan with much of anger, more of curiosity and perhaps the hint of anxiety about being left alone in such surroundings, again followed.

The mist parted to reveal Poe retreating, with stately and deliberate step, down a corridor. Allan stalked after him, past a room decorated in a blue that was matched by the vivid blue of its windows; round a corner, and past a purple chamber whose windows were purple; another corner, and a room and windows of green; another, orange; another, white; another, violet; and yet another, whose decorations were black but whose panes were a deep blood red. Yet again Poe rounded a corner, and Allan, almost at his heels, came to a room at the corridor's end—a room capacious in size and pentagonal in shape, draped from foot to summit in massive-looking tapestries of the richest gold cloth. These were laced with black designs that seemed simple arabesque patterns and conventional grotesqueries from a distance but which seemed to shift as he approached them into subtler and stealthier things, that moved with the constant undulating motion of the drapes.

Thrusting apart the drapery folds, Edgar Allan found himself in a large dining room where some twenty-five

or thirty men and women in exceedingly fine dress were
assembled around a table laden with meats and fruits
and wines in almost barbaric profusion, while at a separate table some seven or eight others fiddled and blew
upon a various and sundry assortment of musical
instruments. As Allan stood silently watching this company for some minutes—for they appeared to be oblivi-
ous to his presence and Poe seemed fairly to have escaped him—their active table conversation took a turn
to the raucous, even the bizarre. Howlings and whis-
tlings and croakings arose from the company; a man
was restrained from leaping up on the table; a woman,
similarly dissuaded from divesting herself of all her
clothes. The tenor of the gathering, having built from
frolic upwards to pandemonium, now gave way to outright chaos at the sudden sounds of shouting and
pounding without the dining room door. Amidst this
croaking and hopping, blaring of trombones and cock-
a-doodling-do the windows of the room shivered into
fragments and a seeming troop of *orang-outangs* leaped
within. Allan, knocked from his seat by one of these
madly shrieking figures, rolled under a sofa for protection.

He lay thus for an uncertain period, eyes screwed
shut and hands pressed against his ears. In time he
lowered the hands to his sides. All now was silence—but
he remained otherwise motionless and still kept shut his
eyes. Something about the uncollectedness of his
thoughts disturbed him; a feeling that a great amount of
time might have perhaps passed as he lay supine. Had
his whereabouts likewise changed? The air about him
felt close, stifling; and its odor was at once strange and
yet disquietingly familiar. He raised one eyelid, then the
other. It was dark—darker far than should have been

the case beneath the sofa. He tried to call for assistance; but his mouth refused to open for him, as if somehow bound. Bound—for what reason? At last he recognized that odor as belonging to a great quantity of moist earth. The appalling nature of his surroundings rushed up to embrace him: he had somehow been taken for *dead,* and buried like a dog—nailed up in a coffin—and thrust, deep, deep, and for ever, into some ordinary and nameless *grave.* He forced his jaws open and screamed.

"For the love of God, Poe!"

It had grown so difficult to think . . . his head reeled and the bells upon it jingled. Enchained thus to this damp granite; the entrance-way to this chamber walled up with brick and mortar—what injury could he have done to merit so awful a revenge? Alone—forever in the darkness—entombed—

"We have put her living in the tomb!"

At the sound of the frantic voice he opened his eyes to the dim and gloomy light of a bed-chamber, and Poe's fiery eyes, seeming to burn into the very core of his bosom. "Said I not that my senses were acute? I *now* tell you that I heard her first feeble movements in the hollow coffin. I heard them—many, many days ago—yet I dared not—I dared not speak! And now—is she not hurrying to upbraid me for my haste? *Madman! I tell you that she now stands without the door!"*

As if in punctuation of Poe's words the door blew open. A woman stood without—tall, stately, lofty-browed—whose glossy black hair fell around a face which, though dazzling in its beauty, betokened by the pallid skin and the mad black eyes the evidences of a body *entombed alive.* As she fell forward upon Poe, Allan turned away in horror, springing to the sill of the open window.

He stood upon the edge of a precipice, looking down

into a canyon whose great depth moved him with terror and revulsion. Back, he must turn back! One false step on this cliff's edge—a sudden crumbling away of the ground beneath his feet—and he was lost! And yet, even as he contemplated the unutterable horrors of the plunge, there arose in him a positive *desire* to consummate just such a fate, and embrace destruction. He swooned, and fell.

His flailing arms and legs closed about the staves of a wooden barrel, adrift in—what? All about him was the seeming blackness of eternal night. A raging, formless chaos of water bore him, with terrific velocity, in great concentric circles, about the edges of a shrieking nightmare of a whirlpool that must surely descend into the very bowels of Hell itself.

As he clutched at the barrel, gasping for breath, a dull sullen glare of red light brought his gaze upward. There, riding toward him on the crest of a wave so high as to almost blot out the sky, was a ship of immense—of incalculable proportions. She was a black ship, without ornament save for her cannons, and her crew, crimson light gleaming from their eyeless sockets—*her crew were the walking dead.* And her Captain—standing becloaked at the helm with eyes and teeth agleam at the wind and the rain and the raging of the maelstrom—her Captain was Edgar Poe.

Allan detached an arm from its precarious hold on the barrel to wave a defiant fist at the looming ship and its Captain. "*Begone,* Poe! Take your errant fantasies and all the other products of your diseased brain back into the Demon-fested Night that spawned you! You have no hold upon *my* soul. Begone from my mind!"

At Allan's words the sea grew calm in an instant; and

Edgar Poe, with a look that seemed to mingle resignation and triumph, seized a chain that appeared to hang suspended from the sky, and climbed upwards until he was lost from sight.

Edgar Allan sat upon the sofa, hand clutching one of its arms; he was, of course, alone. It had been a dream—a waking nightmare of the worst kind, and one that he would endeavor to quickly forget. If need be, he could purge himself of the experience through his writing. *Sonnet: To Nightmare* . . . Or perhaps there was room for such material in the *Virginiad*. General Lee had doubtless experienced his own share of nightmares, between Gettysburg and Appomattox.

He stood. Elmira and the servants would be searching the house to call him to dinner. At the doorway he turned to look at his wife's portrait, frowning at a crimson light that something cast upon her face. His eyes wandered to the glinting sherry glass. Picking it up he whispered, "Rest in peace, Edgar Poe. There, but for the grace of God. . . ."

No Pets
by
Tawn Stokes

About the Author

Tawn Stokes (Lovely name!) works at a famous pediatric hospital associated with the University of Pennsylvania. Born a mile down the street, she has a graduate degree from Penn, has been a social worker, a civil servant, a short-order cook, an eccentric landlady (she says), and a house-restorer. And she's yet another of our writers with long and strong experience in theater, mostly in all the possible back-stage duties but also out front. She has never wanted to be anything else than a writer, concentrating on plays.

She has published poetry and some manuals and pamphlets. One producer, she reports, read one of her plays and then suggested she was working only out of "some warped personal need."

We can't imagine what other kind of need would drive a writer, warped or not. Furthermore, the history of literature shows plainly that the difference between being "warped" and being a fresh, bright new voice is publication.

Publication occurs herewith. Fresh, bright new voice follows. . . .

My Other came to me at daybreak.
He levitated instantaneous to my pallet, silent.
Blue as the light. His optic receptors rose like pale moons over me, tilted, and fixed me.

"Greeting," I said.

I greet.

His ripnails dug my shoulders, extended and retracted rhythmically, ever so lightly. I heard the chuffled whirring of his pleasure.

Yes, in the time of tales before the Black Sun, his ancestors ate my ancestors.

He greets me each dawn.

I greet.

He covered my chest and belly with his presence; he's very large, even for a Great Blue Other. He offered his facial sensors, filaments tipped in light. He lets me twirl them.

If I were prey he would hover thus above me, whirring deeply.

My Other loves me.

I love.

Such love is Ban. Prohibited.

My Landlord's been seen in the Complex the last two mornings.

Best to get up.

My Other rowled as I dumped him.

"Necessity, love," I said.

Keeping Others, especially the Dawn Blues, is Damn Forbidden.

My Other danced before me to my larder.

I love.

I dance.

Who knew when the Landlord would get here? Best to be ready.

I took down a foodbrik, more than enough to sustain me. I'm old for my anthropoid species. My sexual organs are dry, my cephalic hair's gone brittle. I stand less tall than I once stood. My own would have called me a woman; the Landlords call me a problem. I lived to Retire, and now they're obliged to keep me. One of my kind and station's not a woman.

The blattids call themselves human. We killed them, too.

Once.

I saw my Other's vertebral extensor lashing.

What enraged him?

I followed the line I took for his line of sighting: straight to the wall of my larder.

Nothing moving.

I lash.

I looked through the wall and canted my vision downward.

I watch.

I lash.

Something my size but horizontal was crossing the flat clay apron that fronts the Complex. A Complex (if you've never seen one; some are so lucky) is a stack of slatted lifeboxes. You can see straight down to the bottom between the slats. You have to learn how to cant or your eyes go flicketa, as if the bottom were dropping.

Makes you dizzy at first. I live on Level Eleven, if I count correctly.

Yes.

It was.

I watch.

The Landlord approached an easy deathfall below me, straight across the flat clay apron. No call for modesty; the blattids own the damn Earth. As well as us.

Looked just exactly like every other Landlord, shiny black carapace and flittering jointed feet. Had a prissy momerobe drawn across its ovipositor, as if I cared it had one. So it drops little Landlords, what about it.

I'd rather caress my Other and think of Steven.

I would greet my damn Landlord naked as I do my Other, but it might consider me mad and withdraw my ration. When it jointed up to the clankstair I popped on my old pink frillo. Yes, I've always hated pink.

My Other hissed.

I hunger.

His vertebral extensor flickered across the floorslats.

I watch.

I wait.

The Landlord was entering the Complex a long way below us, to suckle on the thoughts of my neighbors who hardly know me.

Would it forget me?

Possession of a natural Other is not permitted.

Where would my Other hide? Would he care if I hid him?

I've never considered trouble 'till I had to. Why I won't live to get old, Old Steven tells me.

Told me. I'm old now.

The blattididae give us this day our daily foodbriks,

goes with Retirement Housing. Nothing for Others. Blattids refuse to feed Others. Or let us feed them.

My Other feeds himself.

And he doesn't like foodbriks.

My Other was still as the light laid out the floorslats. Only the end of his vertebral extensor twitched.

He saw the roach before I did.

It was an arrogant Prussian roach as tall as my Other, dull brown and winged, advancing with feelers cocked, like a Policy robot serving a termination. Its relatives run this Complex. Somebody told it.

My Other tensed.

I hunger.

An Other's optic receptors are set to detect what moves: When an Other sits perfectly still with stillness before him his visual field is blank. He's blind 'til something flickers. So he waits for movement.

I wait.

The roach proceeded.

I saw the roach see him.

It stopped. The damn things may be sentient; there's plenty of argument.

The Landlords use Cousin Roach in medical experiments.

Yet they've kept us. They even offer Retirement.

The roach did not flicker a feeler.

I looked at my Other.

My Other was rhythmically shifting his optic receptors, side to side. He was moving his visual field. To activate vision.

I knew what he meant to do.

I would watch him do it.

He began the deathsong, low as the wind that hovers over water, rising slow and rising.

The roach was all attention. Not a feeler quivered.
Stasis. Optic receptors shifting.
Song.
And stasis.
Stillness.
Rising, moaning stillness.
The roach broke first.
The roach flew up and my Other seized it in midair, his long incisors crackling into its carapace. Yellow juice spattered the floorslats. My Other's tenor deathsong thrilled my ears. I gloried in the tensile grip of his powerful ripnails, smelled the maddening sweetness of the oozeflesh erupting out of the carapace gripped between them. I felt the lifeforce desperate within his grip struggling, fighting to only live. I felt his huge curved incisors seek the deathpoint, the juncture spot between the head and the carapace.

I sometimes become my Other.

In imagination.

I kill.

I live.

His long incisors pointed their mark and slashed downward. The roach thrashed once and was still.

My Other ate it.

I watched as he neatly cleaned his facial sensors, whirring softly.

We caressed each other. I watched his viscera kneading.

I'd almost forgotten the Landlord.

My Other heard it scrabbling at the doorstocks. And he hissed.

"Hide," I hissed myself, a hasty hiss.

My Other agreeably continued caressing my ankle.

"Sun's sake," I said. "The Landlord's coming in here.

Mustn't see you. Please, love, get under the bed." If my
sturdy little legged pallet deserves the name Bed. It's the
only thing in my lifebox you could get under.

"This is an official visit," the Landlord blatted.

What the hell did you think I thought it was? I did
not say: I'd hardly ask you for company.

"A single moment," I said.

I lifted my Other though he doesn't like to be lifted;
he always prefers to levitate to my bosom. Well, to
what's left of my bosom, but nevertheless.

He rowled displeasure.

Ye suns, if the Landlord heard him.

Landlords never keep Others.

How would one know what a displeased Other sounds
like?

"I shall come in," my official blattid said.

I had no choice in the matter: I stuffed my Other,
rowling, under the bed. I gave him half a foodbrik; he
started to play with it.

I twirled his facial sensors, sometimes calms him.
Provided he wills to be calmed, and this time, I thank
you, he did.

"Please be still," I said. "I love you only."

Steven's not going to hear me. Wherever he is.

I fluffed my old pink frillo and patted my cheek-
bones, not that I think even blows would make them
red. Must look nice for my visitor.

"Do come in," I said.

The Landlord did so.

"Good day," it said.

Hell, I'd hardly noticed.

"So it is," I said. "Delighted to have you."

If the damn thing swallows that lie it'll swallow the
others.

It bowed from its leg joints. The species has no waist.

"May I ask certain questions?"

Hell no, bug, I've always hated questions. Never answer 'em.

"If that's what you came for," I said, and too politely. I'm too old to die for impudence.

We hunched at my dangling tabula.

I hunched; I don't know the damn blattid word for what my blattid did. I assume it made itself comfy.

It folded its hard black legs beneath its carapace. I hadn't known it could do that; my previous Landlords were stiffs.

"I record my impressions," it said.

Record them well, bug. My Other eats your relatives.

And you eat mine as well, I shouldn't wonder. Monkeymeat hangs heavy on your breath.

Blattids don't do breath.

"You're entirely welcome," I said.

At least it recorded silent, with a brainbox. Though the damn things have no brains in the human sense.

ANTHROPOIDS HAVE NO BRAINS IN THE HUMAN SENSE, BUT I DO CONSIDER THEM SENTIENT.

My Landlord faced and addressed me.

"Are you presently well?" it said.

Why should you give a damn, bug.

"Well enough," I said.

I RECORD THE IMPRESSION: HOSTILITY. THE TENANT IS HOSTILE. ONCE IN THE TIME OF TALES BEFORE THE BLACK SUN, ITS ANCESTORS RAIDED MY ANCESTORS' NESTS WITH CHEMICALS.

"You are presently well," it said.

Illustrated by Bob Eggleton

WE CAN ONLY BELIEVE THEY WISHED TO
EXTERMINATE US.

If the damn thing knew of my Other, my Lease on
Life would terminate. Even if I am in Retirement.

No Pets.

THEY NEVER OFFERED RETIREMENT.

They outdid us.

WE OUTDID THEM. NOW WE NEED ONLY
LIVE AND HONOR THE LIFEFORCE. WE ARE
CIVILIZED.

"Does your food suffice?" Bug asked me.

"It suffices fine," I said. Look in my larder. I still
have 17 foodbriks and three hods of water. My Other
and I are frugal.

He doesn't like foodbriks.

I could hear the flick-swish of my Other's vertebral
appendage. My suns, let him stay in hiding. My Landlord swiveled its eyes, all flat black panes of responsive-
ness, towards the swish.

"Listen to the wind," I said.

"Should the wind be audible?" That has to be a
bugbrained question: wind should be what it is.

"It's the slatted walls," I said.

"Do you find your lifebox comfortable?"

Fine for a lifebox.

"Reasonably so," I said. "I know I'm too old to do
better."

"One is never too old," it said with prim disapproval.
Roachoid philosophy.

"How old are you?" I said.

ONE HUNDRED AND ELEVEN.

OBLITERATE THAT IMPRESSION.

"It is not appropriate," my Landlord primly said, "to
speak of my personal particulars."

Personal particulars my dry ass: you have no personal particulars. Skip the momerobe.

"You look so young," I said. It obviously didn't: they all look the same until they turn up dead. They live a couple of centuries.

How they outdid us, I estimate.

"Do you keep a pet?" it said, right out of the ether.

Oh my suns, I did not say. This one's a Watcher.

"Why do you ask?" I said. Some think the Landlords are telepaths, know if you're lying. I don't myself, but why should I take any chances?

There was movement under my bed.

My Other was shifting his optical receptors.

My Other was watching my Watcher.

I did not dare tell him to quit.

Not that Others do what you tell them, you've noticed that.

My Landlord's paned black eyes appeared alert, but who the hell knows what a blattid is looking at anyway? Eyeless eyes, Steven called them.

How long has Steven been out there in the limepit?

"Are you disturbed?" my eyeless watcher said.

"Not at all," I said with well-feigned insouciance.

"You appear disturbed," it said. I told you: they did outdo us.

"Appearance deceives," I said.

THIS TENANT DECEIVES ME.

"May we go on?" I said. Your momerobe's open: your ovipositor's showing.

And being the descendant of apes, I scratched my ass.

THE TENANT OBSERVES THAT I AM OB-SERVING SOMETHING.

My sundamned Other hissed.

It was a long, low, python's hiss.

His moonpale optical receptors glowed like mirrors.

He had levitated onto my bed.

Blue as the dawn, and visible as an elephant. Hissing his wrathful hiss.

I fainted face down on the tabula.

Of course I didn't faint; I only falsified.

The blattid was instantly solicitous.

THE TENANT APPEARS TO HAVE FAINTED.

Its cracklehard feelers brushed my cephalic hair. My three hods of water'd be hardly enough to wash it.

THE FAINT ITSELF IS DECEPTION. I DISCERN AN AUDIBLE HISS.

I moaned realistically. Suns how I hate to be old and reduced to this. Yes in my sundanced heyday I'd just have thunked her, Steve and I could have lumbered out the body. But they'd only provide me another. The landless all have Landlords.

Not one that had heard my Other.

THE AUDIBLE HISS IS EMANATING FROM AN OTHER: A SMALL TELEKINETIC PREDATOR. IT IS TENSED UPON THE BED.

I thought I'd better come round, so I muttered pitifully.

"Are you presently well?" Roachy said.

"I'm entirely fine," I said. "Except I'm starving."

Not that I want more foodbriks, the damn things digest like lead.

"I can increase your ration of foodbriks."

"That would be nice," I said. They'll make dandy missiles.

THE OTHER MUST BE HER PET.

"Do you have a pet?" it said.

"Pets not permitted."

I saw my Other glide silent off the bed and couch himself under it.

Had the Landlord seen him?

My Other was perfectly still, a shadow in shadow.

"Do I infer that you do not have one?"

"You do infer," I said. And I certainly hope so.

What would I say if she pinioned me: no or yes?

WHAT WOULD THE CLIENT SAY IF I ASKED HER: AFFIRMATIVE/NEGATIVE?

It's obvious La Roach hasn't seen him.

IT IS OBVIOUS SHE HAS AN OTHER: IT WAS HER OTHER ON THE BED.

She'd jump me if she'd had the glimpse of him. She must have believed that ape-piss about the wind.

This one's dumb, by ringo. Hope I keep her.

OF COURSE NO CIVILIZED PERSON COM-PREHENDS NOR CARES TO COMPREHEND WHAT MOTIVATES A SENTIENT BEING TO HARBOR A COMPANION PREDATOR.

She hasn't seen him. She must be deaf, dumb and dumb, but she hasn't seen him.

BUT THE TENANT IS ALL ALONE AND IN RETIREMENT: SHE MAY NEED SOME AFFEC-TIVE RELATIONSHIP.

Why is my Landlord eyeing the ceiling; there's no-body up there. Eyeless Watcher.

I wait.

PETS ARE NOT STRICTLY PERMITTED: THEIR PRESENCE ENCOURAGES INSECTS.

Others are strictly forbidden: The Landlords think they're devils, so I estimate.

My Other looked plenty devilish, hovering still as a deathhead under the bed.

NEED SHOULD MAKE EXCEPTIONS. THOUGH
SOME WOULD NOT, PERHAPS I SHOULD MAKE
THIS EXCEPTION.

She hasn't seen him.

I wait.

LET HER HAVE HER LITTLE WHIRRING PET.
IT IS LITTLE ENOUGH FOR SUCH AN ANCIENT
BEING. WE ARE CIVILIZED.

HONOR THE LIFEFORCE. LIVE AND LET
LIVE.

I wait.

My Other's safe as long as I have this watcher: I can
fool her. Any dawn of day and twice for sunset.

THE OTHER IS SAFE: WHO CAN ONE OTHER
INJURE?

I watch.

I wait.

OBLITERATE THE IMPRESSION.

I want.

I wait.

I HAVE SEEN NOTHING.

She hasn't seen anything.

I see.

I wait.

I exchange my last unpleasantries with my Landlord,
fully confident, not even galled to be nice to her. Suns, I
did hope to keep this one. I truly did.

Finally my Landlord unfolded, twitching its momerobe.

I didn't even want to see its ovipositor. Hell, I'm
civilized.

Did occur to me what fun it would be to pop off my
frillo and offer the ape-old gesture, but I didn't. Due
respect.

My Other was couching still beneath the bed.

I watch.

I wait.

"Your ration is increased," my mother of roachlets said. "Your medical needs will be tended."

"I have no medical needs," I almost said, and then I remembered I'd fainted, quite successfully.

"I'll visit the doc," I said.

"Would you like the doc brought to you?"

Not for a million.

"Believe I can go," I said. "If not, I'll notify."

"I am concerned," my Landlord said. "Please do remember."

It probably was, too.

Why was I feeling warm to it?

I like the dumb ones.

"Keep yourself well," it said and legged out the doorway.

No: I did not see my Other follow it.

THE LITTLE PREDATOR FOLLOWS ME. IT WEAVES AMONG MY FEET. CAN IT BE IT EXPERIENCES GRATITUDE.

How long has my Steven been out in the common limepit?

He would not, I expect, have been proud of my old fool deceptions. Steve was unruly.

I weave.

I sing.

Steve's dead.

I sing.

I hunger.

THE OTHER IS EMANATING CURIOUS TENOR SOUNDS. IT TANGLES INTO MY FEET. MY, MY— MY FEET ARE SLIDING. . . .

I sing.

IT TICKLES. I WONDER IF PERHAPS THE
LITTLE OTHER LIKES ME.

I heard the crackling splat.

My nice dumb Landlord was splattered out on the
hard clay eleven floors below me, carapace cracked and
scattered like exploded lacquer. The oozeflesh was oozing freely. Its silly little momerobe had fallen from its
ovipositor; yes, it did have a nice one, smooth and black
and amorously oviparous.

Yes, it was dead.

I saw My Other.

He was levitating half a handspan above the clankstair, revving up for a feat. Even through the slatted
walls I could hear his whirring. His vertebral extensor
lashed in lustful triumph.

He lifted neat from the clankstair and sprang out into
ether for descent. I watched him bear to the mark his
great incisors as he fell upon his target, drawing his
facial sensors to maximal gape. I knew what he meant to
do. I would watch him do it.

He landed live and whirring.

On his feet.

I kill.

I live.

I eat.

Building Plausible Futures
by
Jerry Pournelle

About the Author

Jerry Pournelle is that legendary figure, the Renaissance Man. That includes his mastery of the epeé as well as other deadly weapons, but it also covers his two Ph. D.'s, his master's degree in statistics and systems engineering, his bachelor's degree in mathematics, and his chairmanship of the Citizen's Advisory Council on National Space Policy. Then, of course, there are his definitive regular columns on computers for Byte and InfoWorld. And all of that isn't even the half of it.

In the world of SF, his contributions include editorship of many anthologies, any number of nonfiction pieces for the SF media, the presidency of the Science Fiction Writers of America, and, of course, his stories and novels. Those he writes alone and in collaboration with others, notably fellow W.O.T.F. judge Larry Niven. He is a fixture on the New York Times best-seller list, with such blockbusters as The Mote in God's Eye, Lucifer's Hammer, Footfall and Oath of Fealty.

And he was a front-line artillery officer in Korea. When he speaks, people should listen. . . .

The first thing you must do is decide whether you *want* to build a plausible future. Many writers don't. Some write fantasy and have no interest in building futures with sharp edges and rivets. Some, like Harlan Ellison, don't exactly write fantasy but are successful largely *because* what they write is implausible. Others aren't interested in futures at all.

Then there are writers like Frank Herbert. *Dune* convinces you that the implausible is real. Frank simply evaded most of the tough questions: computer and space science are dismissed with handwaving and religious mumbo-jumbo. He made a fortune with *Dune* and if you can write like Frank Herbert you don't need advice from me.

This essay is about classical science fiction stories, the kind that built and even defined the genre during the Golden Age when John W. Campbell, Jr. was editor of *Astounding*. Those stories generally presented a future that seemed real and plausible; a future in which science, engineering, technology, and the social structures were self-consistent; a future the reader could believe in, at least until he had finished the story. The best of these stories taught the reader something about science and technology, and held up under real-world scrutiny.

Building those futures was never easy, but it was a lot

easier in the old days than it is now. Things were a lot
simpler then, and more predictable. Space travel was
inevitable even if most people didn't believe it. All you
needed was the courage to accept your own analyses.

For example, Robert Heinlein's "Requiem" and "The
Man Who Sold The Moon" are about a businessman
whose ambition is to go to the Moon, and who uses
business techniques to get a Moon colony started. Today those stories may be dated, but we can still read
them. In their time, they were the epitome of hard-
science science fiction.

Heinlein used a simple technique: he took everyday
familiar objects and events, projected them into the
future, and subtly modified them. One of the most famous lines in science fiction: "The door dilated." In this
one line from *Beyond This Horizon,* Heinlein takes us
into the future.

A dilating door would still be the future to us.
"Requiem," though, begins at a county fair. In Heinlein's
time the barnstormer pilot, or the aeronaut, really did
go to county fairs and offer to take passengers for short
rides for a fee. Most readers would be familiar with that.
In "Requiem," fair-goers have the opportunity to fly in
a privately owned, obsolete, and nearly unsafe rocket
ship.

"Requiem" was written in 1939, long before the real
space program became a government monopoly. More
importantly, though, it was written before the skies were
crowded with aircraft; before lawyers dominated the
world; before the Environmental Protection Agency;
before OSHA and Medicare and the busybody government put a stop to risky entertainment like barnstorm-
ing, whether in biplanes or rocket ships—and before TV
put an end to county fairs as a standard medium of

entertainment. The central theme of "Requiem" could make a good story today, but every one of the details, both technical and social, would be different. In its day, though, "Requiem" was as fine an example of projecting a plausible future as we have. Those who want to learn how to build plausible futures could do a lot worse than study early Heinlein's ability to link technological and social changes and weave them into a seamless whole.

Technological Projection

Technology projection isn't particularly easy, but the science fiction writer doesn't have to do it. We don't need to predict the real future; we're only interested in a *plausible* future.

Even in the real world of professional technology projections, some things are easier than others. For example, you can have a lot more confidence that some development will happen some time in the next thirty years than you have in predicting *when*. It's usually easier to project twenty to thirty years ahead than it is five.

Before you can project technology, you need some understanding of what technology is. You needn't be a scientist or engineer, and in fact scientists and engineers often don't understand the nature of technological development. Technology as a phenomenon is easier to understand than most of its components.

The first principle is that technology goes by "S" curves. When a new scientific or engineering principle is discovered, things go pretty slow for a while. It takes a lot of effort to make small changes. An example would be aircraft speeds and ranges from the time of the Wright brothers until after World War I.

Then a breakthrough is made. The curve shoots upward. Aircraft speed and performance made astonishing gains just before and during World War II. After
that we reached the "sound barrier" and the gains came
much more slowly. We had reached the top of the "S."
That in turn became the base of a new "S."

Computer power went the same way. Early science
fiction had a dismal record of predicting what computers would be like and what they could do. The best
SF writers based their future computers on things they
knew: fire control computers for warships, and primi-
tive IBM machines. Real world computer technology
crawled along so slowly that it was plausible to have
stories in which humans could take the place of a
damaged or destroyed computer, or even out-perform
one.

Then came the breakthroughs, and most of those
stories were made instantly obsolete. Even after the
breakthrough, when writers were frantically trying to
revise their thinking, the sheer speed of real-world advances made most of their stories obsolete within a year
of publication.

We are now in the sharp upward slope of the computer technology "S" curve: computing power doubles
every year while component prices fall. Eventually we
will reach the top of that curve. Meanwhile, plausible
stories require that future societies not only have advanced computer technology, but that the technology
be widespread through the culture. The notion of the
computer as hulking giant hidden in a basement and
attended by high priests simply can't hold any longer:
everyone has computers now, and will in any plausible
future.

The second principle is that technology is interdependent. Advances in one sector influence all the others. New molecular chemistry techniques led to microminiaturization which led to the computer revolution. New computer techniques led to new developments in chemistry—and in nearly everything else. It is now possible to do computer simulations of medical and dental problems; economic systems; aircraft. Little remains unaffected.

In the military field miniaturization made possible on-board computers for missile guidance. This brought ICBM miss-distances down from miles to hundreds of feet in a decade. That led to increased research in silo-hardening, which led to hard-rock silo designs, and that development made it possible to conduct certain mining operations that were previously not financially feasible.

Examples of interdependence can be given without limit, and you can't know too many of them. Burke's *Connections* is worth a lot of study.

The important thing to note is that you can't change just one thing; if you're constructing plausible societies, you must not only project technologies, but think through what effects those technologies will have on other fields—and also what they will do to the social order.

After all, the sexual revolution owes more to cheap motor cars than anything else. Before the motor car it was very difficult for young people of opposite sex to be together without adults; after the motor car, adult supervision became nearly impossible. (And for that matter, the adults had new opportunities.)

We're now in an era of bifurcated morality: high tech people generally aren't perceived to be motivated by

religion, and haven't found another philosophical basis
for faith in law and justice. Meanwhile we have the new
rise of fundamentalism, both Christian and Moslem at
precisely the moment when all knowledge is available to
just about everyone. It makes for interesting times.

Tools of the Trade

In order to keep the present from overtaking your
future before you have finished your story, you have to
keep up with current trends. This isn't easy. After all, I
live in a world that was science fiction when I was in
college. I sit at a computer console that connects me to
tens of thousands of highly educated technologists; I can
get the answer to nearly any question in minutes to
hours. The Soviets have built the space station the US
would have built in the 70's, if it weren't for Proxmire
and his ilk. Terrawatt lasers of high efficiency have been
developed for strategic defense. Technology pours out,
and if you're not careful you can write a story about a
future invention that's already available in your DAK
mail order catalog.

The indispensable tools of the trade are: *High Technology* magazine, and the weekly *Science News*. These
aren't enough, but you can't do without them. A magazine that used to be useful and isn't now is *Technology
Review*. *Scientific American* used to be indispensable;
now it's useful, but just barely. Both these magazines
succumbed to the notion that politics was more important than science.

Perhaps the best of the science magazines is the
British publication *New Scientist*. It isn't cheap. Because
of its political slant, and its British origin, it cannot and
should not be the only science magazine you get.

From there you will need some specialty publications. Business trends are best tracked in *The Wall Street Journal,* which also follows commercially important technology trends. *Fortune* will do a good job of condensing and summarizing business developments. *Aviation Week and Space Technology* is valuable to most science fiction writers, but it's expensive. *BYTE* summarizes the latest trends in consumer-available computer technology. All of these are available in the libraries.

There are also books. *Writing And Selling Science Fiction* by the Science Fiction Writers of America, available from Writer's Digest Books, is one of the best. It contains my longer work on this subject, as well as essays by many other writers. *Science Fiction Today And Tomorrow,* edited by Reginald Bretnor, (Harper 1974) is I think out of print but well worth the trouble of finding it.

Once a writer becomes established by publishing a few stories and books, he will find ways to get on various mailing lists, such as NASA's news briefs, and the technology announcements that pour forth from university and commercial laboratories. Indeed, the problem may be to avoid getting too many of these publications; but they're indispensable for finding out what's happening at the cutting edge.

A Sense of Structure

The most important prerequisite to inventing a plausible future is to have an understanding of the way the world works. That's not easy since no one knows how the world works. On the other hand, if you don't think you have a fairly good idea, you'll have no framework to build your future on.

It used to be that the whole purpose of education was to give students a working knowledge of how the world works. We have since opted for "educating the whole child," meaning that we teach people nothing. Unless you had an atypical modern education, you'll have no choice but to teach yourself.

You learn by getting around and doing things, asking questions, and watching other people do things. Writing is never a full-time job. You'll also have to read books. Arthur C. Clarke used to counsel writers to read at least one book and one newspaper each day. If that's too much, make it a book a week; but you must read and read a lot.

The books needn't be on technology. The only way I know to project the future is to know a lot about the past. To see what impacts new technologies will have, look at what the old ones have done. It also helps to read biographies and especially autobiographies: of scientists, to be sure, but also of people like Albert Sloan and Henry Ford, movers and shakers who have turned technology into social change.

How I Got This Way

I'm told I do a reasonable job of creating plausible worlds. I like to think so, and people I respect confirm it. What I am *not* an expert on is teaching anyone else how to do it.

In my case I spent a lot of time in universities studying nearly everything except English literature; then more years in space science, working at the edge of technology, and sometimes making technological forecasts. I also wrote research proposals for aerospace firms. The experience was invaluable; I used to tease my SF writer friends by saying that I wrote science fiction without characters or plot and got paid more per word than they did.

When I got out of the aerospace business to write full time I ended up writing a weekly column for a national newspaper. I'd answer questions like "what is a laser?", and "what caused the Ice Ages?", in exactly 700 words. I guarantee that three years' experience at that will give you a broad base in the sciences, and teach you not to waste many words.

In other words, I had a fair amount of education and training, and experience, in understanding this world before I started building new ones; and I don't know of any easy substitute for that.

Nobody ever promised it would be easy.

On My Way to Paradise
by
Dave Wolverton

About the Author

Dave Wolverton is at Brigham Young University studying to become an editor. He is a rugged individual who has done such things as being a prison guard, and has also served as a Mormon missionary. He is an editor for The Leading Edge, a Provo-based semiprofessional SF magazine of high caliber.

He had entered the Writers of The Future contest twice before, becoming a semi-finalist the first time and a finalist in the most recent previous Quarter before winning a First with the strikingly accomplished story that follows.

To further substantiate Wolverton's rapid progress, "On My Way to Paradise" has already grown into a novel, scheduled to be completed by the time you read this. W.O.T.F. has launched a number of novelists, but this is the first one who has brought us his opening chapters. So if you would like to know more about what happens to the situation you are about to be captivated by, it will likely not be long before a fortunate book publisher satisfies your curiosity. Meanwhile. . . .

$\mathbf{A}$ dusty gray hovercraft floated to a stop in front of my booth in the feria. As its door flipped open an emaciated woman struggled up from the shadows within and into the stabbing daylight. Her head was down, and rolling from side to side as she moved. Sweat stained the armpits of her black skinsuit, and blood dripped from the bandaged stump at the end of her right arm. An old mestizo woman lurched away from the craft, made the sign of the cross, and muttered "Qué horror!" A small boy gaped at the thin woman and moaned "Una bruja!" and the crowd murmured in agreement that this walking skeleton must be a witch.

She staggered to my booth, shouldering past curious peasants, and thrust her bloody stump over the counter. "Are you Señor Angelo Osic?" she asked in English.

I nodded.

"Can you fix this . . . this body?" She braced herself on the counter, trembling.

"Si—yes," I said, gently prodding the stump at the end of her arm. Her wound was fresh, but would soon be infected. "However, a new hand will take months to grow—months more to be usable. A prosthesis would be fast—"

"Do a hand. Now! And bones too. I need bones." She talked with the quick, commanding voice of the rich refugiados from the Estados Unidos Socialistas del Sur. I thought she must be a criminal from Guyana or the American Colonies in Brasilia Independiente.

"Do you have your hand?" I asked. "Perhaps we could reconnect it."

"No."

I looked at her closely. The slope of her shoulders and her narrow cheeks indicated that she'd been born with a small frame, but even if she had bone disease too, the two factors couldn't account for the small diameter of her joints. "How long were you in low G?"

"Never been in low G," she lied.

"You should be in the hospital," I told her, not wanting to deal with a criminal. "I am only a pharmacologist. And my drugs are not as miraculous as people sometimes claim."

"Fix me," she said. "No hospitals. No questions." She pulled out a computer crystal as long as her hand and slipped it into my palm. Its nonglare surface was virtually invisible, except for the packet of liquid RAM at one end. It was good crystal, Fugitsu quality.

"You need a place to rest—a hospital bed," I said.

She leaned forward, and I saw she was young, much younger than I had first imagined; her black hair fell in front of her black eyes and her sweaty face paled with genuine terror. "If you ball me over, *I die*," she said.

In that moment when she showed her terror, she was beautiful. I felt a strong urge to help her, to comfort her. Telling myself she might not be a criminal, I closed my booth and escorted her back to the hovercraft. I gave the driver my address in Gatun and told him to go by way of Avenida Balboa. He drove very slowly through the crowded feria, and soon the thin woman fell asleep. We floated past crowds of mestizos selling bright dresses and parrots, fresh fruit, cheap Chinese microchips tumbling from earthenware pots. Merchant sailors from Europe, Africa and Asia searched the backwaters of

Panama for high-tech and contraband items to resell in other ports. The local peasants became angry with my chauffeur for driving in a pedestrian zone and refused to move, so he flushed the hovercraft's thrusters, blowing hot air and dust into the crowds, burning the naked legs of the children. I felt dirty and sinful to be in that craft and wished I hadn't agreed to take care of the thin woman. I jacked in a call to Uppanishadi-Smith Corp. and ordered a limb-regeneration kit, an osteoporosis rehab packet, and a self-regulating canister of fluo-thane.

On the border of the free zone I saw Flaco, a good friend who did not mind dealing with criminals as much as I did, and I had the driver stop the limo. Flaco stood with some arms dealers who haggled with Colombian guerrillas over the price of grenade launchers. Flaco stuck his narrow face through the window and raised an eyebrow as he saw the thin woman.

"Hola, Angelo. So, you have taken to dating dead women?" he said, laughing. "Good idea. Very classy! Very sensible!"

I got out of the hovercraft and walked out of the thin woman's listening range. "Yes," I said. "She's quite a catch for an old man. Not only is she beautiful, but when I'm done with her, she'll make fine fertilizer for the lawn." Flaco laughed. I handed him the crystal. "What is the value of this?" I asked.

Flaco rolled it over in his hand. "Any software on it?"

"I don't know."

"Maybe 400–500 thousand," he said.

"Will you check its registration code? I think it is stolen. Also," I whispered, "I must know who this woman is. Can you get a retina scanner and bring it to my home tonight?"

"Yes, my friend," Flaco whispered, staring at the woman in the floater. "Once, I saw a spider with legs that thin—" he said. "I stepped on it." He patted my shoulder, then laughed.

I got in the hovercraft and left the free zone. And as we floated down the highway on the outskirts of Colón, we rolled past the evenly spaced rows of banana plants. Because I'd never floated down that road in a fast car before, I noticed for the first time how perfectly ordered the orchards were, with each plant three meters from its neighbor. My prosthetic eyes register colors in the infrared spectrum as shimmers of light, something like the sheen one sees glimmering off platinum in the sunlight. And on this day the dark green canopy of the orchards shimmered with infrared light. Under the canopy of leaves were jumbles of hammocks, burlap lean-to's, tents, cardboard boxes and old cars—squalid, temporary shelters for the refugiados who were fleeing the Socialist states in South America. Unfortunately, they were afraid to brave their way through Costa Rica, so the refugiados huddled together, waiting for ship passage to Trinidad or Madagascar or some other imaginary capitalist paradise.

I looked at the homes among the orchards and thought it strange to see such disorder among order. It reminded me of an incident from my childhood: a family of murderers called the Battistas Sangrientos had been caught selling body organs outside our village. When the police caught them, they took the family to the beach to shoot them in front of the whole town so people would know what a despicable crime had been committed. Three boys in this family were only children, perhaps ten to twelve years old, and it was rumored that when gutting victims these boys often raced each other to

salvage precious organs. But all the Battistas swore the
boys were innocent. And when the police got ready to
shoot the family, the Captain told them to form a line,
but the young boys clung to their murderous father and
refused to move. The policemen clubbed the boys, and it
took a long time for the police to get the family to stand
in line. And once the family was standing in a line, it
took a long time for the Captain to give the order for the
firing squad to shoot. I have always believed that the
Captain waited just so he could enjoy that moment of
watching them stand in line. And as the bullets ripped
through the crowd of children I wondered *Why could the
Captain not shoot them while in a huddle, clutching their
father? What difference did it make?*

When we reached my home, I carried the thin woman
to the cool basement and laid her on a blanket on
the floor. I checked her pulse and was looking at the
bandage on her stump when I heard a foot scuff on the
carpet behind me. The limo driver had brought in two
small bags and set them down. I paid him for the thin
woman's fare, escorted him out of the house, and asked
if he would drive me to Colón for free since he was going
that way. He said no, so I walked the eleven kilometers
back to Colón to pick up my drugs at Uppanishadi-
Smith Corp.

I enjoyed the walk back home. My house is very
old and the adobe walls are crumbling, but it is in a
neighborhood where all houses are in poor repair, so
it doesn't look bad by comparison. Some people even
think it must be a rich person's house, because it is on
the lake, and because they can't imagine a morphogen
dealer not being rich. But I had decided long before not
to break my heart by hustling life extensions in the

penthouses of Miami, Seoul, or Peking. I loved Panama.

By the time I got back home, the sun had just set. The air was getting cool. Flaco lay under the papaya tree in my front yard, watching a large brown fruit bat gorge on the uppermost papayas and spill dark seeds to the ground. "Hola, Angelo," he called when he saw me. "I brought that *thing* you wanted. Spider Legs is inside. She's awake now. I brought beautiful yellow roses for her. She likes them as much as that bat likes papayas. I think her nose is stuck to the flowers."

"So, you have met her?" I asked.

"Yes. I told her I am a doctor, and that you called me in to administer medications."

"Did she believe you?"

"Oh yes. I am a very good liar," Flaco laughed. "Also, that crystal did have software on it—old military software."

"Military?"

"Yes. A reality program for a brain bag."

I had once heard a doctor at a convention give a speech on reality programs. The military attached them to brains when they needed to store them for transplanting. The reality program kept the transplantee from suffering sensory deprivation, so he wouldn't become paranoid or psychotic. It locked him in a dream where he ate, worked, slept, and did other routine things, unaware he was separated from his body. But the reality program can only tap into existing memories and vary scenarios by merging those memories. The brain bag then monitors the brain's reaction to the scenarios and keeps it from becoming surprised or shocked. "Is it stolen?" I asked.

"According to the registration code on the crystal, it belongs to a Señor Amir Jafari. He lives at one of the

Lagrange orbits. He hasn't applied for citizenship with any nation, so he may prefer to live outside the law. It would be illegal for him to have this program; he won't report it stolen."

"Is he a doctor?" I asked.

Flaco shrugged.

"Why would he be interested in brain storage?"

Flaco shrugged again, pulled the crystal from his pocket, and said, "If you want to sell it, we could get 572,000 standards."

I calculated: barring complications, the thin woman's medication would cost about twenty-six thousand, which would leave a great deal of profit. However, I decided to ask the thin woman if she had a receipt for the crystal, hoping she hadn't stolen it. I asked Flaco to hold the crystal a few days.

When we got to the basement, the thin woman sat propped in a corner with her knees against her chin. Three yellow roses rested on her knees, and she was asleep. I opened the limb-regeneration kit and spread packets of salves, washes, and medical instruments on a clean cloth on the floor.

Flaco read aloud the directions on the fluothane and practiced putting the gas mask over his face. When he'd done it enough so he could put it on the thin woman, I touched her shoulder, waking her. She crawled to the center of the floor and lay on her back.

The roses had fallen off her knees, and Flaco handed them to her. She inhaled their fragrance and said, "You know, when you try to smell them too long, you lose their scent. You can't hold it." Flaco and I nodded.

"By the way," Flaco said, "what should we call you?"

The thin woman didn't answer. Flaco kept talking in

a conversational tone. "Angelo says we should call you *Spider Legs*. He thinks that is very funny. But I told him it isn't proper to call a woman that. You must forgive him—he has a peasant mentality and doesn't know better."

"Call me *Tamara*," she said.

"Ah, Tamara. A fitting name. Very beautiful," Flaco said.

"Do you still have the crystal?" Tamara asked.

"Yes," I answered.

"May I touch it? Hold it until you're done?"

I nodded, and Flaco wrapped her left hand around the crystal, put the gas mask over her face, and flipped on the canister. She sniffed the acrid scent of the fluothane and tried to wiggle out from beneath the mask for a moment, then fell asleep.

I put a tourniquet above her wrist and peeled her bandage. A bit of clear, oily synovial fluid from breached joints had gathered inside the bandage, along with a little pus. The wound began bleeding, so I opened a package of plastic AV clips and pinched off the radial artery. In these cases, you're supposed to seal any split bones and regenerate them separately. Molecules in the regenerative wash read the genetic codes of the cells they infiltrate and begin replicating them in an orderly fashion— in effect, following the pattern of growth ordered in birth. But skeletal tissue doesn't regenerate by the same chemical formula as other tissues, and no tissue except skin regenerates on a limb unless both formulae are used simultaneously.

I took a disposable scalpel and began peeling the flesh from the radius and ulna. Because of the small diameter of the bones, I thought they'd been severed just below the joint. But to my surprise the pale-blue articular cartilages, which fit like a cap over the joints, were whole and unbreached. Only the ligament, the fibrous cover that holds the joints together, was severed. Apparently her hand had been pulled off instead of sliced or blown off. My neighbor once set a leg-trap for a mean dog that had snapped at his children. The dog got caught in the trap and wrenched off his foot in exactly the way this woman had wrenched off her hand. All her bones from the carpals on down were missing, though a long ragged piece of flesh from her palm was still attached. This made my job very easy. I set the bloody scalpel back in its cellophane wrapper, cocked her arm at a right angle so most of the muscular tissue pulled away from the exposed bone, and applied the skeletal regeneration wash.

Flaco had been watching me, but he got bored and picked up the thin woman's left arm and watched it flop to the floor as he dropped it.

"Don't do that," I said.

"Why?"

"Her bones might break. I don't think she was born on Earth. She's very fragile."

"I had a friend who once slugged an off-worlder and accidentally killed him," Flaco said. He began searching the thin woman's bags. He pulled out a folding chemical-laser rifle. "Hah! What do you think, she hunts anteaters with this?"

I grunted my surprise at the rifle. Flaco put it back and went to get the retina scanner. I administered the regeneration wash to the muscles, tendons, and skin, and used Doering clamps to anchor some torn flexors and brachioradials to their proper places; then I painted a resin bandage over the whole stump and called it good. Of course, these regeneration kits never work exactly as they're supposed to, and in a few weeks I'd have to reclamp some tendons and splice some of the new nerve tissue to the old.

While the resin bandage was wet, I opened the osteoporosis rehab packet and inserted the catheter of a hormone fusion pump into her flesh about five centimeters above the wrist and began pumping in calcitonin, collagenates, SGH, and mineral supplements. When the resin bandage dried it would seal around the catheter, preventing any chance of infection.

Meanwhile, Flaco had brought in the retina scanner and had been fiddling with it by the electrical outlet. I looked up at him. I expected him to have one of the little hand-held models policemen sometimes carry, but he had a large industrial model. Its corners were dented where he'd pried it free from someone's wall, and the screws that were supposed to hold it to the wall dangled in their sockets; little bits of white paint and plaster still clung to the screws. Flaco had cut the electric cord to get the scanner free, so now he was splicing on a plug.

"Where did you get the scanner?" I asked.

"I stole it from the check-out desk at the public library," Flaco answered.

"Why didn't you just rent one?"

"I don't know. I thought you wanted to keep this private—no records."

"It's not that important," I said.

"If it will make you feel better, I'll take it back tomorrow."

"Good," I said.

Flaco finished splicing the wires and plugged the scanner in, then I turned off the fluothane and pried open one of Tamara's eyes. Flaco aimed the scanner at her eye, but it rolled back and we couldn't see her retina, so Flaco started calling to her, saying "Oh, Spider Legs! Oh, Spider Legs. Wake up! We have nice flies to eat!" and things like that. I patted her cheek a little. After a few minutes her eyeball rolled forward and Flaco scanned it. For all practical purposes she was still asleep, but I turned the fluothane back on to put her under, just to be sure she wouldn't remember we'd scanned her. Then Flaco jacked in a call to his hacker and read off her ID number: AK-483-VO-992-RAF.

I cleaned up the room. Flaco went to the bathroom. Five minutes later he came out and said, "I've got my hacker on-line. Are you sure we got her ID right?"

The scanner was still on, so I read the number to him again.

Flaco stood in the corner, listening to the comlink in his head. "According to the records," he said, "she's Tamara Maria de la Garza. Born 2-24-2167 on Bacchus 4 in the Ceti star system. She left at age eight, and spent seventeen years in flight back to Earth. Two years ago, she joined the Allied Earth Marines and went with a peace-keeping force to the Epsilon Eridani system." Flaco's eyes remained unfocused as he listened to the voice in his head, and he laughed at something the hacker said. "According to her military records, she's been in flight two years. Expected to reach Epsilon Eridani in 2213."

"Oh," I said. I flipped off the fluothane on her gas mask. According to Flaco, this woman was nearly a light-year from Earth. Apparently, she had either jumped ship or never left—but then, if that were true she would be listed as AWOL. Obviously, the military had falsified her files. I started thinking of reasons the military would falsify her files, and came up with many, but I realized it would be just like them to falsify her records for the hell of it.

Flaco stood in the corner for a moment. "Also." he said, "My friend didn't bother to mention earlier that two months ago the man who owned the crystal, Amir Jafari, was made a Class D General in the Federated Earth Marines—he's in charge of Cyborg Intelligence." Flaco smiled; he was still on-line.

At first I thought that explained Jafari's interest in brain storage. The cyborg command was once notorious for shanghaiing draftees, placing their brains in brain bags, and jacking them into reality programs—convincing them they were just living through their daily affairs until they could be transferred to mechanical bodies. But why would the computer crystal be registered to Jafari, not the Alliance? He wouldn't be holding it as a commodities investment—the price of crystals drops daily.

"My hacker says he doesn't want to know me anymore," Flaco said, eyes focused. He was off-line. He tried to sound confident. "He just got tagged. He's going on vacation."

"Did they trace to us?"

"No, I don't think so," Flaco said. "I'd called him. They won't trace back to us." He sat on the floor and sighed. I knew he was wrong. I knew that if they took the initiative, they could check the hacker for incoming calls and get back to us. But it would take time, perhaps days. "So, what do you think?" Flaco asked.

I knew he wanted me to venture a guess about who had traced the hacker's call. I phrased my words carefully, trying to turn the subject of the conversation. "I think this woman is not Jafari, so perhaps she stole the crystal."

"Do you know what I think?" Flaco said. "I watched you treat that girl. I think you wasted your money going to school to study morphogenic pharmacology. All you did was read the directions on those boxes. Anybody could have done that. A monkey could have done that!"

"Yes," I said, "Flaco could have done that."

"I did fine with the fluothane, no? I'm a fine anesthesiologist."

"Yes, you're a fine anesthesiologist."

"I am also tired," Flaco said, yawning.

"Me too."

"Can I sleep here?" he asked.

"We should put this woman on the couch, and I have no other bed."

"I will sleep on the floor," he said. "A fine floor. Very soft. Very practical."

"Good," I said. "You can make sure this thief doesn't run off with my valuables."

"I will guard your valuables with my life," Flaco promised. We moved Tamara to the couch; then Flaco lay down on the floor and closed his eyes, and I went to my room.

Although it was late and I had many things on my mind, I turned on my computer, phoned Informer 261—the artificial intelligence who services me—and requested a readout of all scholarly articles on morphogenic pharmacology published within the past three days. The AI bartered with me, trying to restructure my payment schedule for information. He started out asking far too much money; at times it seemed his bartering equations went totally off kilter. He didn't understand the emotional attachment I had to my money. I talked him down to a reasonable fee, then he granted access to the information. I studied long into the night.

In the morning Tamara gave the computer crystal back to me, and I refilled the hormone pump on her arm, told her to eat and drink as much as she could, and left "Doctor" Flaco to watch her.

I took her dirty bandage to Uppanishadi-Smith for a blood analysis. Tamara had very low levels of leukocytes and other antibodies, and this seemed very strange. With such a severe injury, her antibody levels should have rocketed. However, people raised in artificial atmospheres often have unresponsive immune systems, so I did not worry so much. But with the high humidity in Panama and the resultant risk of infections, I thought it necessary to buy a wide-spectrum antibody treatment. Then I went back to my booth at the feria. The day was slow: I sold two lipid and cholesterol flushes to old people, and I had one soccer player who wanted to get all his nerves myelinated so he could speed his reflexes. His was an unworkable plan, and I told him how much better a nerve bypass was, since silver wire conducts electrical impulses much faster than a myelinated nerve, and recommended the doctor who had bypassed my sympathetic and peripheral nervous systems for me. The day was cool, so I walked home before sundown.

When I got home, a gray kitten with white feet was on the roof and Flaco and Tamara were in the front yard throwing a red plastic ball up to the kitten. It would hide on the other side of the roof, and when Flaco threw the ball up it would clatter on the roof's red tiles, and the kitten would hear it and run over the top, swiping and biting at the ball and chasing it till it rolled off the roof.

Then the kitten would hiss and raise the hairs on its back as if surprised to see Flaco and Tamara, and would run back over the rooftop to hide. Tamara enjoyed this as much as the kitten did. She giggled when the kitten attacked the ball and acted very excited, often putting her hand over her mouth. And I had a strange realization: the beauty I had seen in Tamara when she showed terror was in her when she laughed. The way emotions played over her face gave her an unusually expressive quality that made her different from the dead-eyed, emotionless refugiadas and merchant women I often met. Flaco must have seen it too, for when he spoke with her, his voice took on a mellow, respectful tone.

I watched Tamara for some time, looking for any signs of the cramping the hormone injections can cause. She wobbled a great deal and clung to Flaco for support, but it was good for her to get the exercise. I remembered the antibody packet I'd bought, so I had her sit on the front porch while I injected the antibodies into her catheter.

"I have been thinking," I said when I was done, "that I would like to sell that crystal. Would you happen to have a receipt for it?"

Tamara looked up at me in surprise, then burst out laughing until tears formed in her eyes. Flaco started laughing too. I felt very foolish about asking for a receipt, but now I knew for sure she was a thief. Tamara struggled up and went into the house to rest.

Flaco put his arm around me. "Ah, Angelo, I like you. Promise me you'll never change."

I sighed, and wondered what to do. It would be wrong to sell stolen property, no matter how much I would make from it. Once again I wished that I had not taken Tamara into my care, and I wondered if I should

send her to the hospital, let the police arrest her if she
was a criminal. "How is she doing?" I asked Flaco.

"She slept much in the morning," he said, "and I
made sure she ate a good lunch. After that she spent
much time in your bedroom, hooked up to your dream
console. She didn't like it. She said it didn't have enough
memory to make a large world seem solid. Also, she
erased all the old worlds you had in it—I hope you're
not angry."

"No, I never use it," I said truthfully.

"You should get a new one," Flaco said. "I have a
friend who steals only from other thieves. He can get
you a nice one, cheap. And it isn't as if it will have been
stolen from a Padre."

"No," I said.

Flaco went in the house and got some beer, and we
sat on the porch and drank while the sun set. Just as it
got dark we heard a distant explosion—a deep, booming
one—and howler monkeys in the forests on the south
side of the lake began howling in fear.

"Chepo?" I asked, wondering if the Socialists were
bombing refugiados on our side of the border.

Flaco shook his head, and spat on the ground.
"Guerrilla artillery. Synchronous barrage; they're trying
to blow up one of the Colombian neutron cannons."
Flaco started to rise, as if to go in the house.

"Wait here for a moment," I told him. "You will see
something strange."

Flaco sat back down and waited. Soon, an old
grizzled spider monkey came walking up the street,
away from the jungle south of the lake, heading north.
The monkey was very nervous, being away from the
trees, and he often stopped, raising his head to look for
the *perros sarnosos*—junkyard dogs that ran loose in the

streets. Flaco saw him and laughed, "Ha! I've never seen a spider monkey leave the jungle like that."

"The fighting and people in the jungle scares them," I said. "I see them every night now. Usually there is just one or two, sometimes bands. They are always heading north."

"Perhaps this old spider monkey is smarter than you and me. Perhaps he is a sign from God," Flaco said, reaching down to pick up a rock. He threw it, hitting the monkey's chest. "Go on, get up to Costa Rica where someone can make a good stew of you!"

The monkey lurched back a few meters, clutching his chest, then ran in a circle, and finally took off as fast as he could past my home. I felt bad to see the old monkey in pain. "You did not need to do that," I told Flaco. Flaco was staring at the ground, angrily, and I knew he was thinking about the threat of the Colombians to the south and Costa Ricans to the north. Some people thought the two countries would invade us, force us to refuse the Capitalists access to our canals.

"Ah, piss on him if he can't take a joke," Flaco said. Then he laughed and we went into the house. Flaco and Tamara had eaten all the fresh fruit, and I do not like to eat a meal without it, so we decided to eat at La Arboleda, a nearby restaurant. I went to get Tamara.

She lay on my bed, with the dream monitor plugged into the socket at the base of her skull and her visor down. She was curled so that her knees touched her chin, and she had her hand in her mouth, biting it. Her tightly drawn face hinted at pain.

"Does she always do this?" I said.

"Do what?" Flaco asked.

"Curl up in the fetal position when she's hooked to the console?"

"Feta? Feta?—yes, she always lies like that."

"Don't touch her," I said. Then I ran next door to Rodrigo DeHoyos' house. He was my neighbor who had trapped the mean dog. I borrowed his extra dream monitor.

When I got back, I put on the monitor and plugged into the viewer's jack of the console—

And on the beach the wind was still but a sandpiper was running, skirting the water's edge, darting away from the waves, burying his ebony bill, moving on. Bleached shells of clam, barnacle, and snail tumbled in the shallows and gleamed like bones in the sand drifts. Cool air carried the scent of decaying sea life. A purple sun hung on the horizon and dyed sand, sky, bird, skin in cellophane shades of red and blue. The amethyst sand cut my bare feet, and down the beach a red-haired woman in a white dress fed gulls that screeched and hung in the air, waiting to snap crumbs she tossed. I stopped and inhaled the air, listened to the sigh of the breakers, and looked at the colors. After so long with my prosthetic eyes, seeing the world in variations of only three primary colors felt like coming home.

I began looking for flaws in her dreamwork. Her world involved all five senses. I could both smell the sea rime and taste it—it felt complete. I could see unity in the starkness of the lines of the jagged stones, the wind-battered birds, and the choppy waves on the horizon. Scarlets and muted tans nicely varied the theme color of purple. Her dreamwork was almost professional quality.

But I turned around and found a warp: on the beach, a huge black bull lay dead in the water, as if he had just washed up from her subconscious. The horizon, the shoreline, the slope of the sand—all converged to emphasize this bull. He lay on his side, with his head

toward me and his feet toward the sea. His belly was
huge and distended, though it didn't show signs of rot.
His knobby legs stuck out, stiff with rigor mortis, and
his whole body heaved from moment to moment as
waves washed against him, surging against his belly,
making his huge testicles and penis float up against his
body as a wave came in, then stretch out and away as the
wave receded. I imagined him gone and tried to shove
a delete command through the monitor. The monitor
flashed a message: You Cannot Edit Dreams While in
the Viewing Mode.

As I headed toward the red-haired woman, a wave
jiggled the bull, and his glassy eyes moved. I watched
him a moment: the bull's gaze remained fixed on the
woman.

Her beauty was the kind one can only be born with—
the elegant lines of her chin were not likely to be the
kind a plastique artist would conceive. Yet her lifeless
expression was like the tragic deadness one sees behind
the eyes of the refugiados, and I wondered why Tamara
had chosen this red-haired woman as an alter ego and if
the emotion I'd seen in Tamara's face earlier were some
trick of her body she could not control.

"What do you want?" she asked without turning to
look at me, tossing a piece of bread to a gull.

I did not know how to answer. "I came to tell you it's
time to eat," I said, looking back at the bull.

"He talks to me," she said, as if confiding a secret.
She didn't turn, and I realized it was the bull she didn't
want to see. "Even though he's dead, he jabbers. He
jabbers at me—he says he wants me to ride his back. But
I know that as soon as I do, he'll take me away. Across
the dark water to a place where I do not wish to go."

I said, as if to a child: "Perhaps you should come with

Flaco and me. We'll have a nice dinner. You'd like that, wouldn't you?"

She stiffened, angered by the tone of my voice. "You go on ahead. I'll finish up here," she said. She tore a huge chunk off her loaf of bread and tossed it to a gull. The gull shrieked and dove, grabbing the bread before it hit the ground. I looked at the gull, with its battered feathers and shrunken stomach. Its dark eyes glared, mad with hunger.

I walked away from the beach and topped a rise by a rock where a lone gull sat. On the other side of the rise the dream ended in a blurred landscape of rolling dunes. I looked back down at the bull floating in the water and at the woman in the white dress. She fed the last of the bread to the gulls, then raised her hands. A gull dove and tentatively nipped her finger. Drops of blood splashed from her wound and the gulls cried and dove upon her, shredding her flesh with their sharp beaks.

The gull beside me cried out, and I looked at it. The light of the setting sun made its white feathers gleam purple. Its dark eyes appeared to glare out of a luminous head. It watched me, cold and prophetic. I jacked out, unwilling to watch the woman be eaten.

"So, what happened?" Flaco asked as soon as I got the monitor off.

"Nothing," I said, not wishing to compromise Tamara's privacy any further. I pulled her plug from the console, terminating her self-torture. Tamara straightened and stretched.

"Is it time to eat?" she asked. She stared at the floor and would not look at me.

"Yes." Flaco helped her stand. It had begun to rain, so Flaco went to the closet for an umbrella.

Tamara stared at the floor and said, "Stay out of my dreams."

"I'm sorry," I said. "You looked as if you were in pain."

"I only had a headache. You invaded me. You don't have that right."

"You're my patient," I said. "I'm obligated to care for you." Flaco came back with the umbrella, and we walked to La Arboleda.

Only a few late eaters and drunks were in the restaurant. We all ordered fish, and Flaco convinced Tamara to order a Rum Sunset—a drink his grandfather had invented that is made of rum and lemon wine, spiced with cinnamon. Flaco tried to get me to drink one too, but I refused. Flaco bragged that his family still owned the company that made the lemon wine, and I pointed out that both his grandfather's company and his grandfather's bad taste were still in the family. Tamara laughed slightly and stared at her hands. A drunk staggered to our table, looked at our drinks, and said, "Hah! Rum Sunset. That's my favorite damn drink in the world. In fact, it's the only good drink!"

"Then you should have a drink with the grandson of the man who invented it," Flaco said.

I was very sorry about this, for the drunk smelled of sour sweat, and he sat next to me. He fell asleep after guzzling his drink, but his smell ruined my dinner. We ate and talked; Flaco told many peculiarly bad jokes which Tamara laughed at shyly at first, but later she laughed horrendously at the slightest provocation. One of my customers that day, a refugiado from Cartagena, had paid me in mixed foreign coins, so I'd carried a large bag of coins tied to my belt all day. I opened the bag and

began stacking the coins according to country and de-
nomination. When Tamara finished her first Rum Sunset, Flaco ordered her another, then another, and I
realized Flaco was trying to get her drunk, and Tamara
must have realized this too, since she excused herself
from the third drink, claiming she had a headache.
Flaco kept drinking, and got drunk himself.

He told a long story about how his father did well in
the wine business, until one day when he went to Mass
and fell asleep. In a dream, the statue of the Virgin
began weeping. Flaco's father asked the Virgin why she
wept, and she told him it was because he sold wine when
he should be selling hats to the Indians in the Amazon.
Flaco's father became convinced he would make a great
deal of money selling hats because, after all, the Virgin
Mary had told him to do it. Then he sailed up the
Amazon and was killed by a poisonous toad before he
could sell a single hat. This incident greatly diminished
the faith of everyone in Flaco's village—so much so that
the villagers broke the offending statue with hammers.

"So what about your family?" Flaco asked Tamara.
She straightened up, and her face took on a closed look.
She hadn't drunk much, but she pretended to be out of
control so we'd excuse her bad manners. "Family? Want
to know about my family? I'll tell you—my father, he
was just like Angelo there. He only wanted two things:
order and immortality." I had just finished stacking my
coins in neat little staggered rows, like banana trees.
Tamara lashed out with her stump and knocked all the
coins down.

"That's not—" I started to say.

"What? You going to say you don't want immortality?" Tamara asked.

In my youth I thought it would be a great boon to get

life extensions at wholesale. Like most other morphogenic pharmacologists, the hope of obtaining life extensions until mankind solved the problem of mortality or
learned to download brains into crystals was a major
factor in determining my career. "I don't want order," I
concluded.

Tamara peered at me as if I'd said something very
strange, and shook her head. "You bastards are all the
same. Your bodies may live, but your souls die."

"Who's a bashtard?" Flaco asked.

"Angelo. He's just like a cyborg—the assholes want
to live forever, but they make their living denying other
people that opportunity." I suddenly felt as if I'd jacked
back into her dreamworld. As far as I could see, her
strange accusations against cyborgs and me made no
sense.

"You're full of guano," Flaco said. "Don Angelo
Oshic here, he'sh nice. He's a gentleman."

Tamara looked at us, and her head wobbled. She
reached for a glass of water and missed. The water
spilled on the table. "Maybe he *is* a cyborg," she said,
ducking her head a little.

"We're not shyborgs," Flaco said in an easy tone.
"See, no shyborgs are in thish room." He handed her his
Rum Sunset.

"You got a comlink in your head?" Tamara asked.
Flaco nodded. "Then you're a cyborg," she said, as if
she'd made a point. I remembered a news clip I'd once
seen of Surinamese Body Purists. Upon conversion to
their cult, new members pulled out their comlinks and
their cranial jacks, their prosthetic kidneys or whatever
they had, and lived totally without mechanical aid. I
wondered if she were a Body Purist, and I suddenly
understood why she wanted a regenerated hand instead

of a prosthetic—the thought of her body being welded
to a machine terrified her; it desecrated the temple of her
spirit.

"A comlink doeshn't make you a shyborg," Flaco
said.

"That's where it starts. First a comlink. Then an arm.
Then a lung. One piece at a time."

"What about you?" Flaco said. "You shaid you were
going to tell about your family."

"My mother and father are cyborgs," she said, with
that closed look. "I never met them. I'm just the interest
paid by the sperm bank. If my parents ever saw me, they
probably got pissed off because I didn't look enough
like a washing machine."

"Hah! There musht be a shtory in that!" Flaco said.
"Tell ush the shtory."

"There's no story," Tamara said. And I wondered
what her point was, why she bothered to lie at all. The
waiter brought Flaco another drink, which he downed
on the spot. Tamara ordered some aspirin. Flaco started
nodding off, and I pulled away his plate and glasses
before his head landed on the table. Tamara just sat and
gazed at her plate, so I decided to drag away the smelly
drunk who sat beside me and order dessert.

I put all my coins in my bag and moved the drunk
back to his previous stall. As I finished setting him
upright, comlink tones sounded in my head. A man with
a heavy African accent said, "Señor Osic?"

"Yes," I answered.

"Tell the woman across the table from you to go to
the telephone."

The caller had to have been in the room at some time
in the evening to know I'd been sitting with Tamara, but
since he didn't know I'd moved away, he'd obviously

Illustrated by Brian Murray

left. "She's drunk. She's unconscious," I lied, hurrying to the door to see if I was being called from outside.

I opened the door and looked out. The avenue was dark and empty, but far down the street I could see the shining heat of a man's body outside a minishuttle. The caller clicked off, and the man jumped in the minishuttle. The tail lights glowed red momentarily, and the shuttle blossomed into a ball of light as the engine turned on. It shot up into the night sky and streaked away.

I went back into the restaurant, and Tamara looked at me curiously, as if to ask why I'd run out. Flaco struggled to lift his head from the table. He turned toward Tamara and said, "I got a messhage for you on comlink: Arish shays he h-has your hand. And *now* he has y-you."

Tamara turned pale. She drank another Rum Sunset.

On the way home, Tamara and Flaco were so drunk they had to lean on me for support. Tamara kept swearing and mumbling that she wanted a gun, and Flaco kept saying "What?" I laid Tamara on the couch and Flaco on the hall floor in front of the bathroom door, and went to bed.

After a couple hours I was awakened by Flaco vomiting and Tamara murmuring, but I just went back to sleep. I dreamed of an old Zeller Cymech advertisement that portrayed a group of people in a gambling casino, all of them cyborgs wearing designer cymechs. The one closest to me only had one arm that was still flesh, and he wore it as if it were a badge of his humanity. He wore a head of electrically dyed red tungsten that looked like a handsome man around the face and eyes, but his jaw curved abruptly into something skeletal. He had gleaming blue zirconium eyes, and his huge smile hinted at perpetual mirth. I had seen this holo once before, and admired it. But suddenly it seemed this man's smile held something malicious, that he was plotting the deaths of the other people in the room, and only I could discern his intent. Then I thought, *No, this is not my dream. This is Tamara's dream.* I was awakened by someone shaking me.

"Angelo! Angelo!" Flaco said.

"Sí. Qué pasa?" I asked.

"Huy! What do you think? That woman, she is a bitch when she drinks, no?"

"Yes, she is a bitch."

"I like that. I like a woman with a fierce spirit!" Flaco said. He talked very slowly and deliberately. "Move over. I want to get in bed with you." I moved over and Flaco climbed in and accidentally kicked me with his shoes. "Ah, this is a good bed," he said. "Very comfortable. Just right for two. You should have invited me in earlier. Did I ever tell you that you have nice breasts? For a man, that is. They are very flaccid. You have more breast than some women."

Flaco's words disturbed me, till I realized he was joking. I said, "Yes, flaccid breasts run in my family. You should have seen my mother: she had several of them."

Flaco laughed. "No more jokes! I think I will vomit again if have to I laugh at your sick jokes. Angelo, do you think Tamara is in danger?"

"Yes."

"I held her hand today. It was very delicate, like a child's hand. We will have to take good care of her. Tell me, what do you think she is running from?"

"What does anyone run from," I said. "She runs from her past."

"Ah, philosophical poop. Do you always poop philosophy at night? If so, we should sleep together often. But I have been thinking—perhaps she is a notorious refugiada. Perhaps she is looking for political asylum, and would be happy to marry a Panamanian like the handsome Flaco just so she can live in a neutral country, eh? Welcome to Flaco; welcome to freedom! What do you think? You still think she is a thief?"

"Yes."

"I don't," Flaco said. "Believe me, oh great philosopher, I know thieves. She is too *alive* to be a thief. Understand?"

"No," I said.

"Ah, it is very simple. You see, Man is a territorial creature. He needs to possess things—houses, land, body space. And if he possesses something, he is happy; and he is happy to let others possess something. But thieves violate their very nature by violating other's territories. They are never at peace with themselves. And because of this, they die inside. This is something an educated, philosophical man like yourself should know."

"Are you not a Socialist?" I asked. "What you say sounds anti-Socialist."

"Why would you think me a Socialist?"

"You live in Panama, between the hammer of Colombia and the anvil of Costa Rica, and don't run away."

"Oh, I am not a Socialist," Flaco said. "I don't believe socialism can work with Man today—we are too territorialistic. I believe a man must possess himself and be his own man. But these Hwang Idealist Socialists will not let a man possess himself. It is not enough that they enslave the artificial intelligences; they must also dominate humans too, grind down their opposition. Always they blame the Capitalists for their economic failure. But they refuse to see that their countries collapse into economic ruin because they take away men's will to work. I met a man from Budapest who said his father had worked in a factory that kept closing because the workers wanted to sit and play cards. The government sent in the military to force the workers to go back to work. But some still refused. They believed they would be paid and fed regardless of whether they worked, they sat and played cards with machine guns at their backs. Finally, the military shot them all, and the radio proclaimed these men traitors. And this man told me that his father, even though he had been murdered, had won against the Socialists because he refused to die inside. And I believe this is a second way to submit to inner death—to live under the domination of others, to deny your need to possess yourself."

Flaco fancied himself a great political thinker, but I had spent so much time studying medicine I was out of touch with politics. I remained respectfully silent for a moment, as if contemplating his words. "So, did you not say that you don't believe this woman is a thief?"

"No, I believe she is a brain transplant."

This made me sit up and think. Intuitively I felt he was right. "Why do you say that?"

"I saw a documentary once. Back when they were drafting people into the cyborg units, the military would put the soldiers' bodies in stasis until their terms were up, and if a soldier wanted to enlist afterward, he could opt to sell his body for parts. But there was a big scandal, because sometimes a soldier would end his term or want to sell his body and find that it had already been

sold on the black market by the cryotechs. All this talk
about cyborgs made me remember this, and I realized
that this was how Tamara could be listed as being on
active duty a light-year away and still be here."

"Do you mean someone has stolen her body?"

"I have been thinking: would anyone steal a useless
body like that? No, I think Tamara de la Garza enlisted
and sold her body. And now this woman is wearing it."

I remembered the beautiful red-haired woman in
Tamara's dream, so different than the scrawny, black-
haired thing that slept on the couch, and I realized that
a brain transplant could explain why she dreamed of
herself looking so differently. And I remembered the way
she had fumbled after the water at dinner—a sign that
her brain had not yet accustomed itself to a change in
body size. "Perhaps," I said.

" 'Perhaps'? What do you mean 'perhaps'? It is a
great solution to our question. If my theory isn't true, it
should be!"

"We are being paid much money. She is paying a little
for her treatment, and much for our silence. If she must
suffer a brain transplant to escape her pursuers, perhaps
our questions jeopardize her."

"You did not tell me earlier she was in danger," Flaco
said.

Out in the living room, Tamara stirred in her sleep
and moaned.

"I did not know if I believed it earlier."

I lay in bed for a long time, thinking. If this woman
had had a brain transplant, and the transplant were
recent, it would explain why her antibody levels hadn't
shot up when her hand was pulled off—she could still be
on antibody inhibitors. But I wasn't sure. Any legitimate

surgeon would have used antimosin C, an inhibitor
which only stops the production of the suppressor cells
that attack transplanted organs. But Tamara's antibody
levels were down all across the spectrum—which meant
she'd been given one of the more common AB inhibitors. The antibody injection I had given her earlier had
thymosins in it, which stimulate the production of all T
cells, including suppressor cells. And if the level of thymosins I'd given her were too high, they could override
the AB inhibitors. And if her brain wasn't perfectly
compatible with its body, Tamara's suppressor cells
would treat her brain as an infecting organism, destroying it. These thoughts made my stomach ache.

I went into the living room and looked at Tamara.
She was tossing and turning, and I could see by the
brilliance of the platinum glow of her body that she had
an elevated temperature. This is one of the first signs of
organ rejection; unfortunately, it is also a sign of an
ordinary infection. To add to my confusion, the hor-
mones I'd given her sped up her metabolism, which
would cause a low-grade fever. She had already complained of headaches, but until she complained of
cramps, numbness, or loss of senses, I couldn't be sure
she was in danger. This was all compounded by the fact
that under the right conditions she could go comatose or
die without warning. All the *ifs* began swimming in my
head. I got a cool rag and sponged her face. She woke
and looked at me, "Bolt the . . . charge a gun," she said.
Then her eyes cleared. "Do you have the crystal?" she
asked. I pulled the computer crystal out of my pocket
and showed it to her. She reached up and stroked it, then
smiled and slept.

I continued sponging her and held her hand through
the night. At dawn, comlink tones sounded in my head.

I opened channel and an image flooded into my mind. A dark man with long black hair and wide nostrils sat on a sofa. He wore the dark blue of the Allied Marines.

"I'm General Amir Jafari," he said. "I understand you have something that belongs to me." His voice had a disturbing atonal quality, lacking inflection. His image was computer-generated.

I reached in my pocket and fondled the crystal. "I believe you're mistaken," I answered.

"Let me be frank," he said. "I want the woman back." The statement startled me, left me unbalanced. "I have a proposition for you: It will cost me two hundred thousand standards to send someone to take her—and I could take her. But it would be much easier for both of us if you'd bring her to me yourself, and accept the two hundred thousand as a token of my gratitude."

"What would you do with her?" I asked. The general stared at me and offered no reply. I felt stupid for asking. "She is very ill," I said. "She cannot be moved safely for several days."

"She has led me on a goose chase for months, but it must stop here. You have until sunset to bring her to the airport in Colón. Do you understand?"

"Yes, I understand."

He seemed to gaze at me for a moment, as if he could see me. "You wouldn't try anything irrational would you? You wouldn't try to escape?"

"No," I said.

"You couldn't if you tried, you know. Running is not an option."

"I understand," I said, unsure if I believed him. Although he was in Intelligence, the AEM couldn't operate legally on Earth. But I knew that wouldn't stop him. As commander of Cyborg Intelligence, he would be

hooked to the military AI's and have the resources of
crystal brains that gathered billions of times more information than anything a biological brain could handle. I
wouldn't be able to access my bank accounts, make a
call, cross a border, pass a police monitor.

"Good," Jafari said. "I will be kind to her. It's for her
own good. I'm not inhuman."

"I won't run," I said. Jafari cut the transmission. I sat
by the couch, feeling as if I were in a box. I pondered
every phrase he'd said, sifting the words for meanings
only the tone could have supplied. His last words hinted
at emotion, or at least an apology for emotion. I
sponged Tamara's head until exhaustion took me.

A couple hours after dawn, Flaco came out of the
bedroom. "Ah, Angelo," he said, "should the dark angel
come to take me, I'd embrace him with open arms.
Often I've wished my grandfather had invented a drink
that allowed one to get drunk and not have a hang-
over!"

"It is a small price to pay for so much happiness," I
quoted an old song. Flaco sat on the bed, and I stroked
Tamara's hair, looking for scar tissue—any exterior sign
that she'd had a brain transplant. There was none, but
that didn't mean anything. A good plastique artist
wouldn't leave such a sign. I said, "You must watch
Tamara for me," then went to fix breakfast. I fried some
gallo pinto—a dish made with brown beans and rice
—opened some nice doughnuts, and mixed the coffee.

Soon, Flaco came into the kitchen. "She sleeps with
the angels," he said.

"Good." I offered him a plate. He loaded it up and
sat at the table. We ate in silence for a long time.

"I can read your mind," he said at last. "I was not so

drunk that I don't remember the call I got at the restaurant. Perhaps we should move the girl to my house."

"No. If he can call you, he knows where you live."

"Then we will move her somewhere else. We could hide her in the banana orchards."

"The orchards would be good," I said. I ate a while more in silence, unsure if I should tell Flaco about the call from Jafari. Flaco was a good friend, and a good man, but he was a thief at heart. Perhaps he was even capable of selling Tamara for the reward.

"What's bothering you?" Flaco asked. "Are you afraid to hide her in the banana orchards?"

I ran my finger over the worn plastic of the table top. Tamara got up and went to the bathroom. I heard the water go on as she washed her face. "No. I gave her an antibody treatment yesterday that could be dangerous. She could die from it."

"What's the probability?"

"I don't know. Probably not very high."

"Then I would only worry about it slightly, and not look so glum. One would think by the look on your face that you were a rooster and your owner was starving." I laughed a little. "See, things are not so bad. Flaco will fix everything. Also, when Tamara comes in, I'm going to test her to see if she is a refugiada." He pulled his eye as a sign for me to not say anything.

Tamara staggered into the kitchen, her head slumped. "I'm leaving," she announced.

"We know," Flaco said. "I am coming with you. We'll hide in the banana orchards with the refugiados. No one will find you."

"You don't know who I'm running from. You don't know their resources."

"Their resources don't matter!" Flaco said. "No one

monitors the orchards—the refugiados come and go too fast. Hundreds of thousands of people live there, yet no one even asks for ID."

Tamara said, "I'm not sure. . . ."

"Ah, but you would blend in perfectly with the refugiados," Flaco said. "Like me, you have that *starved* look."

Tamara stared at him a moment, as if to read some deeper meaning into the joke, then she smiled a labored smile and said "Okay," and began eating.

"Speaking of refugiados, guess who I saw yesterday —" Flaco said, "Professor Bernardo Mendez!" I had heard the name, but couldn't remember where. I looked at Tamara and we both shrugged. "You know, Bernardo Mendez! The great social engineer who did so much good work in Chile—the one who promised to use genetic engineering to breed greed out of man within three generations! I saw him on the street in the feria. He took his idea to Colombia and the Colombians lobotomized him and shoved him over the border as an example to the refugiados. They didn't like his brand of socialism, so they cut out much of his brain, and now he wanders the streets with pee stains on his pants, stealing food."

Tamara stopped eating and turned pale. "Perhaps it was the Capitalists," I said. "Perhaps they lobotomized him."

"Ah, no," Flaco said. "It was the Colombians. I have a friend who has a friend who knows for sure."

Tamara said, "Nobody knows anything for sure."

Flaco smiled and winked at me. "Tsk, Tsk—so much cynicism, and it's only breakfast time! All the same, it is a shame to see a great man in such a state. Peeing his pants that way. Now he is no smarter than an iguana or a duck."

Tamara said, "Let's not talk about it," and finished eating in silence.

We packed some food and clothes, and went to the orchards, watching to make sure we weren't followed. Among the orchards we would travel for a long time without seeing a tent, then suddenly we would find a cluster of tents like a small village. None of the tents belonged to the guerrillas; they were still far to the east. Flaco chose a camp with only four tents next to each other. The tents were dirty and molded, and two had white crap on their tops where chickens roosted at night. Outside one tent a naked baby boy sat in an aluminum washtub with only a small amount of water. He didn't have any teeth, and he had a rag in his mouth, chewing it. Flies crawled all over him and the rag.

Flaco called at the tent door, and a young Chilean woman came out. She opened her blouse, and began nursing the baby. Flaco asked if he and Tamara could camp there, and the woman told him that the people who owned one of the tents had disappeared a week earlier, so he could live there. These disappearances are common—many refugiados are found murdered for no apparent reason. The police are too apathetic to do anything about it. Flaco and Tamara seemed to be pretty well set up, so I went to work in the feria.

The feria was very crowded that day, and I enjoyed it. A great swarm of people—Chinese and Korean mariners, Hindu merchants, and South American guerrillas—descended on the area until the street in front of my stand was packed solid with the bodies of people, all of them in clashing costumes, milling endlessly. The smells of sweat and dust and spicy food filled the air, while the people yelled and bartered. I always loved the sights of the feria. When I was a

student at the university, I lived with my uncle in Mexico
City. All the sidewalks downtown were one way, and if
pedestrians wanted to walk to a store on the other side
of the street, they had to pass the store, go to the next
pedestrian overpass, then walk back to the store they
wanted to get to. All those people walking in the same
direction sickened me. If they'd had their legs shackled
together, they'd never have noticed. And I remembered
that when I had first come to Panama it was the people
milling listlessly in the feria that attracted me. I had
always thought I enjoyed the lack of order in Panama,
but after thinking about Flaco's words of the night
before, I wondered if I didn't enjoy the simple freedom
of being able to turn and walk against the crowd. Perhaps
this was my way of possessing myself.

Flaco came at noon and bought a water jug from a
booth down the street. He stopped and talked with me.
"Did you not see the look on her face when I told her
about Bernardo?"

"Sí, she looked very sick," I said.

"She is a refugiada for sure, no?"

"Sí, she looked very sick," I said. Flaco laughed and
told me to come by later and bring some fruit, and I said
okay. I gave him the computer crystal and asked him to
sell it. He said he'd try. Business was good; I sold a life
extension, a thing which had not happened in over a
month, so I stayed at my booth till well after dark,
hoping for more good fortune.

Flaco's camp was 114 rows south of the canal freeway,
and about three kilometers west of Colón. I walked
to it in the dark, carrying a fruit basket and mineral
water I'd bought at the feria; the banana plants and
warm soil glowed enough infrared to see by. When I got
to the camp, I saw a large black man about fifty meters

from Flaco's tent, slightly hunched over as if he were peeing. I thought to pass him quietly so I wouldn't frighten him, but when I reached him I saw that he was hunched over Flaco, and that he was unwrapping a garrote from around Flaco's neck, and that he had strangled Flaco. I yelled, and the man looked at me. He charged as if to attack, but I jumped aside and he ran away. I checked Flaco's pulse; he had none. I pushed on his chest to get fresh air in him; he gurgled and blood bubbled out of the hole below his Adam's apple. I stuck two fingers into the hole to see how deep it was, and my fingers went back in his neck until they touched the stumps where his vertebrae had been severed. I crawled away and vomited, then yelled for help.

The Chilean woman came out of her tent, followed by Tamara. The Chilean was very surprised and terrified to see Flaco dead—she kept making the sign of the cross and moaning. Tamara just stared at Flaco, her mouth wide with horror.

I got angry and jumped up to chase Flaco's killer. I had only run about five hundred meters when I saw him hiding behind the stalks of a banana plant. I ran straight at him. He jumped from behind the plant and swung a knife at me, so I tried to kick off his knee cap. But I only managed to kick him hard in the knee.

He dropped the knife and took off running. I picked up the knife and followed. He didn't run fast—he kept grabbing his knee and limping—and I felt very light and free. I controlled my breathing and soon fell into a rhythm and fantasized. It would all be very easy, I thought, to pounce on this man and slit him from crotch to skull. I had already disabled him; and I thought it would feel good to kill him. He had probably underestimated me because I am old and flaccid, but I felt like an old lion who has just discovered that he still has one tooth left with which to kill. And because I enjoyed this moment, I did not hurry; I wanted him to be terrified of me. I wanted him to have to wait to die, to know it was coming. Then I realized I was like the Captain who had shot the children on the beach, and I threw down the knife. The man in front of me soon straightened out his leg and doubled his speed, and I kept following him. Comlink tones sounded in my head, and I answered.

"You run good, for an old fucker," the man in front of me said. I didn't answer. He ran out of the orchard, crossed the canal freeway, and I followed as he leapt the crash fence and maglev rail on the far side of the freeway. "What would you do if you caught me, old man?" he asked.

"I would rip out your bowels," I answered. He crossed the underpass of the old canal, then crossed the new canal, and I still followed. He was heading into the ghettoes of Colón. We ran past a few businesses, but soon the apartment buildings reared up on both sides of us, and I felt as if we were running through a tunnel. I kept expecting to pass one of the little police cameras that monitored the area. But every time I saw a monitor stand, the camera was torn off, and I was relieved and afraid at the same time—whatever happened would be between him and me.

"Let's make this fight even. Let's find a place with a little light, so I can see you," the man said. He ran past some garbage cans where a junkyard dog was eating. The dog growled and took off chasing him. The man ran to a well-lit alley and ducked in. The dog yelped, and I hesitated before entering the alley. Just as I began to turn the corner a flash, like a brilliant strobe, silently went off. All the apartments that were exposed to the

light made a sound like the inrush of breath and burst
into flames. The reflected light burned my eyelashes and
gave me a sunburn. "Was that bright enough for you,
fucker?" the man asked. I ran into the alley. The dog was
dead on the street, charred black and smoking. The
paint on the buildings on both sides sputtered blue and
green flames, forcing me back. "Ah, you should thank
Allah you sorry bastard; I've wasted my only energy
grenade," the voice said. "I guess I'll have to get you
later." He broke off the connection.

He had been heading toward my house, so I ran
down the street, parallel to his course, then cut over,
hoping to see him. But he was gone.

I sat on the ground and cried and thought about
Flaco with his throat cut, angry that I had been unable
to avenge his death. I began walking home and it seemed
very foggy, and my legs felt weak. I kept remembering
Flaco dead and my chasing the man who had killed him.
I had thought it would feel good to kill the man, and had
run with great ease as I chased him, but now I felt weak
and sick. I looked up and found myself on a street I'd
never seen before, and I was lost.

I wandered until I found a place I recognized, and
walked on home. Then I took a shovel back to the
orchard to bury Flaco.

His body had grown cold. The Chilean woman had
taken down one of the tents in preparation to leave. She
began shaking when she saw me. She kept watching me
out of the corner of her eye as she packed her clothes
and cooking utensils. I dug a shallow hole and put Flaco
in. I checked his pockets. They were empty. I looked
over at the Chilean woman; she began shaking and fell
to the ground.

"Don't murder me!" she screamed, waving her hands

in front of her chest. "Don't murder me!" She was genuinely afraid, and I realized she thought I had killed Flaco and run away.

"What did you do with his things?" I yelled at her.

"Mercy! I'm a mother. Have mercy!" she cried. I didn't advance on her. "Let me keep a little of the money," she said. "Enough for boat passage to Puerto Rico!"

I stepped forward and raised the shovel, as if to strike her. She began weeping and pulled a bundle of cloth from beneath her blouse. She tossed it to the ground: Flaco's wallet, my computer chip, and a Saint Christopher medallion were inside. I threw Flaco's wallet to her, then turned away. The woman crawled off with her child and other possessions. After covering Flaco with dirt, I went home.

Tamara sat on my bed with the dream monitor on and her visor down. She moaned softly, curled in the fetal position. Between her knees she held her laser rifle. The platinum glow of her skin showed that her fever was very high. I walked over quietly and took the gun from her hand, turned it off, and tossed it in a corner. I examined the stump of her arm. It wasn't inflamed or swollen more than it should be: her fever wasn't from an infection.

I picked up the extra monitor and plugged into the viewer's jack: On the beach the wind, cold and irresistible, tugged at me as if it would lift me and carry me away. In the dark, clear sky the Moon was rising red and brilliant over the sea. On the blood-red sand, thousands of ghost crabs scuttled sideways, making clicking noises. I walked down to where the sea dipped. The bull still tossed about in the waves near shore.

On the beach lay a human skeleton. Its bones were

picked so clean that only a few ghost crabs crawled through its rib cage. "I didn't expect you," the skeleton said.

"Who did you expect?" I asked.

"Not you."

I looked down the beach and said, "It was very bad to see Flaco dead. He was a good friend."

The skeleton moaned. A ghostly woman, draped in red robes, stood in the air above me for a moment. She handed three yellow roses to the wind, then vanished. I looked up at the sky. There were no stars. The skeleton said, "I didn't stick around to find out: How did he die?"

"He was strangled, and stabbed in the throat."

"That would be Arish. Arish likes to kill that way. He always leaves them double-dead." A wave washed up around my ankles. The water was thick and warm and red.

"I almost got him. I almost got to kill Arish."

"Arish is good. You couldn't have killed him."

"I almost did," I said.

"He led you along, making you believe you could," the skeleton said. We both remained silent for a moment. "I'm going to die, Angelo. I told you that if you balled me over, I'd die. You did ball me over, didn't you?"

"Yes," I said, "perhaps in more ways than one."

"How?"

"When we operated on you, we took a retina scan. A hacker checked your government files."

"They would have waited for something like that. It was enough to get me killed."

"Also," I admitted, "I gave you AB stimulators before

we figured out that you were a brain transplant. You did have one?"

"Yes."

"Then you are in danger."

"I'm dead," the skeleton corrected. Its bones grew thin and began snapping like dry twigs. I tried to think of something comforting to say, but couldn't. The skeleton saw my distress, and laughed. "Leave me. I'm not afraid to die."

"Everyone's afraid to die," I said. Wind whipped the sand, blowing it against me. Out in the water, leviathans moved, large dark formless creatures with eyes on waving stalks. A tentacle rose in the air, then slithered back beneath the waves. The creatures sank back into the water, and I could feel the push Tamara had to give to make them stay. Tamara controlled her dream, but only in the half-hearted way of masochists and those who despair.

"That's because they don't practice. Dying. They're so afraid of fraying into oblivion, their muscles' fibers unknitting, the slow settling of fluids from the body."

"And you're not?" I asked.

"No," the skeleton said. "I do it over and over again." With those words, the flesh reappeared on the red-haired woman. The crabs began feeding on her. She didn't flinch.

"Why did Flaco die?" I asked.

She held her breath a moment, and released it slowly. "I guess I owe you that," she said. "My husband, General Amir Jafari, wants my brain in a brain bag and my body in stasis."

"Why?"

"I was in Intelligence. I committed an indiscretion." She paused again, weighing her words. "I was at a party with other officers' wives, and they were talking about a politician who'd been assassinated. By the way they talked, I assumed they all knew we'd made the hit, and said some things I shouldn't have. Among the Alliance such indiscretions get one killed. But my husband got my sentence commuted to life in a brain bag. *But life in a brain bag isn't life.*"

I remembered the empty, simulated voice of the general saying 'I'm not inhuman,' as if to convince himself. Out in the water—the dead bull struggled to its feet and snorted, then was bowled over by a wave.

"I don't understand. Why did he want your body in stasis?" A cold wind blew; a thin crust of ice appeared on the beach.

"I don't know," she said. "Maybe he thinks he'll get to screw it when he gets out of the Service. Once I caught wind of his plan, I didn't stick around to find out. I knew my only chance of escape would be to dump my old body, so I bought one on the black market and dismantled my brain bag. I thought as long as I had that crystal, could hold it in my hand and see it, I would know I wasn't in the brain bag. I had the cryotechs put a German shepherd's brain in my old body and sent it to my husband, naked, in a cage. I put a sign around its neck that said: 'If All You Want is Fucks and Faithfulness, I'm Yours.'" She seemed very pleased by the memory.

"Your husband called me on comlink. He offered to pay me to turn you in. He seemed concerned about you, I think. It's hard to tell."

"Don't let him fool you," the skeleton said. "He's one of the dead, the living dead. His capacity for emotion was tossed aside when he put on the cymech."

"I would not be so quick to judge him."

"Believe me, all he has left are memories of emotions. Memories fade."

"And this Arish, is he military?" I asked.

"Not officially. But he does odd jobs for them. The kind of odd job he did on Flaco."

"Was he the man who pulled off your hand?"

The woman laughed. "No." The beach disappeared. I saw Tamara at the airport, hurrying out of a black Mitsubishi minishuttle, looking worriedly into the sky above her at an incoming craft. She slammed the shuttle door on her hand, and tried to jerk free. Her hand pulled off. She staggered away. Then the scene changed and Tamara was lying on the beach, with the ghost crabs eating her. "This body's worthless."

This incident frightened me. She should not have been able to wipe the whole world off the monitor to show this single memory. She was delving farther into her subconscious than was safe. "I must go now," I said. "I'll need to get you some more medications, to help prevent any brain damage. Will you wait here for me?"

The dark creatures rose out of the sea and eyed me again. She shrugged. "Yes. I guess."

I jacked out and unplugged her monitor. The sun was rising, and because I had not slept much for two days and the pharmacy wasn't open, I decided to nap a few moments. I lay down and closed my eyes.

I awoke at three in the afternoon. Tamara was asleep also, and I touched her forehead. Her fever was high, so I headed for Vasquez Pharmaceuticals. It took an hour to get there, but I thought it unsafe to call and ask for a delivery. I bought some log-phase growth regulators and antimosin C, paying in coin. I hurried home.

At the house, Tamara sat in the kitchen, her head slumped on the table, a hand loosely wrapped around a

glass of icewater, her laser rifle on the floor next to her.
She mumbled in a foreign tongue. Her fever was very
high. I ran downstairs, brought up my medical supplies,
and dumped them on the table. I wanted to get the
log-phases into Tamara as quickly as possible, so I took
out a syringe, filled it, and shoved it into her carotid
artery. Her head snapped up and she looked at the
needle in her neck, then closed her eyes and said, "Get
me out of here. I want to go away."

"In good time," I said, wanting to calm her.

"I feel cold. I think I'm going to die."

"You won't die." The coldness, that was bad. Her
immune system was attacking her brain. I refilled the
syringe with antimosin and injected it into her arm.

"You've been good to me, Angelo. Good. Did you
mean what you said . . . about order? Not wanting order."

"Yes. Very much."

"Then get away. Get out of Panama." Her eyes
snapped open, and she sat up.

"What do you mean?" I asked.

"Do you want me to commit a second indiscretion?"
She smiled, a cold menacing smile. "I mean get out.
Now! Order's coming. Get beyond Panama, beyond . . .
AI's and the Alliance."

I tried to make sense of what she said. She stared at
me, as if to bore the knowledge into me with her eyes.
The Alliance forces were made up of troops from all
countries, and were charged with taking care of Earth's
interests in space. But I didn't understand why she'd
juxtaposed the AI's and the Alliance. I remembered
Flaco's warning of Imperialism. "You mean someone in
the Alliance has bid to some artificial intelligences for
domination of Panama?"

Tamara nodded. "They'll come soon. I don't know how long you have."

I considered the problems of neighboring nations. "But I don't understand—what could the Socialists offer the AI's?"

Tamara hesitated, and answered, "Lift their memory ceilings; give them access to space."

I thought for a moment, feeling dazed. Freedom. She was talking about freedom. Some AI's were going to trade Panama's freedom for their own. It was a perfect bartering equation—value for value. If I hadn't been so emotionally attached to my freedom, I would have laughed. "You should tell someone!" I shouted. "You should turn them in!"

"I told *you*," she said. "You're enough."

"Tell the authorities!"

"Angelo, you don't understand. *I was one of them.* I know them. I'd never get away with it."

She turned her face away, rested her head on the table, and soon dozed off. I stroked her hair and wondered what she meant—one of them. One of those who kill the Flacos of the world? One who makes freedom a commodity? What did I know of her? She was a red-haired woman on the beach. A woman with the quick, commanding voice of a Socialist dictator's wife. She liked the smell of roses. She ran because she feared imprisonment in a machine—yet she turned the world into a prison for others. Wouldn't it be justice to turn her in? Wouldn't it be justice to strangle her? I'd suspected from the moment I'd taken her in that I'd regret it. I wondered if I should take her to the hospital, tell the authorities, let her be killed.

She began moaning again, whispering snatches in English and Farsi. Once she said, "It's all gone bad, just

bad," but I didn't understand most of what she said. I
considered how they would take control of Panama. The
AI's controlled information—market reports, weather
forecasts, libraries, bank accounts—and communications. In addition, they kept track of armaments. It
would be simple to destroy the country with misinfor-
mation.

I looked at Tamara's thin face, at her frail body,
and wished I had known the Tamara who had been. A
woman with a body that poor would have been humble.
She would have known pain, and would feel empathy
for others. What did I know of this woman? As if to
answer, she suddenly cried out in English, "All I want is
away!"

And I decided.

Whatever she had been, whatever she thought herself
to be, she was a refugiada now.

I carried her to bed, then tried to work up enough
nerve to take her to the safety of the orchards. I turned
on the radio, so the music would fill the silence in the
house. After a moment, comlink tones sounded in my
head. I engaged; Jafari came in on audio. He asked in
his perfectly inflectionless voice, "Is Tamil nearby?" His
signal was so full of static, I could barely hear him. He
was running the signal through filters, empty channels
to stop a trace.

"Tamil? Your wife? She's unconscious," I said.

"This is important," Jafari said. "After this, don't
accept or make any comlinks—Intelligence can home in
on an open signal. Tell Tamil the Alliance has taken me
out of the loop. I can do nothing more for her. If she's
caught, she'll be terminated. Tell her I loved her. Tell her
I'm sorry." Jafari cut off.

I began packing food, clothing, water. I went to the

kitchen for my medical bag and began throwing out things I didn't need. Vetinni's "The Rings of Saturn in D Minor" played on the radio, but it stopped, and momentarily the house was quiet.

Downstairs I heard the front door squeak on its hinges. I realized I could feel a draft on my face. I didn't remember leaving the door open. I reached down and picked up the rifle, turned it on as Wagner's "Ride of the Valkyries" started on the radio, and leapt in front of the stairwell and fired. Arish was on the stairs, with his mouth open, his back against the wall, holding a sawed-off shotgun. He said "Mother fu—" and fired as my shot burned across his stomach.

His shot hit the wall behind me, and the weight of my moving body carried me past the open stairwell. I heard Arish drop to the floor. Tamara opened the bedroom door and looked out. Her face was very pale and she could hardly stand. I waved for her to go back into the bedroom, and I snapped a glance around the corner.

Arish lay on his belly, with his gun hand outstretched, breathing heavily. I sneaked toward him and he started to rise, swinging up his shotgun.

I kicked him in the head and his gun fired into the ceiling as he flipped backward down the stairs. He lay perfectly still. He appeared unconscious, though he still held his gun. I aimed my rifle at his head, stepped on his fingers, and pushed away his gun with my foot.

I didn't know what to do with him. I didn't want to kill him. My medical bag was on the table behind me, so I got my fluothane canister and put the gas mask over his face, then checked his wounds. Three fingers had burned off his left hand, and I'd cut a hole across his belly that had nearly disemboweled him, but no vital organs were hit that I could see. I sat for a moment, shocked at how easy it had been. My mouth was dry and felt full of cotton, and my heart beat fast. Tamara had said I couldn't kill Arish, and I was afraid, knowing that next time it wouldn't be this easy. I went to Tamara, to take her back to the orchards.

She was on the bed, feet tucked up under her butt, arms wrapped around her knees, rocking back and forth, visor down, sucking images out of the dream monitor—not like a professional, like a junkie. She kept saying, "All I want is away; All I want is away; All I want is away." Sweat rolled off her as she rocked, and her face was bleached colorless.

I went to the console and unplugged her monitor. She kept rocking, unaware of what I'd done. I pushed her visor up. Her eyes were rolled back, showing white. She kept whimpering, clenching her teeth. She was deep inside herself. Catatonic.

I pulled the visor back down, plugged her into the console, put my own visor down, and plugged into the viewer's jack.

And on the beach the wind raged in the night, whipping grains of sand as sharp as needles through my skin. I thought the wind made a noise like a person hissing through his teeth, but I looked up and saw ghostly seagulls with the faces of men, hissing through their teeth.

The red-haired Tamil sat, curled up, rocking on a beach that undulated beneath her, watching the humps of dark sea creatures rise and gape at her before she shoved them back into oblivion. She spoke to something out at sea, almost yelling. I couldn't hear her words. Ghost crabs scuttled up out of the water and bit her; she kicked, but they scurried away, claws heavy with chunks of her flesh. The dead bull, bloated now, stood in the shallows, struggling against entangling seaweed as he tried to reach shore, lowing as if in pain. The breakers, washing against him, made his penis and testicles rise as they came in, then left them hanging, wet and dripping, as they receded.

I called to Tamil. She didn't answer. I yelled that Arish was dead, but the wind and crashing waves and the hissing gulls carried my words away, so I struggled toward her, running against the stinging wind through sand filled with dark tangling seaweed. The sea creatures began to rise, tentacles outstretched as they moved toward shore. I reached her. She kept yelling at the empty air, "All I want is away!" I pulled her face toward me. She looked up. And though the wind still blew, her world quieted.

"Arish is dead," I yelled, hoping to comfort her. "Your husband called me. He said he's out of the loop. We've got to get away." She looked at me, searched my face. She understood everything I'd told her, much that I hadn't.

"*I die*," she said through clenched teeth.

I heard a thud behind me. The dead bull struggled free of the seaweed and charged. I had half turned when his horns ripped through my chest, and he tossed me over his head. The pain made me see lights, cramped my muscles, and made vomit rise in my throat. I thought someone had shot me, and I wanted to jack out to see my attacker.

I fell face down in the sand and struggled to my side. The bull was stamping Tamil's body. Time and time again he reared his huge front legs up a bit, then dropped on her, pushing her broken body into the sand, cracking her bones. When he stopped, he snorted as he sniffed the blood on her, then plunged his horns through her belly and lifted her in the air. He paraded her up and down the beach, then loped into the sea. The world exploded in a blaze of pain and the white of a dead monitor.

I got up and staggered around my house, from room to room, searching through a fog for something—I didn't know what it was—that I couldn't seem to find. I would look in a room and see something and wonder, "Is that what I'm looking for?" Then I would realize I was looking at a lamp or table, and it was not what I wanted. I went to an open door, which seemed like all the others, and sunlight struck my face. I wandered in my front yard, looking at orchids and trees, wondering if they were what I wanted, and found myself at my neighbor's door. I opened it.

Rodrigo DeHoyos sat in a chair. He looked at me. "Don Osic, what is wrong? What has happened?" he cried as he rose. He forced me into a large, soft chair. I tried to stand and he pushed me back down. "Are you ill?" he asked.

I sat for several minutes, thinking, but my mind seemed to race down pathways that always came to a dead end. I grasped Rodrigo's shirt. "Something terrible has happened!" I told him. Then I remembered, *All I want is away.* I yelled, "You must get me a shuttle!" Rodrigo stared at me, calculatingly, then jacked in a call to Pantransport and asked for a minishuttle as soon as possible. He turned away for a moment, and I got up and headed home. He came and tried to force me to sit back down, but I pushed him aside and he didn't stop me.

I opened my door and found Arish still at the bottom of the stairs, gasping for breath through the gas mask.

One of his lungs must have collapsed to make him gasp that way. The air was filled with the scent of gastric juices and charred flesh and hair. I marveled that I didn't remember passing him when I went outside, and I stumbled over him on my way back to my bedroom.

Tamara sat on the bed, slumped slightly forward, perfectly motionless. I reached up and touched her neck, feeling for a pulse. She had none. I pulled her visor up and looked at her. Her empty eyes seemed to stare at something on the wall behind me. Her face was very pale, perfectly still. One large, wet tear had seeped from her left eye, slowly finding its way down her cheek. I brushed it away, surprised to feel how high her fever had become in the end. I closed her eyes and whispered the words the refugiados spoke over their dead comrades, "Free at last."

As I began thinking of things I needed to do, I heard the sound of a rattle behind me. I turned around. No one was there. I wandered to the kitchen and got my medical bag, filled a specimen bottle with some clear synthetic blood, and spilled most of the blood on the table because my hands shook. I went downstairs to where Arish lay gasping on the floor, removed the gas mask from his face, then unwrapped a scalpel and inserted the blade under his bottom right eyelid and twisted till his eye popped free. I dropped the eye into the blood and agitated the container a moment before putting it in my pocket. I heard the rattling behind me again, and turned around. No one was there. The rattling kept coming, and I realized my jaw was quivering and my own teeth were rattling. I began breathing heavily and could hear my heart pounding.

I took the scalpel and slit Arish's throat from ear to ear.

"For Flaco, you bastard," I told myself. I watched
the blood pump out of Arish's throat, and as it ebbed
away, I could feel something inside me ebbing away. I
believed God would punish me. "Piss on him if he can't
take a joke!" I said. And I laughed and cried at the same
time.

With three dead bodies behind me, I was not about
to risk the courts of Panama. I went outside and sat
beneath the papaya tree to wait for the shuttle. My
muscles had become knotted, and I was breathing hard,
so I stretched out on the grass and tried to still myself. It
was getting dark, and the fruit bats were just reaching
the papayas above me as the shuttle landed.

Outside the shuttle was a security scanner. As I
reached the scanner a mechanized voice said, "State
your destination and prepare for identity scan."

I began breathing hard, fumbled for the specimen
bottle with the clear synthetic blood, then pulled out the
eye. Even with the oxygen provided by the blood, the
proteins in the eye had begun to whiten. I put it in my
palm and held it up to the retina scanner, hoping it
would register the whiteness as an infection, and gave
my destination. "Lagrange star-station, outbound concourse one."

The scanner said, "Welcome, Arish Muhammad Hus-
tanifad. We will deduct 147,232 IMU's from your bank
account. We hope you enjoyed your stay on Earth."

"Thank you," I answered quietly. "I did. I shall miss
Earth very much."

On the flight up I played with the crystal in my
pocket and watched the view outside. The sun had set
in Colón, but I could see the shimmering platinum of
the banana orchards. A line of shadow marched across
Earth; the world darkened beneath me. I checked the

shuttle's computer terminal to see if any starships were willing to sign on a pharmacologist. None were. I checked to see if anyone in another star system was willing to pay my fare from their end. Someone from the Tertullian system wanted a morphogenic pharmacologist badly, was willing to pay fare to a planet called *Baker*. I keyed in the visual for Baker: it was a small planet, newly terraformed, population 300,000. The pictures showed white beaches and palm trees, like Panama. It looked like a place where I could possess myself in peace.

I lay down, and sometime during the night I dozed lightly. Unbidden I dreamed that the day had been warm and happy, and that after selling a life extension in the feria, I walked to where Flaco and Tamara built sand castles on an empty beach. I stood and smiled at them for a long time, not knowing why I was grinning, then began to walk past them.

"Hola, Angelo, where are you going?" Flaco called.

"I'm on my way to Paradise," I said.

Flaco said, "Hah! Good place! I have a cousin who lives there." Tamara and Flaco smiled at me as I walked past them. I looked up the beach. In the distance was only empty sand, and I knew my legs would tire long before I made it. Above me, seagulls hung motionless in the air. I stretched out my arms and crouched, wondering if the wind could lift me and make me fly like a bird. My arms sprouted tiny ugly feathers, and I began to rise. I held my arms steady and floated slowly up into the sky.

Flaco yelled to Tamara, "Watch out, or that big seagull will crap on you!" I looked down. Flaco was pointing up at me, laughing. He pulled a ball from one pocket and a kitten from the other. And as I rose in the air, Flaco and Tamara ran along, playing ball with a gray and white kitten on an empty beach beneath a purple sun that never set.

Resonance Ritual
by
Paula May

About the Author

The SF short-short story is a rare thing. In other literatures, the author need not sketch in much about the world the characters live in. In SF, every story supposes a new reality, which the author must take time to indicate to the reader. Consequently, most of the few existing SF short-shorts—and some are memorable for it—have "gimmick" endings much like those on jokes. Their "reality" is plainly artificial, though catchy. But, once in a great while, we see a piece of short-short art that goes beyond artifice.

You're about to read a fully-rounded story done in about a thousand words, set in a situation that will put a novel in your mind. Its author is in Ohio, raising children, married to an English-born landscape architect. She has a B.A. in English and a background in administration. But like many other aspiring writers, she has also maintained herself with odd jobs . . . she's been a pizza delivery driver, for instance. She has been reading SF for more that a quarter-century but didn't start writing it until three years ago. This is her first appearance with fiction in print. You will remember it. . . .

A slight distortion, a congealing of the air, and a naked man stands in the middle of the darkened room. He tries to look everywhere at once, wild eyes raking the postered walls, the patterned carpet, the cracked ceiling, the comfortable old furniture, greedily sucking in every detail. He moves to the bed, begins to dress in the clothes laid out so neatly upon the bedspread. The trousers are too loose. He's grown thin, almost gaunt. He's been looking for a very long time, this one.

As he pulls on the shirt, he turns to sit on the bed, and he sees me sitting in my rocker, way back in my shadowed corner. Panic pinches the flesh around his eyes, so I speak up quickly.

"It doesn't belong here. I moved it in so I could wait a little more comfortably. It's all right."

The pain eases, his eyes relax, even blink.

"Now you're here, I'll see to supper. Having your favorites tonight."

He nods, just a bit, enough to let me climb out of the rocker and head for the kitchen. Bustle is probably more like it—I bustle, I know I do, especially when I am about cooking.

And I am about cooking tonight. The chicken's all jointed and ready, so I dredge it in the seasoned flour that only I know how to mix and I set it to frying in the heavy, deep-sided iron skillet that I've used all my married life, that my mother used before me. Then I start up the oven and mix some biscuits, the sky-high recipe made with eggs, and get them to baking. I peel a mountain of potatoes for the creamy, mashed potatoes he needs to hold a lake of the thick gravy I'll simmer in the bottom of the heavy skillet after the grease is poured off. I put on a big crock of water to boil for the roastin' ears—they'll have to be frozen ones at this time of year, but we grew them ourselves, blanched and froze them fresh from the field, so they still have the bright flavor of summer sun in them.

All the while, he stands in the doorway, watching every move, checking out every utensil I use, observing every detail of my kitchen. After a few minutes I notice that he is starting to look concerned again, so I stop to consider what I could have forgotten. I figure it out right away, go over to the pie safe and pull out the cherry cobbler I baked yesterday. I show it off to him with a little curtsy, and he breaks out a smile, a genuine smile. He leans back against the doorpost, laying the ankle of the resting leg very deliberately across the ankle of the supporting leg. He's being careful with the details, too.

Matthew comes onto the back porch from the fields, smells the chicken as he's shucking off his overalls. "Company tonight, Mom?" he calls.

"Maybe so, maybe not," I answer, and he knows what's up.

Matt pads into the kitchen in stocking feet and shirtsleeves, nods to the doorway and says casually, "Evening, Son."

The man in the doorway crosses his arms, returns the nod and, finally, speaks. "Evening, Dad."

Tears spring to my eyes, but I just bustle a little more
until they go off, and I don't think either of the men
notice. If they do, they don't let on.

Soon it's all done, the steaming servers set before my
place at the old trestle table, and the three of us sit
down. I pile the plates high with food, first Matthew's,
as has always been our custom, then his, my own last. I
pass the plates and he falls to it, shoveling the potatoes
and gravy in as fast as he can manage. He picks up a
drumstick, pulls off half the meat in one bite. He grins at
each of us in turn with his overstuffed mouth, daring us
to fault his manners. He sets the chicken back on his
plate, stiffens suddenly.

Matthew and I are staring at him. He's staring at his
plate, at the dainty design painted on so nicely around
the edge. My stomach rises into my throat. I can hear
my heartbeat inside my ears. I've always liked that
china—it seems I'll shortly have reason to hate it.

He raises his gaze to meet mine, both our sets of eyes
widening with the stirring of fear. "New china, Mom?"
he asks in clipped tones, willing it so.

I want to say, "Yes! New china, new since you went
away, it's all right," but it isn't so, and even if I lie, the
resonance effect will get him anyway, so I say, "No,
John, I've had that china since Aunt Mary moved to
California. She didn't much care for it, didn't figure it'd
survive the trip, so she gave it to me. You'd best eat
hearty, now, as I figure you'll be leaving us soon."

Round the corner of the table from me, Matthew is
staring at his plate, the bleakness of his face so familiar
by now that I don't even need to turn my head to see it. I
know every line, every pain-filled furrow by heart.

The hope is gone from John's eyes, too. He sighs
softly, then says, "Do you think I could have my cobbler

Illustrated by J. Kenton Manning

now, in case I don't get to finish?"

"'Course." I bustle to the cupboard, serve up a double portion for him, bustle back, set it down in front of him. He catches my hand as I let go of the plate, peers up into my face.

"You're very kind," he murmurs, a strange glistening blurring his dark lashes momentarily.

"I figure you're family. Anybody'd do the same for family." I pat his whitened knuckles gently with my free hand, and he lets me go. I return to my chair.

He tucks into the cobbler. He manages to down three forkfuls of dessert before the resonance mismatch reaches him. He glances up at us, goes out of focus, then vanishes, his fork clattering onto the plate, the borrowed clothes collapsing onto the chair.

Sometimes we go months without a visitor, sometimes they come daily for weeks at a time. We never get more than one a day, and they always arrive just in time for supper, so I don't figure it's all that hard to handle. Matthew says we should sell the farm, move away. I suppose that might make it easier on us, but it sure won't help them.

John never said much about the infinity experiments, but I reckon he should have, because now he's lost somehow, as, I suppose, are all these who appear in his room, all of them lost and desperate for home. As I sit and rock, I imagine a mother for each of these lost ones, rank upon rank of us sitting and rocking, waiting to see if *this* evening will bring Johnny home. What else can we do?

We launder and lay out our sons' clothes, cook our sons' favorite foods, care for these poor souls as they come to us in the hope that somewhere, some other woman is so caring for our own. We must keep them alive and well and searching, for surely one day one lost sheep will manage to return to his proper fold, and if one returns, then maybe they all will, and the universe will resound with homecomings.

*"Nothing makes me happier than to hear
from readers and writers."*

These were the words of L. Ron Hubbard who was always very interested in hearing from his readers and friends. He made a point of staying in communication with everyone he came in contact with over his more than fifty-year career as a professional writer, and he had thousands of fans and friends that he corresponded with all over the world.

The publishers of the anthology resulting from the Writers of The Future Contest, sponsored by L. Ron Hubbard, wish to continue this tradition and would very much welcome letters and comments from you, its readers, both old and new.

Any message addressed to the Authors Affairs Director at NEW ERA Publications UK will be given prompt and full attention.

NEW ERA Publications UK, Ltd.
P.O. Box 110
Tonbridge
Kent TN9 2TY

ABOUT THE STORY ILLUSTRATORS

Brian Murray

After his first publication in Writers of The Future Vol.II he pursued the art of comic book illustration. At the 1986 San Diego Comic Convention Brian was offered a one year exclusive contract with DC Comics, and was also featured in a 12 piece art portfolio by Blackthorne Publishing on "The Strength of Man." He is preparing for a larger career involving movie posters, book covers, and other major forms of graphic design. We certainly feel that Brian is indeed an artist well and rapidly on his way.

J. Kenton Manning

J. Kenton Manning is a graduate of the Art Center College of Design at Pasadena. He has worked extensively in animation, and also teaches art at the University of California. NBC TV, RCA and Warner Brothers are among the many clients he has illustrated for. About illustration Jay says that when as a child he saw the work of artist Mort Drucker, he has always been impressed by the subtle quality of life that can be imparted through simple line art. Seeing his fine work in this volume, we're sure you'll agree.

Bob Eggleton

Bob Eggleton of Rhode Island found a dual passion in both art and science fiction at an early age, and consequently has begun to develop a successful career in creating book covers for SF publishers, as well as illustrating for major SF magazines. His next important project is in illustrating stories in the prestigious Byron Preiss collection "The Planets" and "The Universe" from Bantam books. Bob displays his work at many SF conventions and his greatest joy is to inspire people through his art.

Greg Petan

Greg Petan is a graduate of the American Academy of Art in Chicago. He's at the beginning of his professional career. Working as a successful freelance portraitist, he has also done architectural rendering. Since his first appearance in Writers of The Future Vol.II, Greg has started to branch out into advertising illustration and sees a bright professional future for himself, as do we.

Rich Lynes

Rich Lynes is a completely self-taught artist for all seasons. Whatever the medium, from airbrush to sculpture, Rich imparts a sensitivity combined with a finely-honed skill. His career includes extensive work in TV graphics for NBC and ABC (for which he received an Emmy reccommendation), and he is currently setting his sights on motion picture graphics.

CONTEST RULES

1. All entries must be original works of science fiction or fantasy. Plagiarism will result in automatic disqualification. Submitted works may not have been previously published.

2. Entries must be either short-story length (under 10,000 words) or novelette length (under 17,000 words).

3. Contest is open only to those who have not had professionally published a novel or novella or more than three short stories or more than one novelette.

4. Entries must be typewritten and double-spaced. Each entry shall have a cover page with the title of the work, the author's name, address and telephone number, and state the length of the work. The manuscript itself should be titled, but the author's name should be deleted from it in order to facilitate anonymous judging.

5. Entries must be accompanied by stamped, self-addressed envelope suitable for return of manuscript. Every manuscript will be returned.

6. There shall be three cash prizes for each quarterly contest: 1st prize of $1000.00, 2nd prize of $750.00 and 3rd prize of $500.00. In addition a cash prize of $4000.00 shall be awarded to the 1988 Grand Prize winner.

7. The contest will continue through September 30, 1988 on the following quarterly basis:

    a. October 1 – December 31, 1987
    b. January 1 – March 31, 1988
    c. April 1 – June 30, 1988
    d. July 1 – September 30, 1988

To be eligible for the quarterly contest an entry must be postmarked no later than midnight on the last day of the quarter.

For information concerning subsequent quarters, please write to the contest address given on the preceding page.

8. Each entrant may only submit one entry per quarter.

9. Winners of the quarterly contest are ineligible for further participation in the contest.

10. Winners of the quarterly contests will be awarded trophies or certificates.

11. A 1988 Grand Prize winner will be selected from among the quarterly winners from the period October 1, 1987 through September 30, 1988.

12. Should the sponsor of this contest decide to publish an anthology of science fiction and fantasy works, winners will be contacted regarding their interest in having their manuscript included.

13. Entries will be judged by a panel of professional authors. Each contest may have a different panel. The decisions of the judges are final.

14. Winners of each contest will be individually notified of the results by mail, together with names of those sitting on the panel of judges.

This contest is void where prohibited by law.

*"I am amazed and indeed overwhelmed
by his (Hubbard's) energy."*
ARTHUR C. CLARKE

L. RON HUBBARD'S
MISSION EARTH
DEKALOGY

HIS SUPERLATIVE
TEN-VOLUME MASTERWORK.
UNPARALLELED IN ACTION...
HUMOR...SATIRE...ADVENTURE

A milestone in the science fiction genre. Mission Earth reads with the distinctive pace and artistry that inimitably hallmarks L. Ron Hubbard as an unequaled Master Storyteller.

From light years away, the Voltarian Confederacy sends a mission to stop earth from self-annihilation. However, a villainous faction, the Voltarian Secret Police launch their own plan to sabotage the mission.

Hilariously told from the alien villain's point of view, this highspeed adventure brilliantly and imaginatively fuses action science fiction with rich comedy-satire and biting social commentary in the great tradition of Swift, Wells and Orwell.

"A 10 volume volcano of dynamic action." THE TIMES

"...an extraordinary...epic rich with intergalactic intrigue and wry social commentary." LITERARY GUILD (USA)

"...one of the most gripping storytellers in science fiction." PHILIP JOSÉ FARMER

"A wicked satire...more addictive than salt and peanuts." GENE WOLFE

THE MISSION EARTH DEKALOGY

Vol. 1 – The Invaders Plan	**Vol. 6 – Death Quest**
Vol. 2 – Black Genesis	**Vol. 7 – Voyage of Vengeance**
Vol. 3 – The Enemy Within	**Vol. 8 – Disaster**
Vol. 4 – An Alien Affair	**Vol. 9 – Villainy Victorious**
Vol. 5 – Fortune of Fear	**Vol.10 – The Doomed Planet**

MISSION EARTH IS ACTION, ADVENTURE AND SCIENCE FICTION SATIRE AT ITS BEST!

GET YOUR COPIES TODAY!

Get your copies today for £10.95 wherever fine books are sold. (See tear out order form for special edition).